INTRODUCTION

TO

ELECTRICITY AND OPTICS

INTRODUCTION

TO

ELECTRICITY AND OPTICS

BY

NATHANIEL H. FRANK, Sc.D.

Professor of Physics
Massachusetts Institute of Technology

SECOND EDITION

McGRAW-HILL BOOK COMPANY, INC.

NEW YORK   TORONTO   LONDON

1950

INTRODUCTION TO ELECTRICITY AND OPTICS

IX

PREFACE TO THE SECOND EDITION

In preparing the second edition of this book, the author has been fortunate in having obtained the carefully considered opinions and constructive criticism of those of his colleagues who, during the past ten years, employed this book as a text in teaching the sophomore physics course at MIT, as well as a considerable amount of significant student reaction. It is gratifying that both the scope of the book and the general order and treatment of the subject matter have proved entirely satisfactory. The most significant requirement for an improved second edition seemed to be the need of expanding, and of course improving, the presentation and exposition of the *physical* thinking and principles which underlie the subject. This has been set as the primary goal of the revision, and to accomplish this the book has been largely rewritten. As in the first edition, the requisite mathematical knowledge is only elementary differential and integral calculus, but every attempt has been made to challenge the student continuously in the application of this mathematical background to physical situations.

It seems advisable to list the more important revisions. First, the mks rationalized system of units is now used exclusively in the body of the text, and a short appendix presents in a simple manner the necessary conversion relations to translate any of the material to other commonly employed systems of units. The general plan of introducing the four electromagnetic vectors $\mathcal{E}$, D, B, and H from the outset is still employed, but the manner of introducing D and H, both in empty space and in material bodies, has been revised and clarified. As previously indicated, the over-all subject matter is unchanged, but some new material and many new problems have been added. The major additions are:

1. A new first chapter to provide the student with a sound quantitative background on fields of force and on field concepts in general as used in physics.

2. An elementary treatment of the problem of the metallic sphere in a uniform electric field to help understand the general sort of reasoning underlying the method of electrical images.

3. A concise vector treatment of parallel a-c circuits.

4. The treatment of interference and diffraction has been allocated to two separate chapters and has been supplemented by elementary vector methods of solution.

Applications and worked examples in the text have been held to a minimum consistent with clarity to present a close-knit logical structure of the subject.

A large number of new and varied problems have been added to each chapter. The new problems are of a relatively wide scope of difficulty and, as far as is possible, bear on questions of interest in modern physics. It is hoped that these additional problems will help avoid too much duplication of assignments from year to year.

The author wishes to express his thanks to his colleagues for their critical interest and suggestions and especially to Robert Marlowe for his very able assistance in preparing the manuscript for publication.

CAMBRIDGE, MASS.   NATHANIEL H. FRANK
    June, 1950

PREFACE TO THE FIRST EDITION

This book has been written primarily as a textbook for the use of those second-year students at the Massachusetts Institute of Technology who intend to pursue further studies in electrical engineering, physics, or both. These students have completed a year's course in calculus and one in mechanics and heat utilizing the author's text[1] and are simultaneously pursuing a second course in calculus. The goal to which this book aspires is a compact logical exposition of the fundamental laws of the electric and the magnetic field and the elementary applications of these laws to circuits, to a study of the electrical and magnetic properties of matter, and to the field of optics. The treatment is quantitative throughout and an attempt has been made to imbue the reader with a sound understanding of the fundamental laws (the Maxwell equations) and with the ability to apply them to many and varied phenomena without resorting to special formulas and methods. Thus ordinary circuit concepts and the ideas necessary for the understanding of optics are presented as natural consequences of the basic field equations.

In attempting to carry through the above program in an elementary text, it has been found expedient to depart widely from the usual elementary treatments. The book is essentially divided into two parts. The first half sets as its aim a systematic development of the fundamental laws of the electric and magnetic fields for empty space, confining the discussion of the electrical properties of matter to those of conductors. In this connection all four electromagnetic vectors, $\mathcal{E}$, D, B, and H, are introduced from the very outset; hence the Maxwell equations for empty space are presented in forms which are perfectly general, retaining their validity in the presence of material bodies. The second half encompasses the electric and magnetic properties of matter and is based essentially on the electromagnetic waves in dielectrics leads smoothly to the subject of optics; physical optics is largely emphasized, although one rather long chapter is devoted to geometrical optics.

Since it has become necessary to teach the m.k.s. system of units,

[1] "Introduction to Mechanics and Heat," N. H. Frank, McGraw-Hill Book Company, Inc., New York.

vii

these units have been employed from the very beginning along with the electrostatic system. Electromagnetic units are then introduced at an appropriate place. Thus the student learns the advantages of the newer m.k.s. system and at the same time becomes conversant with the older Gaussian units without which his understanding of much of the literature would be seriously handicapped. In view of the order of development of the subject matter, unrationalized units have been employed throughout and the transition to rationalized units, if desirable, may readily be made at a later stage of the student's education.

The first three chapters are devoted to the subject of the electrostatic field in vacuum. Here, as well as elsewhere in the book, the order of presentation of the topics has been chosen in accordance with the principle of introducing basic concepts one at a time wherever practicable. The concepts and definition of the magnetic field in empty space have been based solely on the mutual force actions of currents or of moving charges, care being taken to stress the magnetic induction vector B as the fundamental force vector. Discussion of magnetic poles is deferred to the second half of the book in connection with the properties of ferromagnetic media. The use of complex numbers is avoided in connection with simple a.c. circuits but the vector diagram method is derived from first principles. The two chapters which conclude the treatment for empty space introduce the concept of the Maxwell displacement current, a discussion of electromagnetic waves in free space, and the Poynting vector. Here the Maxwell equations are formulated in integral form to avoid the premature use of the symbolism of vector differentiation. Traveling and standing waves on an ideal transmission line serve to bridge the usual gap between oscillating LC circuits and the radiation field of an antenna, the latter topic being treated semi-quantitatively.

As previously mentioned, the second half of the book introduces the electrical and magnetic properties of matter on the basis of the Lorenz electron theory. Following a study of the essentially free electrons in vacuum tubes and in metals, the properties of dielectrics in terms of bound electrons and of magnetic media in terms of the orbital motions and spins of the electrons are discussed. The difficult questions of mechanical forces on dielectrics and on magnetic bodies have been relegated to the problems in an attempt to develop critical methods of reasoning in this connection rather than a blind reliance on formulas. A dual standpoint has been adopted in connection with dielectrics and magnetic media: (1) the classical description in terms of dielectric constant and magnetic permeability and (2) the replacement of matter by equivalent charge and current distributions and the consequent reduction of a problem to one for empty space. It is gratifying to find that the treatment of magnetic problems in terms of Amperian currents is fully as simple as the equivalent method of introducing surface distributions of magnetic matter (magnetic poles) and has unquestionable pedagogical advantages. The laws of reflection and refraction of electromagnetic waves at dielectric boundaries are derived from the electromagnetic boundary conditions and the problem of intensity relations for normal incidence is discussed completely. An elementary, but quantitative, theory of the dispersion and scattering of light in gases is extended to give a physical picture of the nature of the refracted wave is isotropic and anisotropic media, the latter leading to the phenomena of double refraction. Fresnel diffraction is analyzed with the help of Fresnel zones and the Fraunhofer diffraction patterns of a single and of a double rectangular slit are worked out completely. The final chapter proceeds to a quantitative discussion of thermal radiation, including an elementary derivation of the law of radiation pressure and of the concept of electromagnetic momentum. A brief discussion of photometry and its connection with general radiation theory is also included.

A number of problems have been included at the end of each chapter. These problems have been designed not only to help the student learn how to apply fundamental principles to many and varied situations— and the working of many problems is essential for a thorough grasp of these fundamentals—but also in some cases to require the student to derive for himself a number of important general results not obtained in the text. A considerable range of complexity has been aimed at in these problems, and it is hoped that not too many of them can be solved by use of formulas alone. It should be pointed out that this book is planned as a guiding textbook and, as such, should be supplemented by laboratory work and descriptive material, especially with regard to experimental methods.

The author would like to express his thanks to a number of his colleagues for valuable suggestions and criticisms and especially to John E. Meade for his able assistance in preparing the manuscript for publication.

N. H. FRANK

CAMBRIDGE, MASS.
May, 1940

CONTENTS

CHAPTER 5

STEADY ELECTRIC CURRENTS

CHAPTER 6

THE MAGNETIC FIELD OF FORCE

CHAPTER 7

THE MAGNETIC FIELD OF STEADY CURRENTS

CHAPTER 8

INDUCED ELECTROMOTIVE FORCES AND INDUCTANCE

CHAPTER 9

ELEMENTARY ALTERNATING-CURRENT CIRCUITS

CHAPTER 19

DIFFRACTION

CHAPTER 20

HEAT RADIATION

CHAPTER 1

FIELDS OF FORCE

The study of mechanics is concerned primarily with the determination of the motions of material bodies under the action of prescribed forces. These motions are obtained by a direct, although not always simple, application of Newton's laws of motion. In contrast to this relatively straightforward program, the study of the forces which act on matter is subtle and complex. In mechanics one is concerned largely with two principal types of forces which were the first to be investigated historically. First, one has gravitational forces, obeying Newton's law of gravitation that any pair of particles attract each other with forces proportional to the product of their masses and inversely proportional to the square of the distance between them. These forces are directed along the straight line joining the particles and are independent of the presence of neighboring or intervening material bodies. The second type of force is the elastic force, as exemplified by Hooke's law.

Next came the study of electric and magnetic forces, and this study forms the content of this book. It is assumed that the reader is acquainted with the qualitative facts concerning various methods of electrifying bodies, such as the historical method of rubbing a rod of hard rubber with fur or a glass rod with silk, as well as the more modern schemes of employing batteries or power lines. When bodies are so treated and placed near together, they exert forces on each other which did not exist before the treatment. We say that the bodies thus treated have become electrically charged. Similarly, the discovery of permanent magnets formed the basis of the first studies of magnetic forces.

The subsequent developments of electromagnetism have yielded not only the widespread practical applications to electrical power production and distribution, to communications in the form of telephone, telegraph, radio, and television, and to the innumerable modern aspects of industrial electronics, but also a remarkable understanding of atomic and molecular forces. Indeed, the success of modern atomic theory in explaining molecular binding and the cohesive forces in

1

solids on an electromagnetic basis suggested that possibly one could trace the origin of all natural forces to electrical and magnetic forces. In recent years, however, the studies of nuclear reactions and radio-activity have shown that nuclear forces, the enormous forces which hold together the elemental particles of which the nuclei of atoms are composed, are probably not electromagnetic in origin, although there are many similarities. Altogether, then, the importance of electro-magnetic forces is so great that the subject of electromagnetism forms one of the major division of physics.

The fact that electrically charged bodies exert forces on each other when not in contact reminds one strongly of gravitational forces. There is, in fact, a great deal of similarity between these two types of forces, although there are important and significant differences between them. The classical treatment of gravitational forces in terms of action at a distance provided the original framework into which the early theories of electric and magnetic forces were cast. In fact, Coulomb discovered in 1785 that two electrically charged bodies whose linear dimensions were small compared to their separation attracted or repelled each other with forces directed along the line joining these charged bodies and inversely proportional to the square of the distance between them. Thus we have an exact parallel to Newton's law of gravitation, and it is not surprising that for many years the theory of electrical forces was essentially the action-at-a-distance theory of gravitational forces. Similarly, it was found that magnetic forces between permanent magnets could be treated in a like fashion, assuming that they contain magnetic north and south poles. The force between poles again is inversely proportional to the square of the distance between them. Of course, single isolated poles were never found in nature, but a magnet can be considered as possessing a pair of equal north and south poles. The later discovery by Oersted that electric charges in motion, *i.e.*, electric currents, produced mag-netic effects was further studied by Ampère, who showed that the magnetic force produced by a current-carrying circuit can be con-sidered as built up from contributions from each infinitesimal length of the circuit. Each of these contributions to the magnetic force again varies inversely as the square of the distance from the current element to the point where the magnetic force is measured. Thus these laws of action at a distance seemed to point to the firm estab-lishment of a theory of electromagnetism quite similar to that of gravitation.

The researches and ideas of Faraday, in the first part of the nineteenth century, marked a significant and important turning point for the theory of electromagnetism. Faraday thought of electric and magnetic interactions not in terms of action at a distance but in terms of fields of force produced by electrical charges and magnets. Since his time there has been a continual trend toward more widespread utilization of the field concept in physics, and indeed present-day theoretical physics is largely concerned with problems of field theory. The importance of Faraday's field concepts lies primarily in the physical significance which he attributed to the field to explain electromagnetic phenomena rather than because of the introduction of the idea of a field. In fact, gravitational fields of force and their properties had already been studied extensively, but they constituted simply mathematical alternatives to action-at-a-distance theories without adding essentially to physical insight into gravitational phenomena. On the other hand, Faraday's field concepts were of utmost physical significance and, as one would expect, contributed greatly to an understanding of just those aspects of electromagnetic interactions which are different from, rather than those similar to, gravitational interactions.

One of the most striking and important differences between electromagnetic forces and gravitational forces is the effect of intervening or neighboring bodies on such forces. The mutual gravitational attraction between a fixed pair of particles is independent of and uninfluenced by the presence of other material bodies. In sharp contrast, the mutual electrical attraction or repulsion between a pair of electrically charged bodies is strongly affected by the presence of even uncharged bodies in their neighborhood. For example, an electrical insulator, or dielectric, placed between two charged bodies sharply reduces the force with which they push or pull on each other. In studying this and related phenomena, Faraday's attention was directed primarily to the dielectric and, in fact, to all space in the neighborhood of charged bodies. He concluded that things of fundamental physical meaning occurred in this otherwise nonelectrified material and believed that the presence of an electrified body in a region of space created a real physical change in this space. The idea of a field of force surrounding a charged body, with lines of force indicating the direction of the electrical force acting on a test body at each point of space, had for Faraday real physical existence. The strength of the field was to be measured by the number of lines (the flux, so-called) per unit area crossing a surface whose normal coincided with the direction of the lines of force. These lines or tubes of force were visualized to possess mechanical strength and to be subject to tensions and stresses.

Faraday's discovery that electrical fields could be induced by changing magnetic fields and that the induced effect in a circuit was proportional to the number of magnetic lines, the magnetic flux, threading this circuit, further strengthened his belief in the reality of electrical and magnetic fields. It remained for Maxwell, some years later, to cast Faraday's ideas into mathematical form and to create a consistent field theory of electromagnetism, which stands to this day as one of the great structures of theoretical physics. From this theory emerged the exciting prediction of electromagnetic waves, so commonplace today, which travel with the observed velocity of light. Thus was born the electromagnetic theory of light, and two hitherto unrelated fields of physics were welded into one. Furthermore, the field theory of electromagnetism became firmly established, and, as previously mentioned, the concept of fields in physics has become increasingly popular and productive with the passing of the years. The fact that electromagnetic effects are propagated with a finite speed is all important in establishing the superiority of the field concept over that of action at a distance. To clarify this statement, let us consider an example comparing gravitational and electromagnetic actions. The gravitational pull of the sun on the earth and the corresponding pull of the earth on the sun depend on the instantaneous positions of these two bodies. Thus the motion of the earth around the sun is due to a force depending only on its instantaneous position relative to the sun, and since the sun may be considered stationary to a good degree of approximation because of its huge mass relative to that of the earth, the motion under this action-at-a-distance force follows the well-known Keplerian laws. In contrast to this, consider an electromagnetic disturbance in the form of a light wave emanating from an atom on the sun and absorbed by an atom on the earth. Since it requires some 8 minutes for light to reach the earth from the sun, the force exerted by the light wave on the absorbing atom does not depend on the instantaneous position of the emitting atom but on its position some 8 minutes before. Thus at best one could talk of a retarded action at a distance to describe this absorption. When one considers the reaction of the absorbing atom on the emitting atom, however, it becomes extraordinarily difficult to formulate any description of the phenomenon in terms of action at a distance. Field theory, on the other hand, provides a relatively simple and straightforward picture by attributing both energy and momentum to the light wave and focusing attention on the interaction between the light wave itself and the absorbing atom.

Because of the overwhelming importance of the field concept, we shall develop the treatment of electricity and magnetism in this book entirely from a field standpoint. Accordingly the remainder of this chapter will be devoted to some of the more important quantitative aspects of fields, and of fields of force in particular, without special reference to their origin. *field theory is important in modern investigat ? the electricity and electromagnetics ??*

1. Scalar and Vector Fields. We now proceed to a more detailed discussion of the concept and definition of a field, as used in physics. We start with simple examples. First, consider a room in which we imagine the temperature measured at each point of space inside the room. The totality of temperature readings as a function of position in space is called a *field*, and more specifically, a *scalar field*, since temperature is a scalar quantity having a magnitude but no directive properties. If the temperature is the same at each point of the room, as it would be if the room were in thermal equilibrium, one says that the field is *uniform.* This is a special but important case. In general, however, the temperature will vary from point to point of the room, a state of affairs only too common when one heats a room with a radiator.

As a second example, consider a region where a liquid or gas is in steady motion. At every point of space one can construct a vector representing the direction and magnitude of the velocity of the fluid particle located at the point in question. In general, we shall have different velocity vectors at different points of the region. The aggregate of these velocity vectors describes uniquely the state of motion of the fluid and is called a *velocity field*. This is an easily visualizable example of a *vector field*. In the special but important case that all the vectors are identical in magnitude and mutually parallel, one calls the vector field *uniform*. For the purposes of this book, we need study some of the properties of only scalar and vector fields, although more complicated fields, such as those describing the stress or strain distribution in an elastic medium, are of interest in more advanced treatments of various branches of physics.

In the case of vector fields, it is useful to map or plot these fields by constructing lines of flow (in the case of a velocity field) or lines of force (in the case of a field of force) which give the direction of the vector velocity or force at each point of space. More specifically, these lines are so constructed that the tangent to a line at a given point yields the direction of the vector in question at that point. Once the field has been mapped with the help of these field lines, there remains only the task of specifying the magnitude of the vector as a function of position to complete the quantitative description of the field.   For a *uniform* field, the field lines form a family of parallel straight lines, and the magnitude of the vector is the same at all field points.   Such a uniform field can exist only in a limited region of space.   In general, the field lines will be curves, and the magnitude of the vector will vary from point to point of space.

If the field quantity at a given point of space is constant, unvarying with time, one calls the field a *static, or stationary*, field.   If not, one is concerned with a *time-varying* field.   In the case of vector fields, the pattern of field lines may or may not vary for a nonstatic field.

Summarizing briefly, we say that a field in a given region of space comprises the aggregate of physical quantities which are functions of position within this region.   If these physical quantities are scalars, one speaks of a scalar field; if they are vectors, one speaks of a vector field.

2. Conservative and Nonconservative Force Fields; Potential Energy.   In mechanics, one learns of the classification of forces acting on material bodies as conservative and nonconservative, and that for conservative forces one can introduce the concept of potential energy. For conservative forces the law of conservation of mechanical energy is valid and forms one of the more useful tools in handling a large class of mechanical problems.   These same ideas can be carried over to the study of fields of force and are similarly of great value in helping one understand the nature of various types of force fields.

For the sake of completeness, we shall review briefly the principal facts concerning conservative and nonconservative forces and potential energy.   Let us start with a very simple example.   Consider a particle moving along a straight line, let us say along the positive x-axis, under the action of a constant force which is directed along the negative x-axis, opposing the motion.   At a given point P of its motion, the particle will have a definite speed and a corresponding kinetic energy. As the particle moves, it loses kinetic energy under the action of the constant force, eventually reverses its direction of motion, and returns along the negative x-axis with ever-increasing speed and kinetic energy.   In particular, when it returns to the point P, it has exactly the same speed and kinetic energy as on the outward trip at this point. The velocity vector is reversed in direction but identical in magnitude. Thus we have the picture of the body losing its kinetic energy as it moves from its initial position P until it reverses, at which point the kinetic energy has been reduced to zero, then gaining kinetic energy on the return trip until, when it returns to its initial position P, it has regained all its initial kinetic energy.   This recapture of kinetic energy when the particle returns leads one to regard the kinetic energy loss in the motion as only an apparent loss of energy and something which is restored to the body when it returns.   Thus the concept of energy being conserved and not lost comes into being, and one introduces the concept of potential energy, or energy of position (in contrast to energy of motion), to keep the books balanced with regard to the total mechanical energy of this motion.

Let us consider this same example from a somewhat different viewpoint.   Suppose that our particle is again located at a point P on the x-axis, but that it is held at rest in equilibrium by the action of an external force F', which must be equal to and oppositely directed to the original force F.   Now let us push the particle from position P to another position Q (in the positive x-direction) and again hold it in equilibrium.   During this displacement we do a positive amount of work on the particle, and the force F does an equal negative amount of work.   All the work which we have done can be regained (as kinetic energy, for example) by allowing the particle to return to its starting point P.   Since this is so, we can think of the work we have done in effecting this displacement as stored in energy of position of the particle, and we say the particle has gained potential energy.   The increase of potential energy is defined as the work we have done, or equally well, as the negative of the work done by the force F during the displacement.   The essential point concerning this definition of potential energy is that it can have a unique meaning *only* if all the expended work can be regained by allowing the body to return to its starting point.   That this is not true for all forces is evident if one considers pushing the body from P to Q against a friction force.   The work done cannot be regained by returning the particle to P and indeed has been lost as mechanical energy.

We now proceed to generalize this idea of potential energy.   In the case of one-dimensional problems, this is simple.   It is evident that any force depending only on position is conservative in the sense that potential energy exists and that no other type of force, such as a force depending on the particle velocity, is conservative.   To see this formally, suppose the force acting is given by $F(x)$ and the particle is displaced from x_1 to x_2.   The work done by this force is evidently given by $\int_{x_1}^{x_2} F(x)\, dx$, and this depends only on the starting and end points, *i.e.*, on the limits of the integral, and not on the details of the intervening motion.   In particular, if the particle returns to its initial position x_1, the two limits become identical, and the integral vanishes.   Thus, the total work done in a round trip is zero, and the force $F(x)$ is therefore conservative.   In the case of two- or three-dimensional problems, the situation is not so simple.   It is still true that only forces which depend on position are conservative, but not *all* forces depending only on position are conservative.   It is necessary that the total work done by such a force on a particle be zero if the particle is moved around *any* closed path and returns to its initial position, and this is not true of all forces which depend only on position.

We are now in a position to state precisely the general condition that a force be conservative and that a potential energy exist.   *A force is said to be conservative if the work done by this force on a body vanishes if the body is carried around any closed path back to its initial position.* This criterion can be stated in an alternative equivalent form which is useful for many purposes: Consider a particle which is moved from an initial position P to some final position Q.   *If the work done by the force acting on the particle is the same for all paths joining the initial and end points, the force is conservative.* One can readily see that both these criteria are equivalent.

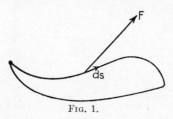

Fig. 1.

The preceding ideas can now be carried over directly to describe fields of force. Consider a field of force of any sort, gravitational, electrical, or magnetic, and let us insert a suitable test body into this field.   There will be a force exerted by the field on the test body, which we denote by F.   We now carry this test body from its original position around an arbitrary closed path as shown in Fig. 1.   The work done by the field on the body as the latter undergoes a small displacement ds as shown is given by

$$dW = F_s\, ds$$

where F_s is the component of F in the direction of ds.   The total work done in performing the complete circuit is obtained by adding the contributions from each element of length ds in the closed path.   If the field is conservative, we have as the condition for *any* closed path,

$$\oint F_s\, ds = 0 \qquad\qquad (1.1)$$

The circle on the integral sign is to remind us that the integral is taken around a closed path.   If condition (1.1) is not obeyed, the field is nonconservative, and one cannot speak uniquely of a potential energy.

It is clear that the lines of force in a conservative field can never be closed curves.

3. Equipotential Surfaces and Potential Energy Gradient. We shall now examine the properties of a *conservative* force field in more detail. Let the force which the field exerts *on* a test body be F, a function of position. If the test body is moved from an initial position A to a final position B along any *arbitrary* path (Fig. 2) connecting these two points, the change of its potential energy will be given by

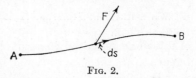

FIG. 2.

$$U_B - U_A = - \int_A^B F_s \, ds \tag{1.2}$$

where U_B denotes the potential energy of the test body at point B and U_A its value at point A. Thus to each point of the force field we can (for a given test body) assign a potential energy U. If the test body gains potential energy in its trip from A to B, one says that the point B is at a higher potential than point A, and vice versa.

It is to be noted that the position in space at which the potential energy is taken equal to zero is arbitrary and is chosen as a matter of convenience. In general, it is convenient to place $U = 0$ at a point where the force F vanishes, but this is not always the most convenient choice. We return to this point in the next chapter in connection with the electrostatic field of force.

Now suppose we have chosen a suitable reference position of zero potential energy. The advantage which has been gained by introducing a potential energy function to describe a conservative field of force lies in the fact that we have replaced a vector field by a scalar field of potential energy. To show that this replacement is complete, we now have to show that one can deduce the magnitude and direction of the force F at any point of the field from a knowledge of the distribution of potential energy. Let us suppose that we know the potential energy U at each point of space, *i.e.*, that we are in possession of a relation of the form $U = \phi(x,y,z)$, where the single-valued function $\phi(x,y,z)$ depends on the particular type of field under discussion. If we wish to know at what points of space a test body will have a given potential energy, say U_0, we set $U = U_0$ and obtain an equation

$$\phi(x,y,z) = U_0 = \text{constant}$$

This is the equation of a surface, and this surface is called an *equi-*

potential surface. There will exist a whole family of these equipotential surfaces corresponding to different values of U_0. Since, by definition, it requires no work to move our test body from one point to any other on the same equipotential surface, it follows that the lines of force must be perpendicular to the equipotential surfaces at every point of space. Thus we have established one relation between lines of force and potential energy. If one has a uniform field of force, as, for example, the gravitational field produced by the earth at points near its surface, the equipotentials consist of a set of parallel planes, the normals to these planes then forming the lines of force. Conversely, if one knows the equipotentials, one can construct immediately the lines of force by drawing the lines which intersect these surfaces at right angles. For example, suppose the equipotential surfaces consist of a family of concentric spherical surfaces with the common center at a point O. Then the lines of force will consist of a set of straight lines radiating in all directions from O, since these lines, being radii of all the spherical equipotential surfaces, intersect these surfaces everywhere at right angles.

Now consider our test body located at a point P in the force field, and suppose we move it a distance ds to a neighboring point. From Eq. (1.2) it follows that its potential energy changes by an amount

$$dU = -F_s\, ds \qquad (1.3)$$

where F_s is the component of the force exerted by the field in the direction ds. This may be written in the form

$$F_s = -\frac{dU}{ds} \qquad (1.4)$$

In words, the component of the force in any given direction is equal to the negative rate of change of potential energy with position in this direction. The space derivative in Eq. (1.4) is known as a *directional derivative*, since its value depends on the direction in which ds is constructed at the point P. This is in accordance with the fact that F_s, being the component of a vector, has a definite direction as well as a magnitude. If one moves from P to a neighboring point on the same equipotential surface as that on which P lies, then for this direction dU/ds is zero since the change in potential energy is zero. If one moves, however, to a neighboring point not on the same equipotential surface, we obtain a value of dU/ds different from zero. That particular direction for which dU/ds has the maximum value possible at a given point is along a line of force (since the maximum value of any component of a vector is the vector itself), and the negative of this maximum rate of change of U with distance is the vector force at the point in question.   This maximum rate of change of potential energy with position is called the *gradient* of the potential energy, and this gradient is a vector directed at right angles to the equipotential surface.   In symbols, one may write

$$F = - \text{grad } U \qquad\qquad (1.5)$$

We have now completed the task of showing how one may derive the properties of a conservative field of force from a knowledge of the potential energy as a function of position.   The converse problem of determining the potential energy from the force field is accomplished by the use of Eq. (1.2).

An example may help to clarify the foregoing.   Suppose one is walking on a hillside and is interested in the changes of elevation, vertical height from the bottom of the hill, with position.   Points of equal elevation form curves called contours, and one often sees maps with these contour lines indicating various elevations.   The contour lines are the analogues of the equipotential surfaces in the case of a conservative force field.   Now suppose that one is located on a contour line at an elevation of 100 ft and wishes to descend to a point of 95-ft elevation.   There are many ways of accomplishing this; all that is necessary is that one move from the starting point to *any* point on the 95-ft contour.   There is, however, a shortest way; that is along the direction perpendicular to the contours and is the direction of *maximum* slope, the line of steepest descent.   It is clear that the maximum rate of change of elevation with position lies along the line of steepest descent (or ascent), and this is the gradient of the elevation.   In the case of our field of force, one moves from one equipotential surface to another differing in potential energy by a definite amount dU along the shortest path by following a line of force perpendicular to the surfaces.   The rate of change of potential energy with distance in this direction is thus the gradient of the potential energy and is the maximum rate of change at the point in

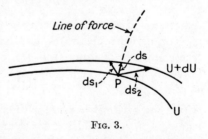

FIG. 3.

question.   This is indicated in Fig. 3, where three directions from P are shown.   For the given value dU, it is clear that ds is shorter than ds_1 or ds_2, and consequently the ratio dU/ds is largest for this direction.

4. The Inverse-square Law. One of the most important fields of force encountered in physical problems is the so-called inverse-square field. For this case, the force exerted by the field on a test body at a point P is directed along the straight line joining the field point P and a *fixed* point O, and its magnitude is inversely proportional to the square of the distance from O to P. According to Newton's law of gravitation, the gravitational field produced by a single mass point is an inverse-square field. As already mentioned, Coulomb's law of force for electrically charged bodies at rest also yields this as the electric field of force produced by a single electrically charged body of dimensions sufficiently small as to be considered a point charge. As we shall see shortly, this is one of the fundamental starting points of our study of electricity, and we shall now derive some of the important properties of this inverse-square field.

We shall first show that this type of field is conservative. To do this, we must prove that the work done by the field on a test body, as

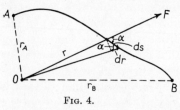

FIG. 4.

the latter is moved from an initial position A to some final position B, does not depend on the particular path connecting A and B, but *only* on the initial and end points A and B. In Fig. 4 are shown the fixed point O and an arbitrary path connecting two points A and B. For the sake of definiteness, we show the force acting on the test body as a repulsive force from the center O. The proof that follows is equally applicable to an attractive force.

Consider a portion ds of the path as shown. The work done during this displacement is, by definition,

$$dW = F_s \, ds = F \, ds \cos \alpha$$

where α is the angle between the force vector F and the displacement vector ds. From the figure, one sees readily that $ds \cos \alpha = dr$, the change in distance from O during the displacement ds, so that we have

$$dW = F \, dr \tag{1.6}$$

If we now write $F = c/r^2$ for the magnitude of F, where c is a positive constant for a repulsive force and negative for an attractive force, the total work done by the field along the path is

$$W = \int_A^B \frac{c}{r^2} \, dr = c\left(\frac{1}{r_A} - \frac{1}{r_B}\right) \tag{1.7}$$

where r_A is the distance from O to A, and r_B is the distance from O to B. Equation (1.7) shows directly that the work done depends only on the end points, *i.e.*, on r_A and r_B, and not on the shape of the path connecting these points. Therefore, the field is conservative, and a potential energy function exists. From (1.2), the difference in potential energy between point B and point A is

$$U_B - U_A = c \left(\frac{1}{r_B} - \frac{1}{r_A} \right) \tag{1.8}$$

There remains only the choice of a convenient origin for potential energy to give it a unique value at all points of space. We shall choose the potential energy zero for points infinitely distant from the fixed point O. This is convenient since the force vanishes at infinity also.

Let us now apply Eq. (1.8) to the case where the initial point A is at infinity, so that $r_A = \infty$ and $U_A = 0$. Then $U_B = c/r_B$, or if we drop the now-redundant subscript B, we have

$$U = \frac{c}{r} \tag{1.9}$$

as the final expression for the potential energy at any point of space, r being the distance from the fixed point O to the point in question. If we use a rectangular coordinate system with O as an origin, we can write the equivalent relation $U(x,y,z) = c/\sqrt{x^2 + y^2 + z^2}$, which is of the form employed in Sec. 3.

The equipotential surfaces are evidently spherical surfaces all possessing the same center, *i.e.*, the fixed point O, and the lines of force are the radii of these spheres, and these lines cut the equi-potentials everywhere at right angles. As a simple check on the use of Eq. (1.4) giving the force components as directional derivatives of the potential energy, we note that for a radial displacement $ds = dr$ from any point in the field, Eq. (1.4) gives

$$F_r = - \frac{dU}{dr} = \frac{c}{r^2}$$

from (1.9). If ds is taken in any direction perpendicular to the radial direction, then the corresponding force component is zero. Thus the radial component F_r is the force vector itself, and we have for this special case

$$F = - \operatorname{grad} U = \frac{c}{r^2}$$

as is to be expected, and F is directed along the radius vector from O to the field point.

5. Example. In order to clarify further the general relations of Sec. 3 between potential energy and lines of force, we shall apply them to a specific example which is not so simple as the inverse-square field of Sec. 4. Suppose we are given the information that the distribution of the potential energy for a conservative force field in the x-y plane, except at the origin $x = y = 0$, is given by the equation

$$U = \frac{ax}{(x^2 + y^2)^{\frac{3}{2}}} \tag{1.10}$$

where a is a constant. (This is actually the potential energy of a force field produced by a tiny electric dipole located at the origin of coordinates, as we shall see in a later chapter. A dipole is a pair of equal and opposite electric charges in juxtaposition.) We wish to find the magnitude and direction of the force vector at any point in the plane and, if possible, derive the equations for the lines of force.

To obtain the x- and y-components of the force vector F, we utilize Eq. (1.4). First, consider the change in potential energy as we move from a point with coordinates (x,y) to a neighboring point with coordinates $(x + dx, y)$. The displacement is in the x-direction, of magnitude dx, and hence we obtain for the x-component of F

$$F_x = - \frac{\partial U}{\partial x} \tag{1.11}$$

In performing the indicated differentiation, we must keep y constant, since x alone varies in this displacement. Similarly the y-component of F is

$$F_y = - \frac{\partial U}{\partial y} \tag{1.11a}$$

keeping x constant.

Using Eq. (1.10) for U, we find readily

$$F_x = - \frac{a}{(x^2 + y^2)^{\frac{3}{2}}} + \frac{3ax^2}{(x^2 + y^2)^{\frac{5}{2}}} = \frac{a(2x^2 - y^2)}{(x^2 + y^2)^{\frac{5}{2}}} \tag{1.12}$$

and

$$F_y = \frac{3axy}{(x^2 + y^2)^{\frac{5}{2}}} \tag{1.13}$$

The magnitude of F is then obtained from

$$F^2 = F_x^2 + F_y^2$$

as

$$F = \frac{a(4x^2 + y^2)^{\frac{1}{2}}}{(x^2 + y^2)^2} \tag{1.14}$$

which is not particularly simple, but which does allow the calculation of the magnitude of the force at each point of the x-y plane.   There remains the question of the direction of the force vector, *i.e.*, the direction of the lines of force.   By definition, the lines of force are to be drawn so that their tangents at every point coincide with the direction of F.   Thus the tangent of the angle which the vector F makes with the x-axis is equal to the slope dy/dx of the lines of force at every point.   Writing this as an equation, we have

$$\frac{dy}{dx} = \frac{F_y}{F_x} \tag{1.15}$$

and, in our case, we have from (1.12) and (1.13)

$$\frac{dy}{dx} = \frac{3xy}{2x^2 - y^2} \tag{1.16}$$

If this can be integrated, the resulting equation is the equation of the lines of force.   In the integrated equation there will occur an arbitrary constant of integration.   The different lines of force describing this field then are obtained by assigning different values to this arbitrary constant.

Equation (1.16) is not easy to integrate as it stands, and indeed the whole problem looks rather formidable when expressed in terms of Cartesian coordinates.   For example, the equation for the equipotentials (more precisely, for the curves representing the intersections of the equipotential surfaces and the x-y plane) which is obtained by setting $U = U_0$ (a constant) in Eq. (1.10) turns out to be of the sixth degree.

The whole problem becomes much simpler to handle if we utilize polar coordinates in the plane, and we shall now proceed to do so, checking the results already obtained and carrying the solution through to completion.   In

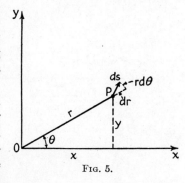

Fig. 5.

Fig. 5 are shown the relations between the Cartesian coordinates (x,y) of the point P and its polar coordinates (r,θ).   We have

$$x = r \cos \theta; \qquad x^2 + y^2 = r^2$$
$$y = r \sin \theta; \qquad \frac{y}{x} = \tan \theta$$

Expressing Eq. (1.10) in terms of r and θ, we have

$$U = \frac{a \cos \theta}{r^2} \tag{1.17}$$

for the potential energy.   The equipotentials are given by $r^2 = k \cos \theta$ (with $k = a/U_0$), which is a much simpler equation to plot than Eq. (1.10).   Now let us compute the radial and tangential components of F.   For the radial component we have, according to Eq. (1.4),

$$F_r = -\frac{\partial U}{\partial r}$$

holding θ constant, since $ds = dr$, and for the tangential component

$$F_\theta = -\frac{1}{r}\frac{\partial U}{\partial \theta}$$

holding r constant, since for this case $ds = r\,d\theta$, as is shown in Fig. 5. Using (1.17), there follows

$$F_r = \frac{2a \cos \theta}{r^3} \tag{1.18}$$

$$F_\theta = \frac{a \sin \theta}{r^3} \tag{1.19}$$

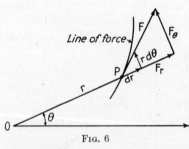

Line of force

FIG. 6

The magnitude of F is obtained from $F^2 = F_r^2 + F_\theta^2$ and is

$$|F| = \frac{a \sqrt{1 + 3\cos^2 \theta}}{r^3} \tag{1.20}$$

which is identical with Eq. (1.14). The proof is left to the student. The equations of the lines of force may now be obtained as follows: The angle between F and the radius vector r is the same as the angle between an infinitesimal length ds of the curve and r (Fig. 6).   Thus we have

$$r\frac{d\theta}{dr} = \frac{F_\theta}{F_r} \tag{1.21}$$

and, using (1.18) and (1.19), this becomes

$$\frac{d\theta}{dr} = \frac{1}{2}\frac{\tan \theta}{r} \tag{1.22}$$

We rewrite this equation in the form

$$\frac{dr}{r} = 2\,\frac{d\theta}{\tan\,\theta} = 2\,\frac{\cos\,\theta\,d\theta}{\sin\,\theta} = 2\,\frac{d(\sin\,\theta)}{\sin\,\theta}$$

and it now can be integrated directly, yielding

$$\ln\left(\frac{r}{\sin^2\,\theta}\right) = \text{constant}$$

or

$$r = b\,\sin^2\,\theta \qquad\qquad (1.23)$$

where b is an arbitrary constant. The solid curves of Fig. 7 are plots of Eq. (1.23) for different values of b; the dotted curves are a few of the equipotentials which, according to Eq. (1.17), are given by $\cos\,\theta/r^2 = \text{constant}$. The equipotentials and lines of force intersect at right angles. Figure 7 seems to display a pattern of closed lines of force, which would contradict the concept of a conservative field. One must remember, however, that our equations do not hold right at the origin, since there both force and potential energy become infinite. (Actually the lines of force start on the positive charge of the dipole and end on its negative charge.) The fact that the lines of force are normal to the equipotentials offers a method of calculating the latter if the former are known. Thus, for example, if we were given Eqs. (1.18) and (1.19) as

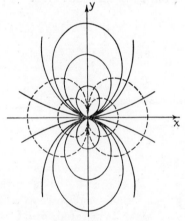

Fig. 7.

the initial data, we would write for the slope of the lines of force, $r\,d\theta/dr = \frac{1}{2}\tan\,\theta$, as in Eq. (1.22). Now, at any point the slope of the curve intersecting a given curve at right angles is the negative reciprocal of the slope of the latter. Hence the equipotential curves satisfy the equation

$$-\frac{1}{r}\frac{dr}{d\theta} = \frac{1}{2}\tan\,\theta$$

$$\tan\,\theta\,d\theta + 2\,\frac{dr}{r} = 0$$

Upon integration, this yields $(\cos\,\theta)/r^2 = \text{constant}$, which checks the potential energy as given by Eq. (1.17).

As a final check, let us rewrite Eq. (1.23) for the lines of force in Cartesian coordinates, differentiate to find the slope, and see if the result checks Eq. (1.16).   Since $r = \sqrt{x^2 + y^2}$ and

$$\sin^2 \theta = \frac{y^2}{r^2} = \frac{y^2}{(x^2 + y^2)},$$

Eq. (1.23) becomes

$$\frac{(x^2 + y^2)^{\frac{3}{2}}}{y^2} = b \qquad\qquad (1.24)$$

and this is of the form $f(x,y) = $ constant.   Differentiating, we have

$$df = \frac{\partial f}{\partial x}\, dx + \frac{\partial f}{\partial y}\, dy = 0$$

so that

$$\frac{dy}{dx} = -\frac{\partial f/\partial x}{\partial f/\partial y}$$

From Eq. (1.24) one finds

$$\frac{\partial f}{\partial x} = \frac{3x}{y^2}\,(x^2 + y^2)^{\frac{1}{2}}$$

and

$$\frac{\partial f}{\partial y} = \frac{3}{y}\,(x^2 + y^2)^{\frac{1}{2}} - \frac{2}{y^3}\,(x^2 + y^2)^{\frac{3}{2}} = \left(\frac{y^2 - 2x^2}{y^3}\right)(x^2 + y^2)^{\frac{1}{2}}$$

hence

$$\frac{dy}{dx} = \frac{3xy}{2x^2 - y^2}$$

which is identical with Eq. (1.16).

To summarize, we have seen how one may find the components of the vector force if the potential energy is known and from this the slope of the lines of force as a function of position.   The latter expression, when integrated, leads to equations of the lines of force.   Conversely, if the components of the field are known, the slope of the equipotentials (more precisely, the intersection of the equipotential surfaces with a plane) may be obtained and, when integrated, yields the equation of the equipotentials.   One may obtain the potential more directly, however, by utilizing Eq. (1.2) and setting the potential energy equal to zero at infinity.   The potential energy U at a point P then can be written as

$$U = -\int_{\infty}^{P} F_s\, ds$$

where the integral is evaluated along any convenient path starting at infinity and ending at the point P at which the potential energy is desired.   A skillful choice of the path of integration may simplify the calculation enormously. For example, if the coordinates of P are (r,θ), we may integrate along that radius vector which makes the desired angle θ with the x-axis, starting at $r = \infty$ and ending at the value of r which brings us to the point P. Using Eq. (1.18) for the radial component of the force, the above integral becomes

$$U = -\int_{\infty}^{r} F_r \, dr = -2a \cos \theta \int_{\infty}^{r} \frac{dr}{r^3} = 2a \cos \theta \left[\frac{1}{2r^2}\right]_{\infty}^{r} = \frac{a \cos \theta}{r^2}$$

which checks Eq. (1.17).

In general, especially for three-dimensional problems, it is not feasible to attempt an integration of Eq. (1.15) or its equivalent in three dimensions. The lines of force are best obtained by graphical methods.

Problems

1. Given a *uniform* field of force in which the force exerted by the field on a test body has the following components:

$$F_x = 0; \qquad F_y = F_0 = \text{constant}; \qquad F_s = 0$$

Setting the potential energy equal to zero at the origin of coordinates, compute the potential energy at a point P of coordinates $(x,y,0)$ by calculating the work done on the test body as it moves from the origin to the point P along the following paths in the x-y plane:

a. From the origin along the x-axis to the point $(x,0)$ and then along a path parallel to the y-axis.

b. From the origin along the y-axis to the point $(0,y)$ and then along a path parallel to the x-axis.

c. Along the straight line from the origin to the point P.

Consider a circle of radius R in the x-y plane with its center at the origin. Find the potential energy as a function of position on the circle, *i.e.*, as a function of the angle θ of polar coordinates for a fixed value of $r = R$. Plot this result as a function of θ.

2. A central force field is one in which the force on a test body located at any point P is directed along the straight line from a fixed center O to the field point P. The magnitude of the force is a function only of the distance r from O to P. (The inverse-square field is a special case of the general central field.)

a. Prove that this central field is conservative.

b. In the case where the force F has a magnitude varying inversely with the cube of the distance from O to P, *i.e.*, $F = c/r^3$ with c a constant, find an expression for the potential energy at any point of the field. Choose the potential energy zero at $r = \infty$.

3. The force exerted on a test body in the x-y plane by a field of force has the components

$$F_x = -\frac{y}{(x^2 + y^2)^{\frac{1}{2}}}; \qquad F_y = \frac{x}{(x^2 + y^2)^{\frac{1}{2}}}$$

a. Find an expression for the magnitude of the resultant force at any point in the plane, and show that it depends only on the distance of the field point from the origin.

b. Prove that the lines of force are a set of concentric circles, the center lying at the origin.

c. Show that this field is nonconservative by computing the work done in carrying a test body completely around a circular path of radius r, starting at the point (r,θ).

d. Compute the work done for the closed path starting at (r,θ), moving out along a radius to the point (r_1,θ), then along a circle of radius r_1 to the point (r_1,θ_1), next inward along a radius to the point (r,θ_1), and finally along a circle of radius r to the starting point. Compare this with your answer to part c.

4. The force components of a conservative field of force in the x-y plane are given by

$$F_x = \frac{a(2x^2 - y^2)}{(x^2 + y^2)^{\frac{5}{2}}}; \qquad F_y = \frac{3axy}{(x^2 + y^2)^{\frac{5}{2}}}$$

where a is a constant.

a. Compute the potential energy (relative to its value at infinity) at a point P with coordinates (x,y) by calculating the work done on a test body by this force as the body is moved from infinity in along the x-axis to the point $(x,0)$, and then along a path parallel to the y-axis to the point P.

b. Repeat the calculation of part a along the following path: from infinity along the y-axis to the point $(0,y)$, and then parallel to the x-axis to the point P.

5. The force on a test charged body in an electric field of force between two long concentric cylindrical surfaces of radii a and b $(a < b)$ is given by

$$F_x = \frac{-cx}{x^2 + y^2}; \qquad F_y = \frac{-cy}{x^2 + y^2}; \qquad F_z = 0$$

where c is a positive constant and the x-y plane is perpendicular to the axis of the cylinders.

a. Construct the lines of force in the x-y plane, and sketch in some of the equipotentials.

b. Calculate the distribution of potential energy for this field, and show that this potential energy depends only on the distance from the axis. Choose the potential energy zero at the inner cylindrical surface.

c. Make a plot of potential energy as a function of distance from the axis.

6. It is possible to produce a force field in a limited region of space such that the potential energy has the form

$$U = a(2x^2 - y^2 - z^2)$$

where a is a constant.

a. What are the force components in this field?

b. Find the equations of the lines of force in the plane $z = 0$, and plot the equipotentials and lines of force in this plane.

7. The potential energy in an electric field of force produced by a "line of dipoles" is given by

$$U = \frac{cx}{x^2 + y^2}$$

with c a constant.

a. Prove that the equipotential surfaces are circular cylinders, obtaining expressions for the radii and for the location of the axes of these cylindrical surfaces.

b. Plot U as a function of x along the line $y = z = 0$.

c. Compute the force components at any point in both Cartesian and polar (cylindrical) coordinates.

d. From your answer to part c, find the polar equation of the lines of force in the x-y plane.

8. Given the distribution of potential energy in a plane

$$U = c \left(\frac{3}{r} - \frac{4}{r^3} \cos^2 \theta \right)$$

where c is a positive constant and r and θ are polar coordinates in the plane.

a. Plot the variations of U with r along radial lines in the directions $\theta = 90°$, $\theta = 45°$, $\theta = 0°$. Where along these lines is the potential energy a maximum? What are the maximum values?

b. Compute F_r and F_θ. How do the direction and magnitude of the force vector vary with r along the radial lines $\theta = 90°$, $\theta = 45°$, and $\theta = 0°$?

c. Where is the force zero? What is the potential energy at these points?

CHAPTER 2

THE ELECTROSTATIC FIELD OF FORCE

In the last chapter we have discussed quantitatively the more important properties of fields of force and of conservative fields in particular. We now turn more specifically to the subject of *electrostatics*, which deals with the laws governing the equilibrium interactions between electrically charged bodies or between electrically charged bodies and uncharged matter. In developing these laws we shall, as previously stated, adopt the field concept from the very outset. Thus, if we have one or more electrically charged bodies at rest, we think of all space being affected by these bodies, and we say that an electric field, or more precisely, an electrostatic field, is established throughout space. If we introduce another charged body at a given point of space, it will be acted on by a force (due, of course, ultimately to the presence of the original charged bodies), and we can use this force exerted on a test charge to describe the field of force. In this chapter we shall be concerned primarily with the study of the nature of the electrostatic field thus produced and shall defer an examination of the details of calculating the field from a knowledge of the charged sources which give rise to it. Of necessity, we shall repeat some of the material already presented in Chap. 1, but only in so far as it applies to the electrostatic field.

1. Electric Charge and Its Conservation: The Electron. One of the fundamental facts concerning electrical forces is that, in contrast to gravitational forces, one may have both attractive and repulsive forces between electrically charged bodies. If two bodies are brought into contact with the same terminal of a battery or power line, or charged by identical methods of any sort, it is found that they repel each other when placed near each other. On the other hand, if the bodies are brought into contact with opposite terminals of the battery, they attract each other. This experimental fact led to the assumption that there exist two kinds of electricity, originally termed *vitreous* and *resinous* after the manner of their production by friction, and now called *positive* and *negative*, respectively. When a body is electrified, we say that *electric charge* has been transferred to the body, positive

22

or negative charge as the case may be.   There is a fundamental law concerning electric charge, *viz.*, *that no net electric charge can ever be created or destroyed*.   Whenever any positive charge is created, there is always created an equal amount of negative charge.   This law, called the *law of conservation of electric charge*, is one of the most fundamental laws of physics.   The experimental basis for this law as given by Faraday will be discussed later.

It was postulated in the early days of the study of electricity that electricity was a fluid, or rather two fluids, present in equal quantities in all matter, and that charging a body consists in adding an excess of positive or negative fluid to it.   Today we are in possession of overwhelming experimental evidence that electricity is atomic rather than continuous in nature and that the smallest charge available in nature is that possessed by an *electron*, one of the fundamental particles of which atoms are composed.   Just why there should exist a smallest charge remains, however, one of the unsolved mysteries of physics. The electron carries a negative charge, and its positive twin, the positron, has been more recently discovered but does not possess the permanence of the negative electron.   As one might expect, the charge carried by an electron is so exceedingly small compared to the ordinary charges with which one has to deal in large-scale experiments, that for many purposes one may still think of electricity as being continuous rather than atomic.   This is the same sort of excellent approximation which can be made in considering matter as continuous rather than atomic in nature for ordinary large-scale applications.

Thus far our discussion has been qualitative, and to proceed to a quantitative formulation of the laws, we must introduce a quantitative measure of charge.   It is characteristic of all physics that a definition of a physical quantity requires (1) a method of making quantitative comparisons and measurements of the quantity and (2) the choice of a unit.   In the case of electric charge, several experimental methods are available for the quantitative comparison of electric charges.   The most straightforward and obvious is the direct measurement of the mutual attraction or repulsive-force action between electric charges and the application of Coulomb's law.   This is possible in principle but is relatively impractical since Coulomb's law applies in its naïve form only to "point" charges.   A far more practical scheme is to employ an electrometer, an instrument which detects and measures electric charge.   The theory of operation of this instrument must be deferred to a later point in our study.   For our present purposes, it is sufficient to state that if an electrically charged body is placed inside a metallic container without touching the walls of the container and if an electrometer is connected to the container as shown in Fig. 8, the instrument will indicate the presence of the charged body.   This indication consists of an angular displacement θ between two originally parallel thin metal foils, or between a metal strip and a thin metal foil as indicated in the figure.   With the help of the electrometer, one can define electric charge by saying that a body carries a charge if it causes a deflection on the instrument when employed as shown. Equal charges are defined as two charges causing identical successive deflections of the electrometer.   One can further demonstrate that the simultaneous introduction of positive and negative charges into

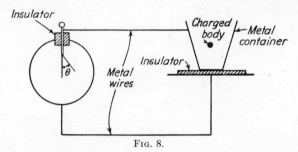

Fig. 8.

the container results in a smaller deflection than the larger of the two deflections when each charge is used separately, and the law of conservation of charge can be studied with this type of instrument.

Thus we have a method of comparing charges, and in order to measure the magnitude of the charge, one must introduce a *unit* of charge. The choice of this unit is, of course, arbitrary.   In the system of units which we shall employ, the unit of charge is defined on the basis of magnetic rather than electrostatic laws, and hence the actual definition must be deferred to a later chapter.   The unit charge so defined is called the *coulomb*.   The charge of an electron is customarily denoted by e and has a magnitude of 1.60×10^{-19} coulomb.   The mechanical units which we shall employ are the so-called meter-kilogram-second (mks) mechanical units.   In this system the unit of length is the meter, the unit of mass the kilogram, and the unit of time the second. From these one obtains the derived unit of force as the newton, which is equal to 10^5 dynes, and the derived unit of energy as the joule, which is equal to 10^7 ergs.

2. Intensity of the Electric Field.   The presence of an electric field in a given region of space can be detected by bringing into that region a so-called test charge, *i.e.*, a small *positively* charged body, and deter-

mining whether a force is exerted on this test charge.   If such a force
exists, we say that an electric field is present, and it would seem reasonable to specify the field by giving the vector force (direction and magnitude) exerted on the test body at each point of space.   This procedure is open to a disturbing objection, *viz.*, the force depends in
magnitude on the size of the charge carried by the test body and hence
cannot be used as a unique measure of the field.   Hence we set up
another measure of electric field strength, the so-called *electric intensity*,
which we denote by $\mathcal{E}$.   The intensity is defined as a vector equal in
magnitude to the *force per unit positive charge* exerted on the test body
and of the same direction as this force.   Thus, if the charge on the
test body is denoted by q, and at a given point of space there is an
electrical force F exerted on it, the field intensity $\mathcal{E}$ at that point of
space is

$$\mathcal{E} = \frac{F}{q} \tag{2.1}$$

or

$$F = \mathcal{E}q \tag{2.1a}$$

There still remains one question to be settled before we can be
satisfied that $\mathcal{E}$ provides a unique measure of the field strength.   If
the force exerted by the field on the test body is proportional to the
charge on the latter, then Eq. (2.1) provides a perfectly satisfactory
definition.   If—and this occurs in many practical cases—the force
per unit charge does depend on the size of the test charge because of
the reaction of the latter on the sources of the field, we must generalize
Eq. (2.1) to remove the ambiguity involved.   Let us suppose that we
bring a number of test charges successively to a given point of space,
and upon measurement we find that the ratio of force to charge does
vary with the size of the test charge.   We proceed to make the magnitude of the test charge smaller and smaller; the force becomes smaller
and smaller, but the ratio of force to charge approaches a definite
limiting value as the size of the test charge is reduced indefinitely.
This limiting value is then defined as the field intensity at this point.
In symbols, we have

$$\mathcal{E} = \lim \frac{\Delta F}{\Delta q} \quad \text{as } \Delta q \to 0 \tag{2.2}$$

Logically, we should adopt Eq. (2.2) as the strictly correct definition
of field intensity, but in many interesting practical situations the
reaction of the test body on the sources is so small that Eq. (2.1) can
be used to a high degree of approximation.

We can now describe the electrostatic field by exactly the same scheme as we have employed for fields of force in Chap. 1.   The lines of $\mathcal{E}$, which give the direction of the field intensity vector at each point, are identical with the lines of force discussed there.   The only difference is that we shall specify the magnitude of the field intensity $\mathcal{E}$ rather than the magnitude of the force vector itself.

From Eq. (2.1) we see that electric field intensity is measured in *newtons per coulomb*, since we express force in newtons and charge in coulombs.   For reasons which will appear directly, the field-intensity units are termed *volts per meter*, and these are identical with newtons per coulomb.   An inverse-square field is a conservative field.

3. Potential; Electromotive Force.   *The electrostatic field of force is a conservative field.*   The proof of this statement is based on Coulomb's law, which states that two point charges attract or repel each other with forces inversely proportional to the square of their separation and that the forces are directed along the straight line joining these charges.   Consequently, the field produced by a *single* point charge is an inverse-square field, and we have proved in Chap. 1 that this sort of field is conservative.   It immediately follows that the electrostatic field produced by an arbitrary distribution of charge is also conservative, since such a force field can be obtained by superposition of the fields of point charges.   The total work done on a test charge in moving it along an arbitrary path from some initial to a final point is then equal to the sum of the works done by the fields of each point charge.   Since each term of the sum is independent of the particular path joining the end points, then the whole sum must also be independent of the path, and the field is conservative.

Thus we can introduce the concept of potential energy of the test charge according to the usual definition that its gain of potential energy in moving from one field point to another is the negative of the work done by the field on it during this displacement.   As in the preceding section, it is useful to refer all quantities such as work and potential energy to unit charge, and we must introduce a few definitions.   *The work done by the field as the test charge is moved from a point A to a point B per unit charge is called the electromotive force along the path joining A and B.*   The work done in moving the charge q (Fig. 9) is, by definition,

$$W = \int_A^B F_s \, ds = q \int_A^B \mathcal{E}_s \, ds \qquad (2.3)$$

using Eq. (2.1). F_s and $\mathcal{E}_s$ are the components of force and field intensity in the direction of motion, respectively.   Thus we have for the emf along this path

$$\text{emf} = \frac{W}{q} = \int_A^B \mathcal{E}_s \, ds \qquad (2.4)$$

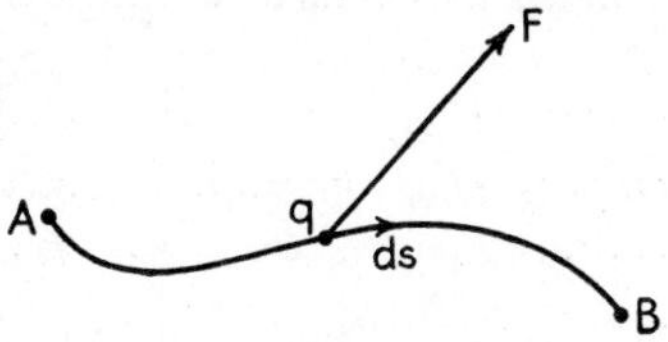

Similarly, the potential energy per unit charge of a test charge located at a given point is defined as the electric potential, or simply the potential, at that point.   If we denote potential energy as before by U and potential by V, we have for the gain of potential energy of the test charge q as it moves from A to B (Fig. 9)

Fig. 9.

$$U_B - U_A = -W = -q \int_A^B \mathcal{E}_s \, ds \qquad (2.5)$$

and the difference of electric potential between these points is

$$V_B - V_A = \frac{U_B}{q} - \frac{U_A}{q} = -\int_A^B \mathcal{E}_s \, ds \qquad (2.6)$$

or the negative of the emf along the path.   If the test charge (remember that it is a *positive* test charge) gains potential energy in moving from A to B, we say that point B is at a higher electric potential than point A, and vice versa.

Furthermore, it is convenient to set the potential energy of the test charge equal to zero at points infinitely distant from the region of space where the electric field exists, making the potential energy zero where the electrostatic force is zero.   If we do this, the potential V at a point P of the field becomes

$$V_P = -\int_\infty^P \mathcal{E}_s \, ds \qquad (2.7)$$

In words, the potential at a point P is the work per unit charge which we must do on the charge to bring it from infinity to the point P *along any path whatsoever.*   Equation (2.7) may be used only if the field intensity at points distant from the sources drops off faster than $1/r$, where r is the distance from the sources to the field point.   If this condition is not obeyed, the integral has an infinite value at its lower limit, and this is decidedly an undesirable choice of an origin for potential.   In any case, however, Eq. (2.6) is applicable.

We now can carry over bodily our complete discussion of conservative force fields and their properties given in Chap. 1 to the electrostatic field by simply referring all quantities to unit charge.   Thus the condition that the electrostatic field is conservative may be written [compare Eq. (1.1)]

$$\oint \mathcal{E}_s \, ds = 0 \tag{2.8}$$

This is one of the fundamental laws of electrostatics.   One can construct equipotential surfaces as the surfaces of constant electric potential, and the electric field intensity bears the same relations to the potential V as the force F of a conservative force field does to the potential energy U.   The lines of $\mathcal{E}$ intersect the equipotential surfaces at right angles, and the component of electric field intensity in any given direction (at a specified point of space) is the negative rate of change of potential with position along this direction.   Thus we have

$$\mathcal{E}_s = -\frac{dV}{ds} \tag{2.9}$$

for any direction s.   The direction for which dV/ds is a *maximum* is along a line of $\mathcal{E}$, and the negative gradient of the potential is the vector field intensity.   In symbols

$$\mathcal{E} = -\operatorname{grad} V \tag{2.10}$$

The reader should refer to the discussion in Chap. 1 at this point for further details.

The unit of potential or of emf in our system of units is one joule per coulomb and is called one volt.   We can now readily see the reason for using volts per meter as the units of electric field intensity.   We have

$$1 \frac{\text{newton}}{\text{coulomb}} = 1 \frac{\text{newton-meter}}{\text{coulomb-meter}} = 1 \frac{\text{joule}}{\text{coulomb-meter}} = 1 \frac{\text{volt}}{\text{meter}}$$

4. Metals as Equipotentials.   We must now recall to the reader the fact that in a general way substances may be classified as conductors of electricity or as nonconductors, or insulators.   In our previous sections we have assumed tacitly that the electrically charged bodies under discussion were either insulators or, if conductors, were supported by insulators, so that the charge residing on them could not escape.   It must be understood that the distinction between an electrical conductor and an insulator is not absolutely sharp, and in fact one finds a continuous gradation from almost perfect insulators, having the property of retaining localized charges almost indefinitely without loss of this charge, to almost perfect conductors, on which localized charge will practically instantaneously spread over the whole conducting body.   From an atomic viewpoint, conductors of electricity are those forms of matter in which some or all of the electric charges of which the body is composed (electrons in the case of metals, ions in aqueous solutions) can move more or less freely under the action of electric forces.   In insulators, on the other hand, the electrons are held more or less rigidly fixed in the atoms of the substance.   If the applied electric forces are large enough to pull electrons from their parent atoms, insulators will become conducting.

In this section we shall concern ourselves with the behavior of good conductors, such as metals, in electrostatic fields.   First let us consider what happens when a metallic body (supported by an insulator) is charged.   The charge transferred to the metal, being free to move, will flow through the metal and finally reach an equilibrium distribution.   This static equilibrium distribution has the following properties:

1. All the transferred charge resides on the surface of the metal.
2. The charge distributes itself on the surface in such a manner that the surface of the conductor becomes an equipotential surface.
3. Every point inside the metal is at the same potential as the surface, so that no electric field exists at any internal point.

The fact that the charge resides on the surface is due to the mutual repulsion of the added elements of charge, which forces them as far away from each other as possible.   Of course, throughout the body of the metal there exists the normal content of electrons, but these are held in equilibrium by the metallic ions.   Since the surface charge distribution is a static equilibrium distribution, there can be no component of electric field intensity parallel to the surface at any point on it. Were this not so, the charge would be accelerated along the surface, and equilibrium conditions would not prevail.   *Thus the electric field intensity vector just at the surface is perpendicular to it.*   The lines of force start from or terminate on the surface everywhere at right angles to it.   Hence the surface is an equipotential.   Now consider the normal content of mobile electrons inside the metal.   For static equilibrium there must be no net force on these charges, and hence the field is zero at every point inside the metal.   Inside ideal insulators it is possible to have a potential gradient without flow of charge, but this cannot occur in a conductor.

The mobility of charge in a metallic conductor gives rise to complicated phenomena which are not encountered in the case of gravitational fields.   Suppose we bring an uncharged piece of metal into a region of space where there exists an electric field.   Different points in the metal will lie, in general, at field points originally of different potentials, so that there will be forces acting on the mobile charges in the metal.   Under the action of these forces, these charges will flow through the metal and redistribute themselves in such a manner that the metal becomes an equipotential.   Although the total charge on the metal is zero and stays so because of the law of conservation of charge, there is brought into being a nonuniform distribution of positive and negative charge on the metal surface.   The resultant of the field produced by these so-called *induced charges* and the original field into which we brought the body is such as to make the whole metal an equipotential.   Thus the presence of a metallic body in an electric field will, in general, modify the field considerably.   This is true whether the metal is charged or uncharged as a whole.

One can make use of the foregoing phenomena to charge metals by "induction," or "influence."   Suppose a charged body is brought near an uncharged metallic body, as indicated in Fig. 10.   There will be

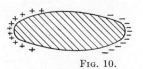 charges induced on the metal surface, as indicated in the figure, electrons being drawn closer to and held by the positive external charge. If now the metal is connected to the

Fig. 10.

earth by a conductor, the positive induced charge escapes, but the negative induced charge is held by the attraction of the external positive charge.   The connection to ground is now broken, and then the external charge is removed.   The metal is now found to be charged negatively, as one expects from the picture.

The action of the electrometer as shown in Fig. 8 can now be understood qualitatively.   Suppose the charge inside the metal container is positive.   It will induce negative charges and hold them on the inner surface of the container.   The remaining metal parts of the system connected to the container (the outer surface of the container, the connecting wire, and the metal-foil leaves of the instrument) will carry an equal induced positive charge.   Some of this will reside on the metal foils, and it is the mutual repulsion of these positive charges which gives rise to the observed angular deflection.

5. The Motion of Charged Particles in Electrostatic Fields.   The problem of finding the motion of a charged particle in an electrostatic field is a straightforward dynamical one when the reaction of the moving charge on the sources of the field is negligible.   If this reaction is not small, the problem becomes quite difficult and requires, in general, advanced methods for its solution.   There are many practical cases of great interest and importance, however, for which the neglect of the reaction on the sources is an excellent approximation, and we shall concern ourselves only with this situation.   The motion of electrons or ions in vacuum tubes affords many practical examples of this type.

Because the force acting on the particle is of electrical origin, the question of correct units often is troublesome, and we shall attempt to clarify this matter by solving a numerical example.   Consider first a particle of mass m and charge e.   If $\mathcal{E}$ is the field intensity at the point where the particle is located, the force acting on this particle will be given by

$$F = e\mathcal{E} \qquad (2.11)$$

according to the definition of $\mathcal{E}$ and the fact that we have assumed that the reaction on the field sources is negligible.   Newton's second law of motion then gives

$$F = e\mathcal{E} = m\frac{dv}{dt} \qquad (2.12)$$

where v is the vector velocity of the particle.   Now $\mathcal{E}$ is supposed known as a function of position, so that the solution follows the usual lines.   Since the electrostatic force field is conservative, one may apply the principle of conservation of mechanical energy.   This takes the form

$$\tfrac{1}{2}mv^2 + eV = \text{constant} \qquad (2.13)$$

since eV is the potential energy and v the speed of the charge e when at a position where the potential is V.   The constant on the right-hand side is the constant total energy of the motion and is determined from the initial conditions.

In the preceding equations, the charge is expressed in coulombs, the field strength in volts per meter, force in newtons, length in meters, mass in kilograms, time in seconds, potential in volts, and potential energy in joules.   The dynamical problem is thus to be solved in the mks system of mechanical units.

Let us consider a very elementary problem.   Suppose an electron of charge -1.60×10^{-19} coulomb and mass 9.0×10^{-31} kg starts from rest and is accelerated by a *uniform* field of intensity 10,000 volts/m. How long does it take this electron to move a distance of 10 cm; what are its velocity and kinetic energy at this time?   We choose an origin at the initial position of the electron and an x-axis in the direction of the field (to the right, let us say).   Since in a *uniform* field the electric intensity is everywhere the same, the force acting on the electron is constant in magnitude and direction, and the problem is the simple one of motion with constant acceleration.   This constant acceleration is, according to Eq. (2.12),

$$\frac{dv}{dt} = \frac{e\mathcal{E}}{m}$$

and since the right-hand side is constant, this can be integrated directly to give

$$
\left.
\begin{array}{l}
v = v_0 + \dfrac{e\mathcal{E}}{m}\, t \\[2mm]
x = v_0 t + \dfrac{e\mathcal{E}}{2m}\, t^2
\end{array}
\right\}
\tag{2.14}
$$

and, since $v = dx/dt$,

In our special case, we have $v_0 = 0$, since the electron starts from rest. Now using the second of Eqs. (2.14), we have for

$$x = -10 \text{ cm} = -0.10 \text{ m}$$

(since the acceleration and motion are *opposite* to the direction of the field because of the negative charge on the electron)

$$-0.10 = \frac{1}{2} \frac{(-1.60 \times 10^{-19}) \times 10^4}{9.0 \times 10^{-31}} t^2$$

$$t^2 = \tfrac{9}{8} \times 10^{-16}$$

$$t = 1.06 \times 10^{-8} \text{ sec}$$

From the first of Eqs. (2.14), we then find for the velocity at this time

$$v = \frac{-1.6 \times 10^{-19} \times 10^4}{9.0 \times 10^{-31}} \times 1.06 \times 10^{-8} = -1.9 \times 10^7 \text{ m/sec}$$

and this is directed to the left, in the direction of the accelerating force but opposite to the direction of the electric field.

The kinetic energy at this point is then

K.E. $= \tfrac{1}{2}mv^2 = \tfrac{1}{2} \times 9.0 \times 10^{-31} \times (1.9)^2 \times 10^{14} = 16 \times 10^{-17}$ joule

We can obtain this last result very quickly from energy considerations. Since the electron moves to the left, opposite to the field direction, it moves from a given point to points of higher potential. Because of its negative charge, however, it loses potential energy and gains a corresponding amount of kinetic energy. The field intensity $\mathcal{E}$, which has only an x-component in our example, is related to the potential according to Eq. (2.9) by

$$\mathcal{E} = -\frac{dV}{dx} \tag{2.15}$$

and, since $\mathcal{E}$ is constant, this gives

$$V_2 - V_1 = \mathcal{E}(x_1 - x_2) \tag{2.16}$$

where V_1 is the potential at x_1 and V_2 the potential at x_2. In our case, $x_1 = 0$ and $x_2 = -0.10$ m, so that we have from (2.16)

$$V_2 - V_1 = 10^4 \times [0 - (-0.10)] = 10^3 \text{ volts}$$

as the potential difference between points x_1 and x_2. The change of potential energy of the electron as it moves from x_1 to x_2 is therefore $U_2 - U_1 = e(V_2 - V_1) = -1.6 \times 10^{-19} \times (10^3) = -16 \times 10^{-17}$ joule. Thus the gain of kinetic energy is 16×10^{-17} joule, and since the particle started from rest, this is its kinetic energy after moving a distance of 10 cm. This checks the answer found above.

In the more general case of a nonuniform field (even for one-dimensional motion), one should apply the law of conservation of energy immediately as the first step toward a solution. Thus in the case of motion along the x-axis, one would write

$$\tfrac{1}{2}mv^2 + eV(x) = \tfrac{1}{2}mv_0^2 + eV_0 \tag{2.17}$$

where v is the particle speed at the point x, v_0 its initial speed, $V(x)$ the potential at the point x, and V_0 the potential at the initial position. It is evident that the right-hand side is the total energy of the motion. Further progress toward a complete solution is then made by writing $v = dx/dt$ and integrating to find the time t as a function of x. The details depend on the form of $V(x)$ and more properly belong to the subject of mechanics.

Problems

The charge on an electron is -1.60×10^{-19} coulomb, and its mass is 9.0×10^{-31} kg.

1. An X-ray tube contains a filament from which electrons are emitted with negligible velocities and a metallic target or anode placed some distance from the filament. The anode is maintained at a potential of 30,000 volts above that of the filament.

a. What is the speed of an electron just prior to striking the anode?

b. How many electrons hit the anode per second if the electric current through the tube is 10 ma. (A current of 1 amp corresponds to 1 coulomb of charge reaching the anode per second.)

c. What is the average force (time average) exerted on the anode owing to this electron bombardment?

d. How much heat is generated per second at the anode?

2. A rigid insulating rod of length l, carrying charges $+q$ and $-q$, respectively, at each of its ends, is suspended from its center by a thread as a torsion pendulum. It is placed in a uniform electric field of intensity $\mathcal{E}$ which is perpendicular to the suspending thread. Assume that the restoring torque exerted by the thread when twisted is negligible.

a. Show that the resultant force on the rod is zero no matter what angle the rod makes with the field.

b. What angle does the rod make with the field direction when in stable equilibrium?

c. If the rod is displaced from its equilibrium position by twisting it so that it makes an angle θ with the field, compute the torque about the axis of suspension acting on the rod when in this position. What is the potential energy of the system in this configuration?

d. If the angle θ is small compared to unity, what sort of motion will the rod perform when released from the position described in part c? What is the period of this motion?

✓ 3. Given an electric field in a limited region surrounding an origin in the x-y plane for which the potential is represented by

$$V = ax^2 + by^2$$

with a and b positive constants.

a. Find the components of the field intensity.

b. Where is the potential a minimum? Where is the field intensity a minimum?

c. If a small charged body of mass m and charge q is placed at $x = A$, $y = 0$ and released from rest, find its ensuing motion.

d. Solve part c if the particle is released from rest at $x = 0$, $y = B$.

e. Find the kinetic equations of motion (x and y as functions of time) if the particle is initially at $x = A$, $y = 0$ and has initial velocity components $v_x = 0$, $v_y = v_0$.

4. An ion of mass 10^{-25} kg carries a charge of 5 electron charges and starts from rest at a point A in a uniform electric field of intensity 1,000 volts/m.

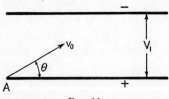
FIG. 11.

It reaches another point B 10^{-5} sec after it starts.

a. Find the distance between A and B.

b. What is the potential at B if the potential at A is -50 volts, referred to an arbitrary origin?

✓ 5. A uniform electric field is set up between parallel metal plates, the potential difference between these plates being maintained at a value V_1. A beam of electrons is shot into this field at the point A of Fig. 11 at an angle θ with the horizontal. These particles have acquired their initial speed v_0 by accelerating from rest through a potential difference V_0.

a. Prove that the electrons will just graze the top plate if

$$\frac{V_1}{V_0} = \sin^2 \theta$$

independent of the charge and mass of the particles and of the separation between the plates.

b. Show that the point of grazing lies to the right of A at a distance such that its ratio to the plate separation is given by $2 \cot \theta$.

6. The potential in vacuum between a long straight wire of radius a and a coaxial hollow metal cylinder of inner radius b is given by

$$V = V_0 \frac{\ln (r/a)}{\ln (b/a)}$$

where r is the distance from the common axis and V_0 is the potential of the outer cylinder. The wire radius if 1.0 mm, and the inner radius of the hollow cylinder is 1.0 cm. $V_0 = 90$ volts.

a. Describe the equipotential surfaces.

b. Find a formula for the field intensity at a distance r from the axis. What is its direction?

c. Find the field intensity in volts per meter at a point 0.5 cm from the axis.

d. An electron is released from the wire surface with a speed of 2.0×10^6 m/sec in a direction perpendicular to the surface. Find its speed when it hits the hollow cylinder.

7. An electron moves along a straight line, the x-axis. The electric potential along this line is given by

$$V = 600 \left(\frac{9}{100x + 12} - \frac{1}{100x + 4} \right)$$

where V is in volts and x in meters. This expression is valid for $x > -0.04$ m, *i.e.*, at all points to the right of the point $x = -0.04$ m. The electron starts with negligible speed and kinetic energy at $x = +\infty$.

a. Find the speed of the electron as it passes the point $x = 0$.

b. Where does the electron reverse its direction of motion?

c. What is the electric field intensity at the point of reversal?

8. The nucleus of a hydrogen atom may be considered a fixed mass point carrying a charge $+e$, equal to and opposite in sign to that of an electron. The potential due to this nucleus is given by $V = 9 \times 10^9 \, e/r$, where e is in coulombs and r is the distance from the nucleus in meters. An electron moves about this nucleus in a circle of radius a.

a. Write an expression for the electrostatic force acting on the electron when in this orbit.

b. What must the speed of the electron be so that this motion is possible?

c. What is the total energy of the electron (kinetic plus potential)?

d. In the normal hydrogen atom it is found that the total energy of the electron is -2.16×10^{-18} joule. What is the radius of the circular orbit?

9. A uniform electric field is set up between two metal plates A and B, and a beam of electrons enters this field, as shown in Fig. 12, midway between the plates with an initial velocity acquired by accelerating from rest through a potential difference of 1,000 volts. The plates are 2.0 cm long and of 0.50 cm separation. The electrons fall on a fluorescent screen 30 cm from the plates and give rise to a visible spot. If the potential difference between the plates is 50 volts, calculate the deflection of the spot from its position when there is no electric field between the plates.

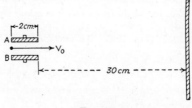

Fig. 12.

10. A three-element vacuum tube may be idealized as follows: A plane metallic sheet (the filament) emits electrons with negligible velocities. Parallel to this filament and 2.0 mm from it is a plane grid of wires (the grid). Another solid metal sheet (the plate) is 10.0 mm beyond the grid and parallel to it. (If you find it necessary, assume that the electric fields between filament and grid and between grid and plate are uniform.)

a. What conditions must hold among the potentials of the filament, grid, and plate so that electrons may reach the plate?

b. For given filament and plate potentials, how does the grid potential affect the velocity of an electron when it strikes the plate?

c. Suppose the grid is made 10 volts positive and the plate 10 volts negative, relative to the filament. What will the motion of an electron be if it leaves the filament with zero velocity? What effect will small initial velocities have on the motion?

11. A charged oil drop of specific gravity 0.90 is held at rest in air by a vertical electric field of intensity 23.1×10^4 volts/m. If the electric field is removed, the drop falls with a constant velocity of 1.09×10^{-4} m/sec. Using Stokes's law with the coefficient of viscosity of air equal to 1.80×10^{-5} kg/m-sec³, calculate:

a. The radius of the drop.

b. The electric charge of the drop.

(This is the principle of the method employed by Millikan to measure the electronic charge.) For Stokes's law, consult Frank, "Introduction to Mechanics and Heat," 2d ed., McGraw-Hill Book Company, Inc.

CHAPTER 3

THE SOURCES OF THE ELECTROSTATIC FIELD

We are now ready to undertake a more detailed discussion of the calculation of electric fields from a knowledge of the positions and magnitudes of the charges which produce them. As has been already pointed out, we encounter at the very outset an experimental fact which, in contrast to the gravitational case, introduces considerable complication. One finds experimentally that the intensity of an electric field produced, let us say, by a number of fixed charges depends not only on the positions and magnitudes of these fixed charges, but also on the material medium in which these charges are embedded and on the presence of neighboring or intervening uncharged material bodies. For example, the force acting on a test charge in empty space is found to be reduced to a fraction of its original value when the sources and test charge are immersed in a nonconducting liquid, such as oil.

This dual dependence of field intensity on both sources and uncharged material media makes it desirable to develop a mode of description which shall distinguish between these two effects. Unfortunately, it is not possible to accomplish this desired resolution in any simple manner which has general validity. A simple separation can be attained only in the special case of a homogeneous medium of sufficient extent that the effects of its boundaries are negligible at all points at which we are interested in the field, and for certain very special geometrical configurations of finite bodies. Accordingly, we shall postpone an examination of these boundary effects and of the modifications introduced by the presence of material media until the second half of this book, at which point we shall undertake a study of the electrical properties of matter. *Here we confine ourselves to the study of fields in empty space*, and for most practical purposes the results so found will be applicable to air-filled regions, since the modifications produced by a gas such as air at atmospheric pressure are exceedingly small and can, in general, be ignored.

1. Coulomb's Law. As we have stated several times in our previous discussion, the basic law of force describing the interaction of electric

37

charges was formulated by Coulomb in 1785 as a result of experiments with a torsion balance. Coulomb concluded that the force of attraction or repulsion between two "point" charges is proportional to the products of the two charges, inversely proportional to the square of their separation, and the forces are directed along the straight line connecting the two charges. The validity of Coulomb's law has been established with a very high degree of precision, the verification being obtained deductively from the fact that the electric field is zero everywhere inside a hollow conductor.

In symbols we express the content of Coulomb's law by writing

$$F \sim \frac{q_1 q_2}{r^2} \qquad (3.1)$$

where r is the distance between the two point charges q_1 and q_2. From our field standpoint we can then write for the electric field intensity $\mathcal{E}$ *due to a single point charge q*

$$\mathcal{E} \sim q/r^2 \qquad (3.2)$$

where r now denotes the distance from q to the field point where $\mathcal{E}$ is measured.

In empty space (and we are considering only this case) the vector $\mathcal{E}$ is directed along the line connecting q and the field point at which $\mathcal{E}$ is measured, away from or toward q, according to whether the field source q is positive or negative. Thus the field of a single point charge is an inverse-square field, the properties of which we have already considered in detail.

We now must introduce a proportionality constant to convert the relations (3.1) and (3.2) into equations in order to develop a quantitative theory, and the choice of this proportionality constant is tied up intimately with the system of units and dimensions to be employed. This matter of units and dimensions will be discussed in the following section. In the system of units which we shall employ, the proportionality constant is written as $1/4\pi\epsilon_0$ (remember that this is in vacuum), where ϵ_0 is called the *specific inductivity*, or *permittivity*, of empty space. Using this particular form for the constant of proportionality, we have from (3.1)

$$F = \frac{q_1 q_2}{4\pi\epsilon_0 r^2} \qquad (3.3)$$

and from (3.2)

$$\mathcal{E} = \frac{q}{4\pi\epsilon_0 r^2} \qquad (3.4)$$

as alternative forms of Coulomb's law.

For the case of the electric field produced by a number of point charges at rest, we calculate the contribution to the resultant electric field intensity vector arising from each charge from Eq. (3.4), and then find the resultant $\mathcal{E}$ by *vector* addition.   In symbols we write,

$$\mathcal{E} = \sum \frac{q}{4\pi\epsilon_0 r^2} \qquad \text{(vector addition)} \qquad (3.5)$$

If we have to calculate the field due to a static continuous distribution of charge, we use integration rather than summation in Eq. (3.5). Since we are adding vectors, however, caution must be employed. The method of calculation is the following:

1. Write an expression for the infinitesimal vector $d\mathcal{E}$ at a given field point due to an element of charge dq in accordance with Eq. (3.4).

2. Resolve this vector into rectangular components, $d\mathcal{E}_x$, $d\mathcal{E}_y$, and $d\mathcal{E}_z$.

3. Calculate each component of $\mathcal{E}$ by integration, *e.g.*,

$$\mathcal{E}_x = \int d\mathcal{E}_x$$

4. Find the resultant $\mathcal{E}$ from its components $\mathcal{E}_x$, $\mathcal{E}_y$, $\mathcal{E}_z$.   We shall illustrate this procedure in detail in a later section.

2. Units and Dimensions: The Rationalized MKS System. Before proceeding further, we must stop to consider the question of units in more detail.   The choice of a suitable system of electromagnetic units has long been one of the most controversial and annoying problems of physics, and it is only in recent years that there seems to be emerging something approaching international agreement on a system of electromagnetic units.   In anticipation of the ultimate universal adoption of this system, we shall employ it exclusively in this book.   The relations between this newer *rationalized mks system of electromagnetic units* and the more frequently encountered older systems of units are presented in Appendix I.

First, let us recall to the reader that the choice of a system of units involves not only the definition of standards and units of physical quantities but also the choice of the dimensions of these various quantities.   The matter of dimensions is handled as follows: One selects arbitrarily a few physical quantities as fundamental and expresses the dimensions of all other physical quantities in terms of these fundamental ones.   In the choice of the fundamental dimensions one is guided by convenience—the number of independent dimensions must be small to be useful—and by the physics of the situation.   Let us illustrate this point for the case of mechanics.   In an absolute system of mechanical units, one chooses mass, length, and time as the fundamental quantities and expresses all other mechanical quantities dimensionally in terms of m, l, and t.   This choice of mass, length, and time is arbitrary and does not represent the minimum number of quantities which could be used.   For example, it is quite simple to set up a system in which all mechanical quantities are expressible dimensionally in terms of length and time only.   To accomplish this, let us consider Newton's law of gravitation in the form

$$F \sim \frac{m_1 m_2}{r^2}$$

and suppose we agree to set the proportionality constant equal to the pure number unity, without dimensions.   Thus the gravitational law becomes $F = m_1 m_2/r^2$, and we now combine this with Newton's second law of motion in the form $F = m \, dv/dt$ (again choosing a proportionality constant equal to the pure number unity).   With the help of these two relations, one can evidently express the dimensions of mass in terms of length and time alone.   Now this scheme, simple as it is, does not enjoy favor in physics because one looks upon the quantities of length and time as being kinematic quantities, useful in describing the purely geometrical aspects of motion without regard to the dynamical aspects of physical problems.   The conviction that mass is a quantity of sufficient physical meaning to warrant its own dimension has resulted in the universal adoption of three, rather than two, fundamental dimensions for mechanics.   In so doing, no attempt is made to preset arbitrarily the proportionality constant in Newton's law of gravitation, and it is written as $F = \gamma m_1 m_2/r^2$, where γ is a quantity whose magnitude and dimensions are fixed by experiment and by the choice of units of mass and length previously adopted.

We face a similar situation in the case of Coulomb's law.   If we set the proportionality constant in (3.1) equal to a pure number, the dimensions of charge become expressible in terms of mass, length, and time.   This is the procedure adopted in the older *electrostatic* system of units, as explained in Appendix I.   This relegates the physical quantity electric charge to a relatively minor position compared to mass, at least dimensionally.   *It is characteristic of our mks system that charge is considered a fundamental quantity, with its own dimension.*[1] In view of the fact that electric charge is conserved (and mass no longer enjoys this privileged position) and is one of the fundamental quantities

---

[1] More precisely, one should label this system the mksc system.

in the physical world, it seems only fitting and proper that charge have its own dimension. Thus we have a system with *four* fundamental quantities (charge, mass, length, and time), in terms of which we express the dimensions of all other quantities.

As already pointed out, the mechanical units are the kilogram, meter, and second, and the unit of charge, the coulomb, is defined on the basis of a magnetic rather than electrostatic law. Once these units have been agreed upon, the magnitude and dimensions of the proportionality constant in Coulomb's law become a matter of experimental determination, not of definition. We write this proportionality constant in the form $1/4\pi\epsilon_0$ for empty space, as is displayed in Eqs. (3.3) and (3.4), and the inclusion of the arbitrary factor 4π characterizes the *rationalized* part of our rationalized system of mks units. As will be evident shortly, the inclusion of this factor has the effect of suppressing a factor of 4π in problems of plane symmetry and having it appear in its more natural place in problems of spherical symmetry. It must be emphasized that this is not a fundamental point but simply one of convenience. The dimension of the permittivity ϵ_0 follows from Eq. (3.3) as

$$[\epsilon_0] = \frac{q^2}{ml^3t^{-2}} = \frac{(\text{coulomb})^2 - \sec^2}{\text{kg-m}^3}$$

A more convenient terminology, however, is obtained from Eq. (3.4). If we remember that $\mathcal{E}$ is expressed in volts per meter, ϵ_0 turns out to be expressed in coulombs per volt-meter. *The coulomb per volt is called one farad*, and hence we shall label ϵ_0 as so many *farads per meter*.

The *experimental* value of ϵ_0 is

$$\epsilon_0 = 8.85 \times 10^{-12} \text{ farad/m} \tag{3.6}$$

As a matter of convenience in calculation, one can also write to a high degree of approximation

$$\epsilon_0 = \frac{1}{36\pi} \times 10^{-9} \text{ farad/m} \qquad \text{or} \qquad 4\pi\epsilon_0 = \frac{1}{9} \times 10^{-9} \text{ farad/m} \tag{3.6a}$$

Summarizing, we now give in Table I a list of the names and dimensions of the physical quantities thus far introduced. The student should construct his own table and add to it as new physical quantities make their appearance as our study proceeds.

3. Gauss's Law: The Displacement Vector D. It has already been pointed out that the electric field intensity of an electrostatic field depends not only on the distribution of charges which give rise to the field but also on the material medium in which these charges are embedded. In the case of infinite homogeneous media, Coulomb's law in the form of the proportionality expressed in (3.2) is valid, but the form employed in Eq. (3.4) holds only in empty space, as indicated by the subscript zero on ϵ_0. There is a property of electric fields, however, which does depend *only* on the distribution and strength of the charged sources producing the fields. This is of such fundamental importance in electromagnetic theory that we shall develop it in a form which retains its validity in general, although as before we confine our attention to the case of empty space at this point and defer a generalization of the definitions involved to a later chapter on the electrical properties of matter.

TABLE I

Physical quantity	Symbol	Name of unit	Dimensions
Mass............................	m	Kilogram	Fundamental
Length..........................	l	Meter	Fundamental
Time............................	t	Second	Fundamental
Charge..........................	$q\ (e)$	Coulomb	Fundamental
Force...........................	F	Newton	mlt^{-2}
Work............................	W	Joule	ml^2t^{-2}
Potential energy................	U	Joule	ml^2t^{-2}
Electric field intensity........	$\mathcal{E}$	Volt per meter	$mlt^{-2}q^{-1}$
Electric potential..............	V	Volt	$ml^2t^{-2}q^{-1}$
Electromotive force.............	emf	Volt	$ml^2t^{-2}q^{-1}$
Permittivity....................	ϵ_0	Farad per meter	$q^2t^2m^{-1}l^{-3}$

For this purpose it is convenient to introduce a second vector, called the *electric displacement* vector, which is denoted by D. *For empty space, this is defined as*

$$D = \epsilon_0 \mathcal{E} \tag{3.7}$$

This definition of the displacement vector, limited as it is in (3.7) to empty space, will be generalized later to include the effects of dielectric media. The vector D in vacuum is identical with the electric field strength $\mathcal{E}$ in direction but differs from it in magnitude and dimensions. Consequently the lines of D which can be used to describe an electric field in vacuum are *identical* with those of $\mathcal{E}$, so that a single field plot suffices, whether one is interested in either or both of these vectors.

The lines of displacement D, or those of field intensity $\mathcal{E}$, which map an electrostatic field of force merely provide information as to the direction of the vectors at each point of space but tell us nothing with respect to their magnitude.   One can insert the latter information by limiting the number of lines drawn in a definite manner, crowding them together in regions of high field strength and spreading them out where the field is weak.   The convention to be used is that the number of lines per unit area which traverse an element of area normal to the field direction shall be made equal to the number of units of the field vector (D or $\mathcal{E}$) at the point where this element of area is located.

Suppose we construct the lines of D due to a single point charge q in empty space according to the above scheme.   These are straight lines radiating in all directions from q.   At a distance r from q, we construct a spherical surface of radius r and center at q (this is an equipotential surface), and this surface is everywhere normal to the field lines.   According to Eq. (3.4), D (and $\mathcal{E}$) has the same magnitude at all points of this surface, and hence the number of lines per unit area crossing this surface is the same at every point.   In other words, the lines are uniformly distributed over the spherical surface.   Since, in accord with our convention, there are $q/4\pi r^2$ lines of D per unit area and since the area of a sphere is $4\pi r^2$, we see that the total number of lines of D crossing this spherical surface is equal to q.   The total number of field lines crossing any surface is called the *flux* across the surface, and we denote the flux of D by the symbol ψ.   Thus we have $\psi = q$.   This flux does not depend on the radius of the spherical surface enclosing q and hence is the same for all such spherical surfaces, independent of their radii.   Hence we see that the lines of D (or of $\mathcal{E}$) cannot start or stop in empty space.   It is further clear from the above that if *any* closed surface is constructed which completely surrounds q, the total flux of D across it must be equal to the enclosed charge q.   When expressed formally as an equation, this is the content of Gauss's law.

The formal statement of Gauss's law is as follows: *The surface integral of the normal component of the electric displacement taken over any closed surface is equal to q, where q is the total charge enclosed by the surface*.   In symbols,

$$\psi = \int_{\substack{\text{closed}\\\text{surface}}} D_n \, dS = q \tag{3.8}$$

where D_n is the component of D along the normal n to the surface. We take the positive direction of the normal as *outward* from the closed surface.   It follows immediately that the flux of $\mathcal{E}$ in empty space across the closed surface is q/ϵ_0.   To obtain a formal proof of Eq. (3.8), we imagine a charge q_1 at a given point O surrounded by an arbitrary closed surface.   Now construct an infinitesimal cone with its vertex at O, intersecting the closed surface in an element of area dS at a distance r from O (Fig. 13).   Let dS' be the projection of dS on a sphere of radius r.   The flux of D across dS is

$$d\psi = \int D_n \, dS = D_n \cos \theta \, dS = \frac{q_1 \, dS \cos \theta}{4\pi r^2}$$

using Eqs. (3.4) and (3.7).

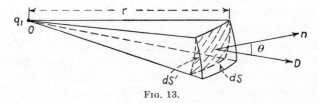

FIG. 13.

Since $dS' = dS \cos \theta$ and dS'/r^2 is the solid angle $d\Omega$ subtended at O by dS', we have

$$d\psi = \frac{q_1}{4\pi} \, d\Omega$$

and if we now integrate over the whole closed surface, we have

$$\psi = \int D_n \, dS = \frac{q_1}{4\pi} \int d\Omega = q_1$$

since the solid angle subtended by any closed surface at a point inside it is 4π.   If the surface encloses a number of charges, q_1, q_2, . . . , q_i, . . . , each charge gives rise to a flux q_i, so that the total flux across the surface becomes $\sum_i q_i = q$, where q now denotes the *total* charge inside the closed surface.   Thus Eq. (3.8) expresses the content of Gauss's law in general, if q in that equation is taken as the total charge enclosed by the surface.   *Gauss's law is one of the fundamental laws of electromagnetic theory.*   Later in our study of the dielectric properties of matter, we shall generalize the definition of D given in Eq. (3.7) and shall find that Eq. (3.8) retains its validity in general with the more general definition of D.   Gauss's law shows clearly that the dimensions of the electric displacement vector D are those of a charge per unit area (a surface charge density), *i.e.*, q/l^2.

Finally, for the case of empty space with which we are concerned at the present, Gauss's law (3.8) may be written in the equivalent form

$$\int_{\substack{\text{closed} \\ \text{surface}}} \epsilon_0 \mathcal{E}_n \, dS = q \tag{3.9}$$

4. Applications of Gauss's Law. Gauss's law provides a simple means of calculating the electrostatic field produced by certain symmetrical charge distributions. Its power lies in the fact that we are free to apply it to any closed surface so shaped that the evaluation of the surface integral $\int D_n \, dS$ (or $\int \epsilon_0 \mathcal{E}_n \, dS$) becomes a simple, straightforward task.

The following examples will illustrate the procedure:

a. Field of a Uniformly Charged Infinite Plane Metal Plate. Suppose the plate is positively charged. The lines of $\mathcal{E}$ will be straight lines normal to the plate because of the symmetry, and the magnitude of the electric field intensity can vary only with the distance of the field point from the charged surface. Now if we construct a closed surface in the form of a cylindrical surface with the cylinder axis perpendicular to the plate, it is clear that everywhere on the curved surface the field intensity is parallel to the surface, and hence the flux across it is zero. The field lines are at right angles to the top and bottom faces, and the magnitude of the field strength is constant at all points of either face. Thus the appropriate Gaussian surface is such a cylindrical surface with the bottom face lying

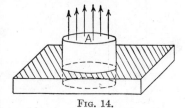

Fig. 14.

inside the metal and the top face a distance d from the top metal surface (Fig. 14). Since the field inside the metal is zero, there is no flux across the bottom face. Hence all the flux emerging from the cylinder arises at the top face. We then have, according to Gauss's law [Eq. (3.9)],

$$\psi = \int_{\substack{\text{closed} \\ \text{surface}}} \epsilon_0 \mathcal{E}_n \, dS = \epsilon_0 \mathcal{E} \int_{\substack{\text{top} \\ \text{face}}} dS = \epsilon_0 \mathcal{E} A = q$$

where q is the total charge inside the cylinder and A is the area of the top face. Denoting the *charge per unit area by* σ (this is the surface density of charge), we have $q = \sigma A$ for a uniformly charged surface, and hence

$$\mathcal{E} = \frac{\sigma}{\epsilon_0} \tag{3.10}$$

Thus the electric field strength is constant, independent of the distance d of the field point from the metal surface. The corresponding value of D is just σ, the surface charge density.

This is an example of a uniform field. In practice, one cannot have a truly infinite metal plate, but for one of finite size the field is practically uniform at points whose distances from the plate are small compared to its surface dimension. This is more nearly true, the nearer the field point lies to the surface. As the field point recedes, it eventually will become so distant that the whole metal plate appears like a point charge, and hence the field strength will ultimately fall off according to Coulomb's law at sufficiently large distances. This is evidently true of any *finite* charge distribution.

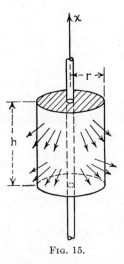

FIG. 15.

The field intensity just outside the surface of any charged conductor, no matter what its shape or size, is given by Eq. (3.10), where σ, the surface charge density, will in general vary from point to point on the conducting surface. The field lines leave the surface normal to it and start out at each point with the magnitude of $\mathcal{E}$ given by σ/ϵ_0. The proof of this statement is identical with the one which we have given, with the single modification that one considers a cylinder of infinitesimal cross section and altitude rather than one of finite dimensions. This is necessary since the charge is not uniformly distributed over the surface, and since the field lines are normal to the surface only in the immediate vicinity thereof.

b. Field of a Long Uniformly Charged Straight Wire. In this case the symmetry is such that the lines of $\mathcal{E}$ are all normal to the axis of the wire. At a given field point P the value of $\mathcal{E}$ cannot depend on the x-coordinate of P (along the wire), since the wire is very long, nor on the angular position of P around the wire, because of cylindrical symmetry. Thus the magnitude of $\mathcal{E}$ can depend only on the distance r from the wire axis to the field point. We therefore construct a closed surface in the form of a cylindrical can (Fig. 15) of radius r and altitude h. No flux crosses the top or bottom faces of the cylinder since the normal component of $\mathcal{E}$ is zero everywhere on these faces. On the curved surface, $\mathcal{E}$ has the same magnitude at all points (since it depends only on r) and is normal to the surface at all its points. Thus the flux of D emerging from the cylinder is

$$\psi = \int \epsilon_0 \mathcal{E}_n \, dS = \epsilon_0 \mathcal{E} \underset{\substack{\text{curved} \\ \text{surface}}}{\int} dS = 2\pi r h \epsilon_0 \mathcal{E}$$

where $\mathcal{E}$ is the magnitude of the field intensity at a distance r from the wire axis. If the charge per unit length on the wire is τ, the total charge inside the cylinder is τh, and Gauss's law requires that

$$\psi = 2\pi r h \epsilon_0 \mathcal{E} = h\tau$$

$$\mathcal{E} = \frac{\tau}{2\pi \epsilon_0 r} \tag{3.11}$$

and we see that the field strength drops off inversely as the distance from the wire. This result is strictly valid only for an infinitely long wire but does give the field at points sufficiently close to a straight wire that their distance from the axis is small compared to the length of the wire Contrast this type of field with that of a *single* point charge.

5. The Field of Fixed Charge Distributions. When one is faced with the problem of determining the field of an arbitrary distribution of charge, the direct application of Gauss's law as given in the preceding section is not feasible in general, and one can proceed by the method outlined in Sec. 1 of this chapter. For the case of the field due to a finite number of point changes, the method requires the straightforward vector addition of the field strengths due to the individual point sources [utilizing Eq. (3.5)] and requires no further comment. The field produced by a continuous distribution of charge can be calculated by integration, and we shall illustrate the procedure with the help of examples.

Let us calculate the field due to a very long, uniformly charged straight wire. Let the plane containing the wire and the field point P be the x-y plane, and construct x- and y-axes as shown in Fig. 16. The contribution to $\mathcal{E}$ from the element of charge dq is shown as $d\mathcal{E}$ in the figure. If the charge per unit length is τ, we have

$$dq = \tau \, dx$$

and the magnitude of $d\mathcal{E}$ is given by Coulomb's law as

$$d\mathcal{E} = \frac{\tau \, dx}{4\pi \epsilon_0 l^2}$$

We must next calculate the components $d\mathcal{E}_x$ and $d\mathcal{E}_y$ of this vector before integrating. These are

$$d\mathcal{E}_x = d\mathcal{E}\,\sin\theta = \frac{\tau}{4\pi\epsilon_0}\frac{dx\,\sin\theta}{l^2}$$

$$d\mathcal{E}_y = d\mathcal{E}\,\cos\theta = \frac{\tau}{4\pi\epsilon_0}\frac{dx\,\cos\theta}{l^2}$$

The components $\mathcal{E}_x$ and $\mathcal{E}_y$ of the resultant field vector $\mathcal{E}$ at P are then

$$\left.\begin{aligned}\mathcal{E}_x &= \frac{\tau}{4\pi\epsilon_0}\int_{-\infty}^{+\infty}\frac{dx\,\sin\theta}{l^2}\\ \mathcal{E}_y &= \frac{\tau}{4\pi\epsilon_0}\int_{-\infty}^{+\infty}\frac{dx\,\cos\theta}{l^2}\end{aligned}\right\} \tag{3.12}$$

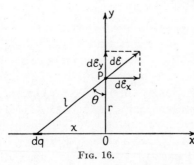

Fig. 16.

From symmetry we see without further calculation that the first integral of (3.12) will vanish, so that the vector $\mathcal{E}$ is normal to the wire. The integrations are readily carried out using θ as the independent variable (Fig. 16). We have

$$x = r\tan\theta; \qquad dx = r\sec^2\theta\,d\theta$$
$$r = l\cos\theta; \qquad \frac{1}{l^2} = \frac{\cos^2\theta}{r^2}$$

so that $dx/l^2 = d\theta/r$, and Eqs. (3.12) become

$$\left.\begin{aligned}\mathcal{E}_x &= \frac{\tau}{4\pi\epsilon_0 r}\int_{-\pi/2}^{+\pi/2}\sin\theta\,d\theta = \frac{\tau}{4\pi\epsilon_0 r}\left[-\cos\theta\right]_{-\pi/2}^{+\pi/2} = 0\\ \mathcal{E}_y &= \frac{\tau}{4\pi\epsilon_0 r}\int_{-\pi/2}^{+\pi/2}\cos\theta\,d\theta = \frac{\tau}{4\pi\epsilon_0 r}\left[\sin\theta\right]_{-\pi/2}^{+\pi/2} = \frac{\tau}{2\pi\epsilon_0 r}\end{aligned}\right\} \tag{3.13}$$

Thus we have found $\mathcal{E} = \tau/2\pi\epsilon_0 r$, coinciding with the result found by utilization of Gauss's theorem and given by Eq. (3.11). We note that the result obtained by Gauss's theorem is evidently valid at all points outside the wire, no matter what the wire radius is, whereas the result expressed in Eqs. (3.13) has been obtained only for a wire of negligible radius.

As a second example, we calculate the field produced by a uniformly charged circular ring of wire of negligible cross section at a point P on the axis of the ring. We take the x-axis as the axis of the ring with an origin at the center of the ring, as shown in Fig. 17. Consider the element of charge dq on an element of length ds of the ring. This is given by

$$dq = \tau\,ds = \frac{q}{2\pi r}\,ds$$

where q is the total charge carried by the ring and r is its radius.

At the point P of Fig. 17, the vector $d\mathcal{E}$ produced by dq has the direction shown and the magnitude

$$d\mathcal{E} = \frac{dq}{4\pi\epsilon_0 l^2} = \frac{q}{8\pi^2\epsilon_0 r} \frac{ds}{l^2} \tag{3.14}$$

If we consider all the infinitesimal vectors due to the various elements of charge dq on the ring, we see that they form a conical array of vectors with the apex at P. Furthermore, according to (3.14) they all have the same magnitude. Resolving these vectors into components, it is

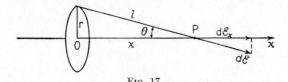

Fig. 17.

evident that only the components $d\mathcal{E}_x$ along the x-axis yield anything to the resultant field, the other components adding up to zero. Thus we have

$$d\mathcal{E}_x = d\mathcal{E} \cos\theta = \frac{q}{8\pi^2\epsilon_0 r} \frac{ds}{l^2} \frac{x}{l}$$

and hence

$$\mathcal{E}_x = \frac{qx}{8\pi^2\epsilon_0 r l^3} \int ds = \frac{qx}{4\pi\epsilon_0 l^3}$$

since $\int ds$ is simply the circumference of the circle. We thus find the resultant field intensity directed along the x-axis at the point P and of magnitude

$$\mathcal{E} = \frac{qx}{4\pi\epsilon_0 l^3} = \frac{q}{4\pi\epsilon_0} \frac{x}{(r^2 + x^2)^{\frac{3}{2}}} \tag{3.15}$$

Equation (3.15) is valid only for points on the axis Ox, as is clear from the derivation.

6. The Use of Potential in Field Calculations. The method of the preceding section, straightforward as it is, becomes cumbersome even in relatively simple problems because of the necessity of dealing with vector summations or integrations. It is in this connection that the introduction of the scalar electric potential simplifies to a great extent the problem of the calculation of electrostatic fields of force. We have already proved that, by virtue of Coulomb's law, the electrostatic field is conservative and hence that a single-valued potential exists. The general scheme of calculation is as follows: We compute the potential as a function of position in the field as the algebraic sum of the potentials due to the point charges giving rise to the field. This is a scalar summation (or integration, in the case of continuous charge distributions) and hence is much simpler to perform than the vector summations or integrations of Sec. 5. Once the potential V is found as a function of position, e.g., in the form $V = V(x,y,z)$, we can derive the electric field intensity immediately from

$$\mathcal{E} = -\text{ grad } V$$

In Cartesian coordinates, this is equivalent to

$$\mathcal{E}_x = -\partial V/\partial x; \qquad \mathcal{E}_y = -\partial V/\partial y; \qquad \mathcal{E}_z = -\partial V/\partial z$$

We now investigate the potential of various charge distributions.

a. Potential of a Point Charge. From Coulomb's law, Eq. (3.4), and the definition of potential difference as given by Eq. (2.6), it follows that the difference in potential between two points A and B in the field of a *single* point charge q is given by

$$V_B - V_A = \frac{q}{4\pi\epsilon_0}\left(\frac{1}{r_B} - \frac{1}{r_A}\right) \tag{3.16}$$

[Compare Sec. 4, Chap. 1; in particular Eqs. (1.8) and (1.9).] Using the convention that the potential at points infinitely far from q be taken as zero [see Eq. (2.7)], we find for the potential at any point P of the field

$$V_P = \frac{q}{4\pi\epsilon_0 r} \tag{3.17}$$

where r is the distance from q to the point P. Remember that V and hence r are scalars. We recall that this is the work per unit charge we must do on a positive test charge to move it along any arbitrary path from infinity to the field point P against the repulsion of the charge q. The points lying on the surface of a sphere of radius r, centered at q, are all at the same potential and thus form an equipotential surface. The field lines are normal to these surfaces and hence are the radii of such spheres. The gradient of the potential at any point is directed radially toward or away from q, and we have

$$\mathcal{E} = -\text{ grad } V = -\frac{dV}{dr} = \frac{q}{4\pi\epsilon_0 r^2} \tag{3.18}$$

which checks Eq. (3.4).

One can demonstrate readily, with the help of Gauss's law, that for the field of any *spherically symmetric* distribution of charge, e.g., a uniformly charged metal sphere, Eqs. (3.17) and (3.18) hold at all points *outside* the charge distribution. For a proof of this by direct integration, see Frank, "Introduction to Mechanics and Heat," Chap. XII. Thus a spherical charge distribution creates a field external to itself which is the same as if the charge were concentrated at the center of the sphere.

b. The Potential and Field of a Dipole.   By a *dipole* is meant a pair of equal and opposite charges separated by a fixed distance. We shall investigate the field of a dipole, having charges $\pm q$ of separation $2a$. Since there is symmetry about the axis of the dipole (the line joining the charges), it will be sufficient to restrict our attention to the plane containing the field point P and the dipole (Fig. 18). The potential at P due to the charge

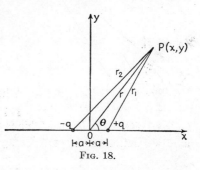

FIG. 18.

$+q$ is $+q/4\pi\epsilon_0 r_1$, and that due to the charge $-q$ is $-q/4\pi\epsilon_0 r_2$. *Since potential is a scalar, the potential at P is the algebraic sum of these two terms.* Hence at P

$$V = \frac{q}{4\pi\epsilon_0}\left(\frac{1}{r_1} - \frac{1}{r_2}\right) \tag{3.19}$$

In order to express V in terms of x and y, the coordinates of P, we use the relations

$$r_1^2 = (x - a)^2 + y^2; \qquad r_2^2 = (x + a)^2 + y^2$$

and Eq. (3.19) becomes

$$V = \frac{q}{4\pi\epsilon_0}\left[\frac{1}{\sqrt{(x - a)^2 + y^2}} - \frac{1}{\sqrt{(x + a)^2 + y^2}}\right] \tag{3.20}$$

The x- and y-components of ε may then be obtained by differentiating Eq. (3.20) with respect to x and y, respectively. In symbols, we have

$$\varepsilon_x = -\frac{\partial V}{\partial x}; \qquad \varepsilon_y = -\frac{\partial V}{\partial y}$$

In the special but very important case where the distance $2a$ between the charges is small compared to r_1 and r_2 (the case of a point dipole), we can simplify Eq. (3.19) as follows. We write

$$V = \frac{q}{4\pi\epsilon_0}\left(\frac{r_2 - r_1}{r_1 r_2}\right) \cong \frac{q}{4\pi\epsilon_0 r^2}(r_2 - r_1)$$

where r is the distance from the dipole to the field point. $(r_2 - r_1)$ is the difference in distance between the two ends of the dipole and the point P, and if the charges are close together, we can write very nearly (Fig. 19)

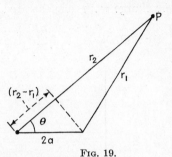

$$r_2 - r_1 = 2a \cos \theta$$

FIG. 19.

so that we obtain for V

$$V = \frac{2aq \cos \theta}{4\pi\epsilon_0 r^2} \qquad (3.21)$$

The expression $2aq$ is the product of the separation of the charges and the magnitude of either of them. This is called the *dipole moment* of the dipole, and we denote it by p. Using this symbol, Eq. (3.21) becomes

$$V = \frac{p \cos \theta}{4\pi\epsilon_0 r^2} \qquad (3.22)$$

as the potential of a tiny dipole of moment p. In terms of the x- and y-coordinates of the field point P, this equation becomes, since $r^2 = x^2 + y^2$ and $\cos \theta = x/r$,

$$V = \frac{px}{4\pi\epsilon_0 r^3} = \frac{px}{4\pi\epsilon_0(x^2 + y^2)^{\frac{3}{2}}} \qquad (3.23)$$

from which $\mathcal{E}_x$ and $\mathcal{E}_y$ may be readily obtained. Further discussion of this field is left to the problems.

c. Potential of a Circular Ring of Charge. To illustrate the case of fields due to a continuous distribution of charge, we consider the example of the previous section and calculate the potential of a uniformly charged ring at a point on the axis of the ring (Fig. 17). In general, for a continuous distribution of charge located in a finite region of space, the potential is given by

$$V = \frac{1}{4\pi\epsilon_0} \int \frac{dq}{r} \qquad (3.24)$$

where r is the distance (always taken positive) between dq and the field point. If we consider the vector[1] $\mathbf{r}$ from dq to P, then in the integration the end of the vector at P is held fixed, and the other end at dq moves over all points of space at which there is a charge. For dq

---

[1] For the sake of clarity, we shall sometimes use boldface type to distinguish vector quantities from the magnitudes of these vectors.

we write $\tau\,ds$, $\sigma\,dS$, or $\rho\,dv$, depending on the problem at hand, where τ, σ, ρ are linear, surface, and volume charge densities, respectively. Referring to Fig. 17, we have in place of Eq. (3.24),

$$V_P = \frac{1}{4\pi\epsilon_0} \int \frac{dq}{l} = \frac{1}{4\pi\epsilon_0 l} \int \tau\,ds = \frac{q}{4\pi\epsilon_0 l}$$

since l is the same for all the elements of charge dq on the ring. This can be written as

$$V = \frac{q}{4\pi\epsilon_0 \sqrt{x^2 + r^2}} \tag{3.25}$$

Equation (3.25) gives the variation of the potential with the coordinates of points *on the x-axis only* and should not be applied at other points. We can, however, find the x-component of $\mathcal{E}$ from Eq. (3.25) at a point on the x-axis such as P. We have

$$\mathcal{E}_x = -\frac{dV}{dx} = \frac{qx}{4\pi\epsilon_0(r^2 + x^2)^{\frac{3}{2}}}$$

which is identical with Eq. (3.15).

Problems

1. Two equal and opposite charges are held 1 ft apart in empty space. What is the magnitude of each charge if they attract each other with a force of 1 lb?

2. Consider two identical particles of mass m and charge e. What must be the ratio of charge to mass if their gravitational attraction is to be equal in magnitude to the electrostatic repulsion? Calculate the ratio of electrostatic to gravitational force for an electron. The gravitational constant is 6.67×10^{-11} mks units.

3. Two pith balls, each of mass 0.02 g, are suspended from a common point by threads, each of length 10 cm. Each is given the same charge, and in equilibrium the threads make an angle of 74° with each other. Compute the charge on each pith ball.

4. In Fig. 20, $q_1 = -80 \times 10^{-9}$ coulomb, $q_2 = +80 \times 10^{-9}$ coulomb, and $q_3 = +10 \times 10^{-8}$ coulomb.

a. Find the magnitude and direction of the force acting on q_3.

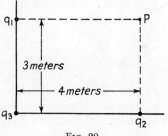

FIG. 20.

b. Find the work required to move q_3 from its position as shown in the figure to point P, keeping the charges q_1 and q_2 fixed.

5. Two equal negative charges, each of magnitude 3×10^{-9} coulomb, are held fixed at a separation of 4.0 cm. Calculate the intensity of the electric field produced by these charges in a plane which bisects the line joining these charges at right angles, at a point 16 cm from the intersection of the plane and the line joining the charges. At what points of the plane is the field intensity a maximum? What is the maximum value of the field strength?

6. Two equal and opposite charges $+q$ and $-q$ are held fixed at a separation $2a$. Using the line connecting the charges as an x-axis with an origin halfway between them, calculate:

a. The field intensity produced by this dipole at any point on the x-axis.

b. The field intensity at any point on a line perpendicular to the x-axis and passing through the positive charge.

c. The resultant field intensity (magnitude and direction) due to this dipole at any point in the x-y plane, using as a y-axis a perpendicular bisector of the line joining the charges.

7. Three equal positive point charges, each of magnitude Q, are held fixed at the corners of a square of side a.

a. Find the magnitude and direction of the electric field intensity at the center of the square and at the fourth corner.

b. Find the potential at these two points.

c. How much work is done on a charge q in moving it from the fourth corner of the square to the center of the square?

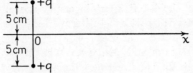

Fig. 21.

8. Two positive point charges, each of charge 3×10^{-9} coulomb, are held fixed at a separation of 10 cm, as shown in Fig. 21.

a. Find expressions for the potential and intensity of the electric field produced by these charges at any point on the x-axis shown in Fig. 21.

b. If an electron starts from rest at a point on the x-axis 10 cm to the right of O, find its speed as it passes through O. How far to the left of O does the electron move?

9. Charges of $+\frac{4}{3} \times 10^{-8}$ coulomb and $-\frac{1}{3} \times 10^{-8}$ coulomb are placed along the x-axis at the points -10 and 0 cm, respectively.

a. Make a plot of the potential as a function of x at any point along the x-axis, also as a function of position on a line perpendicular to the x-axis and passing through the point $x = 10$ cm.

b. At what points on the x-axis is the potential 300 volts? Is the electric field intensity the same at these points?

c. At what point would a third charge remain in equilibrium? Would it be stable equilibrium?

10. A thin glass rod 24 cm long carries a charge of $+16 \times 10^{-9}$ coulomb uniformly distributed along its length.

Compute the potential and electric field intensity at a point on the perpendicular bisector of the rod 5.0 cm from its center.

11. Using Gauss's theorem, prove that the magnitude of the *difference* between the electric field intensity vectors on either side of a very large uniform plane sheet of charge (*not a conductor*) is equal to σ/ϵ_0, where σ is the surface charge density. What is the intensity at a point outside the sheet of charge?

12. Starting from the fact that for electrostatic equilibrium no electric field can exist in the interior of a metallic conductor, show that the charge on a charged metallic body must reside on its surface. Apply Gauss's law successively to a closed surface lying just inside the metal surface and to a closed surface just outside the metal surface. Can a surface charge exist on the *inner* surface of a hollow metallic conductor in electrostatic equilibrium? Justify your answer.

13. Consider a charge q distributed uniformly throughout a spherical volume of radius a with a charge density ρ.

a. Using Gauss's law, show that the electric field intensity at a point inside the sphere is proportional to the distance from the center of the sphere.

b. Derive a formula for the field intensity at points inside and outside the sphere.

c. Construct a plot of the magnitude of the electric intensity against distance from the center of the sphere.

d. Calculate the potential as a function of distance from the center of the sphere for points both inside and outside the sphere.

e. Plot the potential as a function of distance from the center of the sphere.

14. Positive charge is uniformly distributed with a volume density ρ throughout the volume of a very long circular cylinder of radius a. With the help of Gauss's theorem, find a formula for the electric field intensity $\mathcal{E}$ at any point inside the cylinder. Find the potential difference between the axis of the cylinder and a point on its surface.

15. A thin wire bent to form the arc of a circle of radius r subtends an angle θ_0 at the center of the circle. If the wire carries a charge q uniformly distributed along its length, derive an expression for the electric field intensity at the center of the circle.

16. A spherical drop of water 1.0 cm in diameter carries a charge of 2.0×10^{-9} coulomb.

a. What is the potential at the surface of the drop?

b. If two such drops, similarly charged, coalesce to form a single drop, what is the potential at the surface of the drop thus formed?

c. Where is the field intensity largest in parts a and b? What is this largest value?

17. A conducting sphere of radius a carries a charge q. If an infinitesimal additional charge dq is brought up to the sphere from a distant point, calculate the work done in bringing up this charge. What is the total work done in charging the sphere to a potential V, considering the sphere initially uncharged and then charged in the manner described above?

18. One face of a thin circular disk of radius R is charged uniformly with a positive surface charge density σ.

a. Derive an expression for the potential at a point of the axis of the disk at a distance x from the center of the disk.

b. Derive an expression for the electric intensity at the above point. What is its direction?

c. If the disk is 3.0 cm in radius and carries a total charge of 3.0×10^{-10} coulomb, calculate the potential and intensity at a point on the axis 4.0 cm from the center of the disk.

d. Using the data of part *c*, calculate the potential at the center of the disk.

e. Where on the axis is the field intensity maximum? What is the maximum field intensity?

19. A circular *metal* disk of negligible thickness and of radius R carries a uniform surface charge of density σ on its surface.

a. By direct integration of Coulomb's law, find the electric field intensity at a point on the axis of the disk at a distance x from its center.

b. Show from your answer to part *a* that this field intensity approaches the value given by Eq. (3.10) of the text as the disk radius gets larger and larger, keeping the surface density of charge constant.

20. An insulated metal sphere of radius 3.0 cm carries a positive charge of 10^{-9} coulomb and is surrounded concentrically by an insulated hollow metal sphere of inner radius 6.0 cm and outer radius 9.0 cm. The hollow sphere carries a total negative charge of 0.5×10^{-9} coulomb.

a. Using Gauss's law, compute the charge residing on the inner surface of the hollow sphere and on its outer surface.

b. Find the potential difference between the two spheres.

c. Compute the electric field intensity at points 4.5, 7.0, and 12 cm from the center of the spheres.

21. Using the expression $V = (p \cos \theta)/4\pi\epsilon_0 r^2$ for the potential of a point dipole at a point whose polar coordinates are (r,θ) [Eq. (3.22) of the text], calculate:

a. The radial and tangential components of $\mathcal{E}$ ($\mathcal{E}_r$ and $\mathcal{E}_\theta$) at this point.

b. The magnitude and direction of the resultant field intensity vector at this point.

22. Calculate the electric field intensity at any point of space due to two neighboring, parallel, infinite sheets of charge, one carrying a uniform positive surface charge density $+\sigma$ and the other a uniform negative surface charge density $-\sigma$. The planes have a separation d. Calculate the change in potential as one moves from a point outside these planes to a point on the other side of these planes, and show that the change in potential as one crosses this so-called *double layer* is equal to $\sigma d/\epsilon_0$. σd is called the dipole moment per unit area of the double layer.

23. A hemispherical cup of inner radius r carries a charge uniformly distributed over its inner surface. What is the electric field intensity at the center of the hemisphere?

CHAPTER 4

INDUCED CHARGES AND CAPACITY

Electrostatic problems involving conductors are, in general, much more complicated than those discussed in the previous chapter, in which we considered the electrostatic fields produced by systems of *fixed* charges. The complication in the former important class of problems arises from the fact that when a conductor is placed in an electrostatic field, induced surface charges distribute themselves in such a manner as to make the conductor an equipotential. This fact has already been discussed briefly in Chap. 2. One must calculate not only the field but also the distribution of these induced charges on conductors. Since the distribution of all the charges giving rise to the resultant field is not known from the outset, one cannot directly apply Coulomb's law according to the methods explained in Chap. 3. In fact, the solution of these problems can be accomplished only with the aid of more advanced mathematical techniques than are available to us in this book, and only for relatively simple geometrical configurations have exact solutions been obtained.

1. Induced Charges. If an uncharged insulated conductor is placed in an electrostatic field, the law of conservation of electric charge requires that the total charge on the conductor stay equal to zero, so that positive and negative induced surface charges appear in equal amounts. There are just as many lines of force terminating on the negative induced charges as leave the surface from the positive induced charges, in accordance with Gauss's law. Suppose we consider the case of an uncharged metallic sphere placed in the neighborhood of a positive point charge. Some of the lines of $\mathcal{E}$ (or D) originating on the point charge will terminate on the side of the sphere toward the point charge, and an equal number of these lines will leave the other side of the spherical surface. The magnitude of the induced charge of either sign will, of course, be smaller than that of the inducing charge and will depend on how much of the field is intercepted by the conductor.

If a charged body is introduced into the region inside a hollow metal container (with a small opening), practically all the field lines are intercepted, and there appears on the inner surface of the container an

57

induced charge equal to, and opposite in sign to, the charge placed inside the container. If the container is supported by an insulator, one finds on the outer surface of the container a charge equal in sign and magnitude to the charge introduced. If the outside of the container is connected to an electrometer, the leaves of the instrument will diverge because of this charge. Upon bringing the charged body into contact with the inside of the container, no effect is observed on the electrometer, and upon removing the originally charged body, there is still no observable change in the electrometer reading. The charge remaining on the metal container (and electrometer) is thus shown to be equal to the original charge introduced. The above experiment and other similar ones were performed by Faraday using an ice pail as the metal container, and these are known as the Faraday ice-pail experiments. Using this arrangement, Faraday found that if two bodies were electrified by friction inside the pail, no deflection of the electroscope was observed. If then either of the two bodies which were rubbed was removed from the pail, the leaves of the electroscope diverged, thus showing that the bodies were charged by friction. This provided an experimental verification of the law of conservation of charge, showing that the two bodies had acquired exactly equal and opposite charges.

In spite of the difficulties of exact calculation, one can usually obtain a good idea of the modifications of an electric field caused by the presence of a conductor by sketching the lines of $\mathcal{E}$ and the equipotentials. In so doing, one makes use of the fact that the conducting surface is an equipotential, and hence the equipotentials near this surface must bear some resemblance to it. The lines of force must terminate on the conductor surface at right angles to it, and, at some distance from it, both the lines of force and the equipotentials must approach the pattern characteristic of the field in the absence of the conductor. For a typical field of this sort, showing the field resulting from placing an insulated uncharged sphere in a region where there originally existed a uniform field, see Fig. 25.

2. The Method of Electrical Images. The distribution of induced surface charge on a conductor which is placed in an electric field and the resultant field due to these charges and to the original field can be calculated for certain special geometrical conductor shapes by an ingenious method due to Lord Kelvin and called the method of electrical images. We shall explain the method with the help of a simple, but important, example. Suppose we have a large plane conductor, such as a metal plate, placed in the field of a point charge $+q$. Let the distance d of this point charge from the plane surface be small compared to the dimensions of the plane, so that we may treat the latter as infinite in extent. Furthermore, we suppose the conductor grounded (connected to the earth), so that we may take its potential as zero. Now the general condition that determines the distribution of induced charge on the conductor surface is that the combined field of this induced charge and of the external charge (in our case, the point charge $+q$) is such that the potential of the conductor surface is a constant, independent of position on the surface. In our example, this constant potential is zero. The resultant lines of electric field intensity must therefore terminate on or leave this equipotential surface at right angles to it. We now seek to replace the unknown surface charge distribution by a simpler known charge distribution which, in combination with the charges producing the original field, will make the conductor surface an equipo-

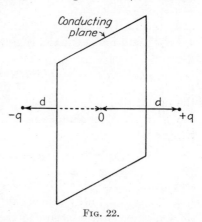

tential. In our example of the point charge and conducting plane, we imagine the conducting plate removed and a second point charge $-q$ placed at a distance d in back of the plane formerly occupied by the conducting surface, just as if it were the optical image of the charge $+q$ in a plane mirror (Fig. 22). The field produced by the two charges in empty space (a dipole field) is such that the plane bisect-ing the line joining them (the loca-

FIG. 22.

tion of the conducting surface in the real problem) is an equipotential. This follows from the fact that every point on this plane is equidistant from the two charges. Thus, at a point P, the potential is

$$V_P = \frac{q}{4\pi\epsilon_0 r} + \frac{-q}{4\pi\epsilon_0 r} = 0$$

Now, since these two point charges create an equipotential surface at the location of the plane conducting surface, they produce the same effect as the induced surface charge distribution and the original point charge $+q$. At any point Q we can calculate the field since the potential there is

$$V = \frac{q}{4\pi\epsilon_0}\left(\frac{1}{r_1} - \frac{1}{r_2}\right)$$

and this yields the field of a dipole discussed in Chap. 3. For the real problem of the point charge and conducting plane, we thus find the field at all points to the right of the plane, since there is no field inside or to the left of the plate.

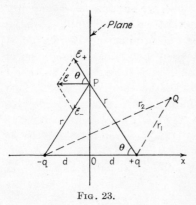

Fig. 23.

To obtain the distribution of induced charge on the conducting plane, we make use of the fact that the electric field intensity at the surface of a conductor is equal to σ/ϵ_0, where σ is the surface charge density at the point in question [Eq. (3.10)]. The intensity $\mathcal{E}$ at an arbitrary point P of the plane is the vector sum of the two vectors $\mathcal{E}_+$ and $\mathcal{E}_-$, as shown in Fig. 23. The vectors $\mathcal{E}_+$ and $\mathcal{E}_-$ are equal in magnitude, each being $q/4\pi\epsilon_0 r^2$, and make equal angles with the x-axis. The resultant is

$$\mathcal{E} = -\frac{2qd}{4\pi\epsilon_0 r^3} \tag{4.1}$$

the negative sign indicating that it is directed to the left, *i.e.*, toward the surface. The induced surface charge density at this point is therefore

$$\sigma = \epsilon_0 \mathcal{E} = -\frac{qd}{2\pi r^3} \tag{4.2}$$

and varies inversely as the cube of the distance from the point charge $+q$. One can readily show that the total induced charge is just equal to $-q$, equal and opposite to the inducing point charge. The proof of this is left to a problem. Thus all the lines of $\mathcal{E}$ leaving the point charge $+q$ terminate on the conducting surface. The force with which the conducting surface and the point charge attract each other is equal to the force with which q attracts its mirror image. Note that although the conductor is grounded (its potential is zero), it carries a charge, held by the attraction of the point charge. It is a common error to suppose that a grounded conductor can never carry an electric charge. Furthermore, it is clear that the problem of an infinite conducting plane in the neighborhood of an arbitrary number of *fixed* point charges can be solved by the above method by superposing the fields of each fixed point charge and its image.

The general idea of replacing an unknown distribution of surface charge by an equivalent simpler charge distribution which produces

the same field external to the conductor is a very useful one. We
shall give a second example employing this guiding principle, although
it is not strictly an image method.   The problem is the following:
Given a uniform electric field $\mathcal{E}_0$ in a region of space.   We introduce an
uncharged insulated metallic sphere of radius R into this region and
wish to find the resultant field and the distribution of induced surface
charge on the sphere.   Let us take the x-axis as the direction of the
original uniform field $\mathcal{E}_0$.   In the absence of the metal sphere, the
potential in the region where this uniform field exists is evidently
given by

$$V_1 = -\mathcal{E}_0 x + C \tag{4.3}$$

where C is an arbitrary constant.   Now suppose the sphere is placed
in position, and let the center of the sphere be the origin of a system of

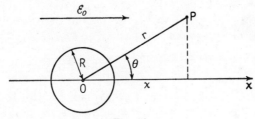

Fig. 24.

coordinates.   If r denotes the distance from the center of the sphere
to a field point P (Fig. 24), and θ the angle which r makes with the
x-axis, the contribution to the potential at P due to the original
uniform field can be rewritten as

$$V_1 = -\mathcal{E}_0 r \cos \theta + C \tag{4.4}$$

If now V_s denotes the potential of the field produced by the induced
charges on the sphere, the total potential V at point P will be

$$V = V_s - \mathcal{E}_0 r \cos \theta + C \tag{4.5}$$

The conditions which now must be satisfied are that (1) the potential
V must reduce to a constant for $r = R$, *independent* of θ, i.e., at all
points on the surface of the sphere, and (2) the potential must reduce
to the value V_1 given by Eq. (4.4) as $r \to \infty$, i.e., at distances from the
sphere large compared to its radius.   Now the only way in which
condition (1) can be satisfied is that V_s must be proportional to $\cos \theta$,
and the proportionality constant must be such that the first two terms
on the right-hand side of Eq. (4.5) cancel for $r = R$.   Condition (2)

will be satisfied if $V_s \rightarrow 0$ as $r \rightarrow \infty$. We have already encountered a potential which satisfies these conditions. This is the potential of a point dipole located at the origin of coordinates, given [Eq. (3.22)] by

$$V_s = \frac{p \cos \theta}{4\pi\epsilon_0 r^2} \tag{4.6}$$

where p is the dipole moment. Thus we have found a simple charge distribution, *viz.*, a point dipole located at the center of the sphere, which produces a field whose potential at points external to the sphere is just that of the field produced by the induced charges. We can therefore replace the induced surface charges on the metal sphere by an equivalent dipole at its center for purposes of computing the electric field outside the sphere. There remains the problem of determining the magnitude of the equivalent dipole moment p. This is done by taking V_s from Eq. (4.6), inserting it into (4.5), placing $r = R$, and setting the sum of the first two terms on the right-hand side of (4.5) equal to zero. Accordingly

$$\frac{p \cos \theta}{4\pi\epsilon_0 R^2} - \mathcal{E}_0 R \cos \theta = 0$$

and we have

$$p = 4\pi\epsilon_0 R^3 \mathcal{E}_0 \tag{4.7}$$

as the magnitude of the so-called induced dipole moment, proportional to the volume of the sphere and to the external uniform field intensity. Using (4.7) in (4.6), we have

$$V_s = \mathcal{E}_0 \frac{R^3}{r^2} \cos \theta$$

and hence Eq. (4.5) gives us finally

$$V = \mathcal{E}_0 \left(\frac{R^3}{r^2} - r \right) \cos \theta + C \tag{4.8}$$

as the potential at any point whose coordinates are (r, θ) and which lies outside the metal sphere where there is a field different from zero.

The components of the electric field intensity are then given by

$$\left. \begin{aligned} \mathcal{E}_r &= -\frac{\partial V}{\partial r} = \left(1 + \frac{2R^3}{r^3} \right) \mathcal{E}_0 \cos \theta \\ \mathcal{E}_\theta &= -\frac{1}{r}\frac{\partial V}{\partial \theta} = -\left(1 - \frac{R^3}{r^3} \right) \mathcal{E}_0 \sin \theta \end{aligned} \right\} \tag{4.9}$$

We note that at the metal surface $r = R$, $\mathcal{E}_\theta = 0$, as we expect since the lines of $\mathcal{E}$ are normal to the surface, *i.e.*, directed along r. The surface density of induced charge is given as before by

$$\sigma = \epsilon_0 \mathcal{E}_r = 3\epsilon_0 \mathcal{E}_0 \cos \theta \qquad (4.10)$$

where we take the value of $\mathcal{E}_r$ for $r = R$, at the surface. Thus we see that the surface charge density is positive and largest for $\theta = 0$, vanishes along the equator $\theta = \pi/2$, and is negative and largest for $\theta = \pi$. One can readily show that the total induced charge on the whole sphere is zero. This, and other details, are left to the problems. Finally in Fig. 25 we show the sphere, the equivalent dipole at the center, and a few of the lines of force. The dotted lines indicate some of the equipotentials.

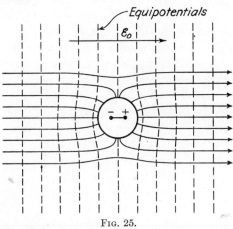

Fig. 25.

3. Capacity Coefficients; Condensers. If an isolated charged conducting body, such as a metal sphere, is charged, its potential (relative to that of an infinitely distant point) is raised or lowered, depending on the magnitude and sign of the charge imparted to it. In fact, the potential is proportional to the charge carried by the sphere. If the body is not alone, however, and there are other conducting bodies in the neighborhood, the potential of the first body will depend not only on its own charge but also on the charges and positions of all its neighbors. This is true whether the bodies carry a net charge or whether they carry induced charges, or both. Of course, at least one of the conducting bodies must be charged as a whole if an electric field is to exist. It can be shown in general (although we shall not attempt the proof here) that for a system of conducting bodies in equilibrium, the potential of each is a *linear* homogeneous function of the charges carried by both itself and all the others. Conversely, the charge on each conductor is a linear function of the potentials of all the bodies, itself included. The constant coefficients appearing in these linear equations (charges in terms of potentials) depend only on the geometrical configuration of the system, not on its electrical state, and are called the *capacity coefficients* of the system. In our work we shall confine our attention to the case of *two-body* systems, for which these relations become comparatively simple.

Let us consider two uncharged metallic bodies in empty space, insulated from each other and far removed from other conductors or charged bodies. If we transfer a quantity of charge from one body to the other, as can be done by connecting them for a moment to opposite terminals of a battery or power line, one of the bodies will carry a charge $+q$, the other a charge $-q$, and there will exist a potential difference between the two bodies. Such a two-body system is called an electrical *condenser*, or *capacitor*. The potential difference between the two so-called *plates* of a condenser is proportional to the magnitude of the charge transferred from one plate to the other. *The ratio of the magnitude of the charge on either plate to the potential difference between them is called the electrical capacity, or capacitance, of the condenser.*

If q is the magnitude of the charge on either plate and $V_2 - V_1$ denotes the potential difference between them, the capacity C is given by

$$C = \frac{q}{V_2 - V_1} \tag{4.11}$$

The capacity C of a condenser is by definition a positive quantity, and its value depends only on the geometrical configuration of the system in empty space. It also depends, as we shall see later, on the medium in which the field produced by the charges on the condenser plates exists, but this does not concern us at the present stage of our study. As before, we confine our attention to the case of empty space (or air, since to a good degree of approximation the effect of the air can be generally neglected).

The unit of capacity, one coulomb per volt, is called one farad. It has dimensions given by $[C] = q^2 t^2 m^{-1} l^{-2}$. All the lines of $\mathcal{E}$ (or of D) in the field of a condenser which leave the positively charged plate of a condenser must terminate on the negative plate since the charges on the plates are equal and opposite and there are no other charged bodies in the vicinity. The general problem of determining this field for bodies of arbitrary shape, so that the potential difference may be calculated, is virtually impossible; hence capacities are usually determined experimentally. There are, however, several simple and important geometrical configurations for which theoretical calculations may be made without difficulty, and we shall examine a few of these.

a. *The Parallel-plate Condenser.* The condenser consists of two parallel metal plates, each of area A, separated by a distance d, which is small compared to the surface dimensions of the plates (Fig. 26). If the left-hand plate carries a charge $+q$ and the right-hand plate a charge $-q$, the electric field produced by these charges will exist practically only in the region between the plates. There will be a so-called fringing field near the ends, but this can be neglected if the plates are large enough compared to their separation. In the figure are indicated the lines of ε (or of D) originating at the positive charges, which are uniformly distributed on the *inner* surface of the left-hand plate, and terminating on the corresponding negative charges on the *inner* surface of the opposite plate. Note that the distribution of charge on each metal plate is confined to its inner surface, being held there by the attraction of the charge on the opposite plate. This is quite different from the case of a *single* thin charged plate of large area, in which the charge is uniformly distributed over both surfaces of the plate. The field between the condenser plates is a uniform field, and the application of Gauss's law to a cylindrical surface of the sort shown in Fig. 14 and employed in Chap. 3, Sec. 4, for the case of a single infinite metal plate, uniformly charged, gives, as the magnitude of ε,

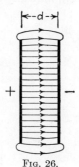

Fig. 26.

$$\varepsilon = \frac{\sigma}{\epsilon_0} \qquad (4.12)$$

and, correspondingly, $D = \sigma$, where σ is the surface charge density on the inner surface of the condenser plate. The lines of force are directed from left to right as shown in Fig. 26, so that the left-hand plate is at a higher potential than the right-hand one. Now by definition the potential difference between the plates is equal to the work per unit charge we must do in pushing a positive test charge from the right-hand to the left-hand plate against the field. Since the field is uniform, the vector ε is constant in magnitude and direction at all points between the plates, so that the potential difference between them has the magnitude

$$V_2 - V_1 = \varepsilon d \qquad (4.13)$$

To obtain the capacity of the condenser, we require an expression for

q, the charge on either plate.   From Eq. (4.12), we have

$$q = \sigma A = \epsilon_0 \mathcal{E} A \qquad (4.14)$$

Using the defining equation (4.11), there follows for the capacity of a parallel-plate condenser (neglecting fringing at the ends) in vacuum or air

$$C = \frac{q}{V_2 - V_1} = \frac{\epsilon_0 A}{d} \qquad (4.15)$$

Equation (4.15) shows that the capacity increases with increasing area and decreasing separation of the plates.   Furthermore, we can now give a simple physical interpretation of the permittivity ϵ_0.   It is numerically equal to the vacuum capacity of a parallel-plate condenser of plate area 1 m² and separation 1 m, or better, since we should satisfy the condition that the plate separation be small compared to its surface dimensions, the capacity of such a condenser with plates of area 100 cm² and separation 1 cm.

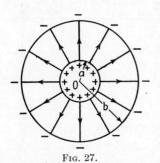

Fig. 27.

b. *The Spherical Condenser.*   The condenser consists of a metallic sphere of radius a and a concentric hollow metallic sphere of radius b surrounding the first (Fig. 27). The spherical symmetry of the condenser requires the charges on the inner and outer spheres to be distributed uniformly over their surfaces.   Suppose the inner sphere carries a positive charge $+q$.   Then the outer sphere will have an equal negative charge uniformly spread over its inner surface.   The inner sphere is evidently at a higher potential than the outer one.

Applying Gauss's law to a closed spherical surface of radius r, $a < r < b$, one finds that the field intensity vector at any point on this surface has a magnitude given by

$$\mathcal{E} = \frac{q}{4\pi\epsilon_0 r^2} \qquad (4.16)$$

and is directed outward along r.   The electric field is the same in the region between the spheres as if the charge $+q$ were concentrated at the center O.

The potential difference between the plates is, by definition,

$$V_a - V_b = -\int_{r=b}^{r=a} \mathcal{E}_r \, dr = -\frac{q}{4\pi\epsilon_0} \int_b^a \frac{dr}{r^2} = \frac{q}{4\pi\epsilon_0} \left(\frac{1}{a} - \frac{1}{b} \right) \qquad (4.17)$$

where V_a and V_b are the potentials of the inner and outer spheres, respectively. From Eq. (4.11), the capacity of this spherical condenser is then

$$C = \frac{q}{V_a - V_b} = \frac{4\pi\epsilon_0}{(1/a) - (1/b)} = \frac{4\pi\epsilon_0 ab}{b - a} \qquad (4.18)$$

If the inner radius of the outer sphere is very large compared to a, Eq. (4.18) gives

$$C = 4\pi\epsilon_0 a \qquad (4.19)$$

as the *capacity of an isolated conducting sphere of radius a.*

   c. The Cylindrical Condenser.   The condenser consists of a metallic cylinder of radius a and a concentric hollow cylinder of inner radius b surrounding the inner cylinder.   If the length l of the cylinders is very large compared to their separation, the field between the cylinders is essentially that produced by a uniformly charged straight wire of infinite length lying along the cylinder axis.   For this case, a calculation similar to those of the preceding examples yields, as the *capacity per unit length* of such a condenser,

$$C' = \frac{C}{l} = \frac{2\pi\epsilon_0}{\ln (b/a)} \qquad (4.20)$$

The proof of this formula is left as a problem for the student.

   4. Condensers in Parallel and in Series.   In many practical cases one is interested in the capacity of systems of condensers when they are connected to one another in various manners by metallic wires.   At first sight it might seem that one would have to employ the general theory of capacity coefficients to carry through a calculation of this many-body problem.   We have seen, however, that the electric field due to the charges on the plates of a condenser is confined almost entirely to the region between the plates. The presence of other conductors in the neighborhood of a condenser has no effect, provided only that they lie outside the field produced by the condenser.   This is the case in practice, and hence we proceed with the calculation treating each condenser as if it were far from any of the others.

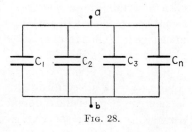

FIG. 28.

   Suppose a number n of condensers are connected in parallel as shown in Fig. 28, and a difference of potential is established between points

a and b, a being at the higher potential.   For convenience in notation we denote the potential difference $V_a - V_b$ between a and b by V_{ab}. V_{ab} is the same for all the condensers by virtue of the electrical connection, and the total charge on the system is the sum of the charges on the separate condensers.   For the individual condensers we have

$$q_1 = C_1 V_{ab}; \; q_2 = C_2 V_{ab}; \; \cdots \; ; q_n = C_n V_{ab}$$

Adding all these equations, there follows

$$q_1 + q_2 + \cdots + q_n = Q = V_{ab}(C_1 + C_2 + \cdots + C_n)$$

and since a single condenser equivalent to this combination would acquire the same charge Q when its plates have a potential difference V_{ab} between them, its capacity would be

$$C = \frac{Q}{V_{ab}} = C_1 + C_2 + \cdots + C_n \qquad (4.21)$$

Thus the capacity of a single condenser equivalent to a number of condensers in parallel is equal to the sum of the individual capacities.

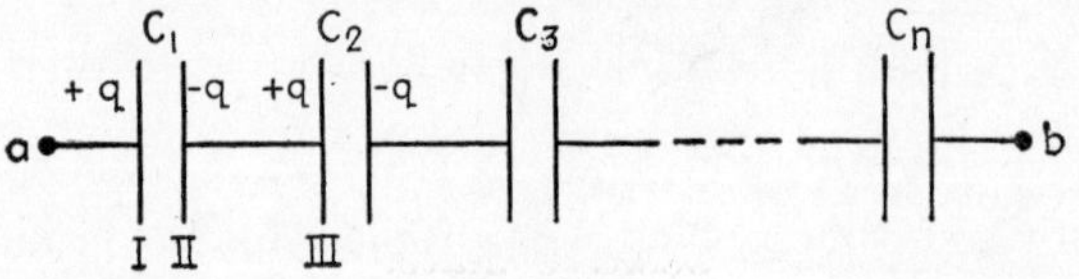

Fig. 29.

If we connect the condensers in series, we obtain the arrangement shown in Fig. 29.   Suppose we establish a definite potential difference V_{ab} between the terminals a and b by connecting them to a battery. Let the positive charge on plate I be $+q$.   There will then be an equal negative charge $-q$ on plate II, since all the lines of ε (or of D) leaving plate I terminate on plate II.   Now plates II and III are connected together by a conductor, and this insulated system is originally uncharged.   The law of conservation of charge then requires that when plate II acquires the charge $-q$, plate III must acquire an equal and opposite charge $+q$.   Thus we see that the charges on the individual condensers are all equal in this series connection.   If $V_1, V_2, \ldots , V_n$ denote the potential differences between the plates of the condensers $C_1, C_2, \ldots , C_n$, respectively, we must have

$$V_{ab} = V_1 + V_2 + \cdots + V_n$$

since the work one must do to move a test charge from b to a is equal to the sum of the works done in moving through the fields of the individual condensers.

For the separate condensers we have, remembering that they carry equal charges q,

$$V_1 = \frac{q}{C_1}; \; V_2 = \frac{q}{C_2}; \; \cdots \; ; \; V_n = \frac{q}{C_n}$$

Adding these equations, there follows

$$V_{ab} = \frac{q}{C} = q \left(\frac{1}{C_1} + \frac{1}{C_2} + \cdots + \frac{1}{C_n} \right)$$

where C is the capacity of a single equivalent condenser. Hence we have

$$\frac{1}{C} = \frac{1}{C_1} + \frac{1}{C_2} + \cdots + \frac{1}{C_n} \tag{4.22}$$

as the formula for calculating the capacity of a single condenser which is equivalent to a number of condensers in series.

5. Energy Stored in a Condenser; Energy in the Electrostatic Field.
Let us compute the work which must be done in charging a condenser. To do so, we imagine the charge brought from one plate to the other in successive steps, during each of which equilibrium conditions prevail, an infinitesimal quantity dq in each step. Consider the process at the stage where the charge on the plates is q and the potential difference between them is V'. In bringing up an additional charge dq from the negative to the positive plate, we must do an amount of work

$$dW = V' \, dq \tag{4.23}$$

since V' is the work per unit charge we must do in transferring a charge from one plate to the other. Since, by definition,

$$V' = \frac{q}{C}$$

where C is the condenser capacity, we can rewrite Eq. (4.23) as

$$dW = \frac{q \, dq}{C}$$

and then find for the total work required to charge the condenser to a total charge Q,

$$W = \frac{1}{C} \int_0^Q q \, dq = \frac{Q^2}{2C} \tag{4.24}$$

If the final potential difference is V, this can be written as

$$W = \tfrac{1}{2} C V^2 \tag{4.25}$$

(This energy can be thought of as stored potential energy in the condenser, since it can all be regained.) For example, in a parallel-plate condenser one could allow the plates to come together under the action of their mutual attraction and thereby raise a weight. This sort of argument may be employed to calculate the force with which one condenser plate attracts the other. Let the condenser plates have a separation x, and suppose the condenser has been charged, the plates carrying charges $\pm Q$ and insulated so that no charge can escape. If

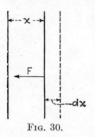

FIG. 30.

we now separate the plates by an additional amount dx (Fig. 30), we must do an amount of *mechanical* work

$$dW = F\,dx \tag{4.26}$$

where F is the magnitude of the force of attraction of the plates for each other. Since the system is electrically isolated, this work must be stored up as additional electrostatic energy in the condenser. We can calculate this increase of stored energy in the condenser by noting that the capacity decreases, and hence, according to Eq. (4.24), the stored energy increases. We write for the energy U, in accordance with Eqs. (4.24) and (4.15),

$$U = \frac{Q^2}{2C} = \frac{Q^2 x}{2\epsilon_0 A} \tag{4.27}$$

and if x is increased by an amount dx, the increase of U is

$$dU = \frac{Q^2}{2\epsilon_0 A}\,dx \tag{4.28}$$

Equating (4.26) and (4.28), there follows for the attractive force

$$F = \frac{Q^2}{2\epsilon_0 A} = \frac{\sigma^2 A}{2\epsilon_0} \tag{4.29}$$

where σ is the surface charge density on either plate. From this we find for the *force per unit area* (a normal stress) acting on the charged surfaces

$$\frac{F}{A} = \frac{\sigma^2}{2\epsilon_0} \tag{4.30}$$

(This expression turns out to be valid for any charged surface, although we have derived it only for a special case.) It is important to note that in this derivation the charge on the condenser plates was maintained constant while the plates were moved. One might well ask, "Why not calculate the work done during the motion dx of one of the

plates, keeping the potential difference between the plates constant?"
Such a calculation would not directly yield the correct value of the
attractive force because the constant difference of potential would
have to be maintained during the motion by an *external* device, such
as a battery. The battery would then deliver energy to or absorb it
from the condenser when the plate separation is changed. Hence it
would be incorrect to identify the mechanical work done with the
increase of electrostatic energy in the condenser.

Returning to the question of the energy stored in a parallel-plate
condenser, we can write this energy according to Eq. (4.24) as

$$U = \frac{Q^2}{2C} = \frac{\sigma^2 A^2}{2C} = \frac{\sigma^2}{2\epsilon_0}(Ad) \qquad (4.31)$$

using the fact that the capacity $C = \epsilon_0 A/d$. It is interesting to write
this expression in terms of the electric field intensity vector. Since
we have $\mathcal{E} = \sigma/\epsilon_0$ for the uniform field of the parallel-plate condenser,
Eq. (4.31) takes the form

$$U = \tfrac{1}{2}\epsilon_0 \mathcal{E}^2 (Ad) = \tfrac{1}{2}\mathcal{E}D(Ad) \qquad (4.32)$$

where the last equality is obtained with the use of the defining relation
$D = \epsilon_0 \mathcal{E}$. Now Ad is just the volume of space between the condenser
plates where there is an electric field, and the stored energy is proportional to this volume. Thus for this case we can think of the electrostatic energy as stored in the electrostatic field with an *energy density*
(energy per unit volume) equal to $\tfrac{1}{2}\epsilon_0 \mathcal{E}^2 = \tfrac{1}{2}\mathcal{E}D$. One can prove in
general (with the help of methods beyond the scope of this text) that
the above interpretation is possible for any arbitrary electrostatic
field. It takes work to establish such a field, and we can think of this
work as being stored up as potential energy of the field, distributed
throughout space with a density given, as above, by

$$u = \tfrac{1}{2}\epsilon_0 \mathcal{E}^2 = \tfrac{1}{2}\mathcal{E}D \qquad (4.33)$$

where $\mathcal{E}$ and D represent the magnitudes of the field intensity and displacement vectors at the point where the energy density is being calculated. The utility of this notion of energy being distributed throughout space will become evident (as does the whole field concept) when
we later investigate time-varying fields and electromagnetic waves.
Equation (4.33) holds only for empty space as written with the factor
ϵ_0, but we shall later see that a very similar relation holds in material
media. For a given field, one can compute the total electrostatic

energy by integrating over all space, so that

$$U = \frac{\epsilon_0}{2} \int \mathcal{E}^2 \, dv \qquad (4.34)$$

where dv is an element of volume.

Problems

1. Prove by direct integration that the total charge induced on an infinite conducting plane by a point charge is equal to and opposite in sign to the point charge.   Use Eq. (4.2) for the surface density of induced charge.

2. In the preceding problem, derive an expression for the fraction of the total induced charge on the plane which lies inside a circle whose radius equals the distance of the point charge from the plane, the center of the circle being the point of intersection with the plane of a perpendicular from the point charge.

3. An electron is located at a distance of 10^{-8} cm in front of a large plane metallic plate.

a. Calculate the force exerted by the plate on the electron in the above position.

b. What is this force when the electron is a distance x from the plate?

c. How much work does it take to pull the electron to infinity starting from the point $x = 10^{-8}$ cm?

d. Through what potential difference in volts would an electron have to move to gain the amount of energy calculated in part *c*?

4. A long wire of radius 1.0 cm is supported parallel to and at a height of 10 m above the earth's surface.   If it is maintained at a potential of 10,000 volts above ground potential, find the charge per unit length on the wire. What is the electric field intensity at a point on the earth's surface directly below the wire?   Use the method of images, assuming that the charge distribution on the wire has the cylindrical symmetry of an isolated wire.

5. An uncharged metal sphere of radius R is placed in a region of space where there previously existed a uniform electric field.   Show, by integrating the expression (4.10) of the text for the induced surface charge density on the sphere, that the *total* induced surface charge is zero.

6. An uncharged metal sphere of radius 3.0 cm is placed in a region where there previously existed a uniform electric field of field intensity 10^5 volts/m.

a. Find the total *positive* charge induced on the sphere.

b. What must be the separation between this positive charge concentrated at a point and an equal negative point charge, if the dipole moment thus formed is to be equal to the induced dipole moment on the sphere?

7. A parallel-plate condenser has plates of 100 cm² area separated by a distance of 1.0 mm.

a. Calculate the capacity of this condenser in microfarads.

b. If the plates of this condenser are connected to the terminals of a 100-volt battery, what charge resides on the plates?

8. Considering the earth as an isolated spherical conductor, calculate its capacity in microfarads. The radius of the earth is 4,000 miles.

9. Derive Eq. (4.20) for the capacity per unit length of a long cylindrical condenser.

10. The potential difference between the inner and outer conductors of a cylindrical condenser is maintained at 2,800 volts. If the diameter of the inner conductor is 0.70 cm, and the inside diameter of the outer conductor is 1.9 cm, what is the maximum electric field intensity inside the condenser? Where is the field intensity a maximum?

11. A 0.01-μf condenser is alternately charged to a potential difference of 5,000 volts and discharged through a spark gap, 500 times per second. What is the energy dissipated per discharge? What is the average rate of power dissipation?

12. Because of the presence of electrons, the potential V between the plates of a parallel-plate condenser at a distance x from the left-hand plate is given by

$$V = V_0 \left(\frac{x}{d}\right)^{\frac{4}{3}}$$

where V_0 is the potential of the right-hand plate and d is the plate separation.

a. Find an expression for the electric field intensity at any point x between the plates. What is its direction?

b. Applying Gauss's law to the surface bounding the volume of space between the plates (but not including the plates), find an expression for the number of electrons N in this region, if $-e$ is the electronic charge and A the area of each plate. Neglect end effects.

13. A parallel-plate condenser of plate separation d has its plates maintained at a difference of potential V_0. A thin sheet of paper carrying a uniformly distributed positive charge of surface density $+\sigma_0$ is inserted between the plates and parallel to them. This sheet of positive charge is located at a distance a from the plate of higher potential, and at a distance b from the other plate ($a \neq b$).

a. Using Gauss's law, find the electric field intensity as a function of position between the plates.

b. Under what conditions will the electric field between the sheet of charge and one of the condenser plates vanish?

c. Find the surface charge density on each condenser plate.

14. A small metal sphere, positively charged, is held fixed inside a hollow uncharged metal sphere. The centers of the two spheres do *not* coincide. At any point P in space outside the larger sphere the potential is found to be given by the relation

$$V = \frac{7.5}{r}$$

where V is in volts and r is the distance in meters from the center of the larger sphere to the field point P. What is the charge on the small metal sphere?

15. Three condensers of capacities 2, 4, and 6 μf, respectively, are connected in series, and a potential difference of 200 volts is established across the whole combination by connecting the free terminals to a battery.

a. Calculate the charge on each condenser.

b. Find the potential difference across each condenser.

c. What is the energy stored in each condenser?

16. The three condensers of the preceding problem are connected in parallel and then connected to the same battery as before.

a. What is the total charge on all three condensers?

b. What is the total energy stored in all three condensers?

17. The 4- and 6-μf condensers of the preceding problems are connected in parallel and then connected in series with the 2μf condenser. The potential difference across the whole combination is 200 volts. Calculate the total energy stored in the condensers and the charge on each.

18. Two condensers, one charged and the other uncharged, are connected in parallel. Prove that when equilibrium is reached, each condenser carries a fraction of the initial charge equal to the ratio of its capacity to the sum of the two capacities. Show that the final energy is less than the initial energy, and derive a formula for the difference in terms of the initial charge and the capacities of the two condensers.

19. Two condensers of capacities 5- and 10-μf are each charged to a potential difference of 100 volts, and the negative plate of the 5μf condenser is connected to the positive plate of the 10μf condenser.

a. What is the total charge on the two plates which are connected together?

b. If the other two plates are now connected together, what is the potential difference across each condenser when equilibrium is established?

20. Show that the attractive force per unit area between two parallel condenser plates can be written as $F/A = \frac{1}{2}\epsilon_0 \mathcal{E}^2$, where $\mathcal{E}$ is the field intensity between the plates. From this find the law giving the variation of force with plate separation if the potential difference between the plates is maintained constant (by connecting the plates to a battery).

21. A parallel-plate condenser of plate areas 100 cm² and a separation of 2.0 mm is permanently connected to a 100-volt battery. Using the results of the preceding problem, compute the work done in separating the plates to a distance of 4.0 mm, the potential difference staying constant. Does the electrostatic energy stored in the condenser increase or decrease during this process, and by how much? How does this compare in magnitude and sign with the mechanical work done in effecting the plate separation?

22. Two condensers, each of 10 μf capacity, are connected in parallel and charged to a potential difference of 1,200 volts. The external charging battery is then disconnected. If the plates of one of the condensers are separated so that its capacity becomes halved, compute:

a. The potential difference across each condenser.

b. The charge on each condenser.

23. A parallel-plate condenser has circular plates, each of radius 20 cm, separated by a distance of 1.0 cm. The condenser is charged to a potential difference of 3,000 volts, and the plates are then insulated so that no charge can escape from them.

a. What is the energy stored in the condenser?

b. A large uncharged sheet of metal 2.0 mm thick is inserted parallel to and between the condenser plates. How much work is done by electrical forces in the process of inserting the metal sheet?

c. What is the potential difference between the condenser plates after the metal sheet has been inserted?

24. Assuming the validity of the expression $\sigma^2/2\epsilon_0$ as the outward force per unit area on any charged conducting surface (σ being the surface charge density), calculate the maximum charge which can be put on the surface of a water drop of 2.0 cm diameter. The surface tension of water is 7.2×10^{-2} newton/m. What is the potential at the surface of the drop under these conditions?

HINT: The maximum charge is that for which the outward electrical force just equals the surface-tension force.

25. For the problem of the point charge and conducting plane, calculate the force of attraction between charge and plane by integrating the expression $\sigma^2/2\epsilon_0$ over the area of the plane. Show that this equals the attraction of the point charge for its image.

26. An isolated metal sphere of radius R carries a charge q. Find the radius of a concentric spherical surface such that one-half the electrostatic field energy resides inside this spherical surface.

27. Show that the expression $Q^2/2C$ is the energy stored in a spherical condenser by integrating the energy density $u = \frac{1}{2}\epsilon_0\mathcal{E}^2$ over the region between the plates. Use the volume between two spheres of radii r and $r + dr$ as a volume element.

28. Assuming that an electron is a sphere of radius a, with its charge uniformly distributed over its surface, calculate an expression for the total electrostatic energy in the field produced by a single electron. Assuming further that this energy is equal to mc^2, m the electronic mass and c the velocity of light (3.0×10^8 m/sec), calculate the radius of an electron.

CHAPTER 5

STEADY ELECTRIC CURRENTS

The basic laws describing the equilibrium behavior of conductors are altered when *static* equilibrium is disturbed, *i.e.*, when there is motion or flow of electric charges in the conductor. When the charges in a conductor are in motion, the electric field intensity just at the conductor surface need not be perpendicular to the surface. The conducting body is *not* an equipotential, as it is for *static* equilibrium of the charges in it, and an electric field will exist inside the conductor. Consider, for example, a charged condenser in electrostatic equilibrium. If we connect the two plates with a metallic wire, we have, at the instant of contact, a single conducting system (the two condenser plates and the wire) with a difference of potential between two of its parts. Since this is not a possible equilibrium state, electric charge flows in the wire from one plate to the other until all points of the system attain the same potential. We say that an *electric current* is present in the wire connecting the plates, and, in this example, the current is *transient*, or nonsteady, equilibrium being reestablished in a very short time. One can say that positive charge flows from the plate of higher potential to that of lower potential, or that negative charge flows in the opposite direction, or both. No matter which of these alternatives is adopted, it is necessary to adopt a convention as to the direction of the electric current. We do so by *defining the direction of flow of positive charge as the direction of the electric current.* When an electric current is set up in a material medium such as a metallic conductor, it is usual to denote the current as *conduction current*, whereas, if charged masses such as electrons or ions transport the charge directly by moving from one point to another, the current is called *convection current*. The essential point is that electric charge is transferred from one point to another, the whole of mode of description closely paralleling the corresponding mode of description of heat flow. In the case of heat flow, one describes the transfer of energy rather than of charge, and the analogy between heat flow and flow of charge is so close that the student will do well to draw parallels constantly between the two phenomena.

76

1. Definitions of Electric Current and Current Density.   The electric current crossing a definite surface is defined as the charge crossing this surface per unit time.   In symbols, we write

$$i = \frac{dq}{dt} \tag{5.1}$$

where i is the current and dq the charge transported across the surface in time dt.   The direction of the current is the direction of flow of positive charge.   For many purposes it is necessary to introduce the

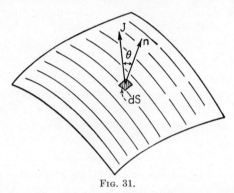

Fig. 31.

idea of *current density*.   Consider an infinitesimal element of area in a medium carrying an electric current, and choose this elementary area so oriented that its normal coincides in direction with that of the electric current.   If we denote this elementary surface element by dS_n (the subscript n is to remind us of the orientation) and the current crossing it by di, then the *current density* J at this point is defined by

$$J = \frac{di}{dS_n} \tag{5.2}$$

The current density J is a vector; Eq. (5.2) gives its magnitude, and the direction of the normal n is its direction.   If the vector J is known at every point of an arbitrary surface in a region where there is flow of electric charge, we can obtain the total electric current traversing a finite area as follows: The current crossing an element dS of this area is $J_n \, dS$, since only the component of J normal to dS contributes to the charge crossing this area.   The total current is then the sum of the contributions from all the elements of area of which the finite area is composed.   Thus we have (Fig. 31)

$$i = \int_{\text{area}} J_n \, dS = \int J \cos \theta \, dS \tag{5.3}$$

In our mks system the unit of current of one coulomb per second is called one ampere, and the corresponding unit of current density is one ampere per square meter.

2. The Steady State; Equation of Continuity. Consider a conducting medium carrying an electric current, and let us imagine that at each point in the medium we construct the curent-density vector J. The totality of these vectors forms a *vector field* of flow just as in the

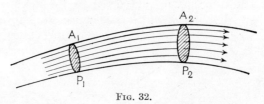

Fig. 32.

case of the flow of fluids or of heat. One can construct lines of flow which give the direction of the current at each point of space and also tubes of flow, just as in the case of hydrodynamics. In this chapter we confine our attention to the case of the *steady* or *stationary* state, for which the pattern of flow lines is fixed in space and does not vary with the time. The current density maintains a definite unvarying value at each point of the medium although it may vary in both magnitude and direction from point to point. Thus the vector field of flow is a *static field*, even though there is motion of electric charge. In the applications with which we shall be concerned, we shall have to deal largely with currents in metallic wires. In these cases we have a bundle of stream lines within the wire (the current being along the length of the wire), which we lump together into a single tube of flow.

The law of conservation of electric charge places a definite restriction on the pattern of lines of flow, and this leads to the so-called *equation of continuity*. We shall derive this law for the steady state. Consider a single tube of flow, as shown in Fig. 32, and let the cross sections of this tube at points P_1 and P_2 be A_1 and A_2, respectively. We assume that the current density J is constant at all points of either area. This involves no loss of generality, since we can make these areas as small as we please. Consider now the volume of the tube lying between the areas A_1 and A_2. In the steady state the charge entering this volume per unit time across A_1 must just equal the charge leaving per unit time across A_2. Otherwise the charge in this volume would increase or decrease indefinitely, in contradiction to the assumption of a steady state. The law of conservation of charge does not allow the net creation or destruction of charge inside the volume.

Since both A_1 and A_2 are constructed normal to the lines of flow, the current across A_1 is $i_1 = J_1 A_1$ [Eq. (5.3)], and that across A_2 is $i_2 = J_2 A_2$, so that the equation of continuity requires that

$$i_1 = i_2$$

or

$$J_1 A_1 = J_2 A_2 \tag{5.4}$$

where 1 and 2 refer to any pair of points in a tube of flow.

This equation may be extended readily to the case where a tube of flow branches into two or more tubes of flow, as in the case of linear metallic circuits where more than two wires meet and are connected at a single point.   In Fig. 33 are shown schematically the tubes of flow corresponding to three conductors connected at a junction point P.   Choosing areas A_1, A_2, and A_3 as shown, one finds easily that the continuity equation takes the form

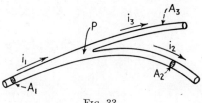

Fig. 33.

$$i_1 = i_2 + i_3$$

or

$$J_1 A_1 = J_2 A_2 + J_3 A_3 \tag{5.5}$$

The extension to the case of more than three conductors connected at one point is obvious.

The law of conservation of charge requires that, *for the steady state*, the lines of electric current density (and hence the tubes of flow) form a pattern of *closed* curves and cannot start or stop at any point in the conducting medium where this current exists.   This statement can be easily formulated mathematically to obtain a somewhat more general form of the continuity equation than those which we have already written.   Consider any *closed* surface such that the enclosed volume lies totally within the current-carrying medium.   From the foregoing we see that the *net* charge entering or leaving this enclosed volume across its bounding surface must vanish, and hence we can write

$$\int_{\substack{\text{closed} \\ \text{surface}}} J_n \, dS = 0 \tag{5.6}$$

This is the general form for the equation of continuity for the steady state. Equations (5.4) and (5.5) can be obtained directly by applying Eq.

(5.6) to the particular cases described by them. Equation (5.6) must hold for *every possible* closed surface in the region under consideration, as is evident from its derivation.

3. Sources of Electromotive Force. Thus far we have considered only the geometrical description of electric currents, and now we must inquire into the methods by which such currents can be set up and maintained. We start with the simplest case of a metallic wire. If one maintains a constant potential difference between the ends of the wire, it is found that a steady state is established in which a constant current is carried by the wire, and a steady evolution of heat is observed. This generation of heat represents a continual dissipation of energy, which must be supplied by the device which maintains the constant difference of potential between the ends of the wire. *Any device which maintains a definite difference of potential between two points*, known as the terminals, is called *a seat of electromotive force.* If a conducting wire is connected between the terminals of a seat of emf, a steady current will be set up, and a definite potential difference will be maintained between the terminals. This potential difference will, in general, be different for different currents, but in any given case it will be constant, and the seat of emf will continually supply energy to the electric circuit thus formed, forcing positive charge *internally* from its low-potential to its high-potential terminal. One important characteristic of an electrical system carrying a steady current must always be kept in mind: *Although there is a steady flow of electric charge around the circuit, the distribution of potential and consequently of electric field is static, unchanging with time, and this electrostatic field is maintained by the seat of emf.* Consequently, the basic laws of the electrostatic field are valid for steady electric currents; *i.e.*, the field is conservative, and the flux of the displacement vector across any closed surface is equal to the charge inside this surface. The steady-state flow of electric charge is a stationary condition, in which the electric charge at any *point* in the system is constant, independent of time. This has already been formulated quantitatively as the equation of continuity [Eq. (5.6)].

Let us examine the situation more closely for the case of a typical seat of emf, a battery. First, let us suppose that we have a charged parallel-plate condenser constructed with copper plates. If the charged plates are dipped into a dilute sulfuric acid solution (a conducting medium), the electric field between the condenser plates sets the charged ions in the solution into motion; an electric current is built up which discharges the condenser. When equilibrium is again reached, the plates are at the same potential, and the electric field between the plates has been reduced to zero. Were we to perform the above experiment with an initially uncharged condenser, there would be no change when the plates are dipped into the solution. If, however, we substitute a zinc plate for one of the copper plates and dip the *uncharged* condenser into the sulfuric acid solution, we find the surprising result that a difference of electric potential appears and is maintained between the plates, the copper being at a higher potential than the zinc. Thus there exists an electrostatic field between the copper and zinc plates which tends to send current from the copper to the zinc and destroy the difference of potential. Since this does not happen, and the potential difference stays unaltered, we must assume the existence of forces inside the cell which are not due to the electrostatic field and which we shall denote as *nonelectrical* or *chemical* forces. In equilibrium, then, the chemical force tending to drive an ion from one plate to the other is just equal and opposite to the force exerted on this ion by the electric field. The classification of forces inside a seat of emf into electrical and nonelectrical is to a large extent an arbitrary one. It is analogous to the classification of forces in mechanics as external and internal. Here the distinction depends on the choice of the mechanical system on which the forces act, and this is arbitrary. Once the system has been defined, however, the distinction between external and internal forces is obvious. Similarly, we define our electrical system as the system of conductors and charges giving rise to the electrostatic field, and then any forces other than electrostatic will be termed nonelectrical, no matter what their physical origin. Returning once more to the chemical cell, let us imagine that we move an ion inside the cell from the negative to the positive plate. The work done by the electric field during this motion must be just equal and opposite to the work done by the chemical forces. Thus the work per unit charge done by chemical forces in the above motion is just equal to the potential difference between the terminals (this is true *only* on open circuit, *i.e.*, when no conductor is connected externally between the terminals of the cell) and is called the *emf of the cell.* It is in this manner that we can employ the idea of emf as a measure of the work per unit charge done by the nonelectrical forces which must act in any seat of emf.

There is an alternative method of describing the above situation which enjoys considerable popularity, in which one uses the term emf to denote the work done per unit charge by both nonelectrical and electrical forces on a test charge carried around a *closed path,* part of which lies inside the seat of emf.   Although there is no essential difference between the two modes of description, it often causes confusion.   Let us imagine that we have a cell on open circuit and that we carry a charge around a closed path such as that shown in Fig. 34.

The work done per unit charge in the portion of the closed path *AB* which is external to the cell is just V_{AB}, the drop of potential between

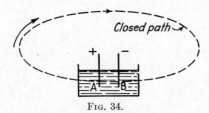

the plates.   Inside the cell, we have equal and opposite electrical and nonelectrical forces, so that the net work done by all the forces for the path *BA* inside the cell is zero.   In either mode of description we have the fundamental result that *the electromotive force of a seat of emf is measured by the potential difference between its terminals on open circuit.*

Fig. 34.

In symbols we write

$$E = V_{AB} \qquad \text{(open circuit)} \qquad (5.7)$$

One fundamental point must be insisted upon once again.   Since we have an electrostatic field of force maintained by virtue of the action of the seat of emf, even when there is a steady electric current, we still are able to write the fundamental relation of electrostatics for $\mathcal{E}(= - \operatorname{grad} V)$

$$\oint \mathcal{E}_s \, ds = 0 \qquad (5.8)$$

or, in words, the work done by the electrostatic forces per unit charge around *any closed* path is zero.   This is just another way of stating that the field is conservative and that a potential exists.

4. Ohm's Law for Linear Conductors.   We return now to the case of a simple series circuit, a single metallic wire of uniform cross section connected to the terminals of a seat of emf.   Since a constant potential difference is maintained between the ends of the wire, there must be present an electrostatic field within the wire.   Under the influence of this field, a steady unidirectional current i (a so-called *direct current*) is maintained.   If now the potential difference between the ends of the conductor is changed, there is a corresponding change in the steady current, and one finds experimentally that the ratio of potential difference to current is *constant*, independent of the current, provided the temperature of the conductor is held at a constant value.   *This is the essence of Ohm's law.*   Denoting the potential difference by V_{ab}, a and

b referring to the ends of the wire, then Ohm's law states that

$$\frac{V_{ab}}{i} = \text{constant} \tag{5.9}$$

This constant ratio is called the *electrical resistance* of the conductor for this steady direct current.   Note that Ohm's law states an experimental fact concerning the behavior of conducting bodies and in this sense should be looked upon as describing a property of matter rather than as a fundamental electrical principle.   If we denote this constant resistance by R_{ab}, Eq. (5.9) becomes

$$V_{ab} = iR_{ab} \tag{5.10}$$

The unit of resistance, one volt per ampere, is called one ohm.

Ohm's law as embodied in Eq. (5.9) or Eq. (5.10) holds for any portion of a linear conductor, a and b then referring to any two cross sections of the wire.   For a homogeneous straight conductor of uniform cross section carrying a direct current along its length, the equipotential surfaces *inside* the conductor are cross-sectional areas of the conductor normal to the direction of the lines of electric current, and the electric field inside the conductor is uniform and directed along the lines of flow.   We return to this point in the next section.

Since heat is evolved as long as the current is maintained, we think of the expression iR_{ab} as a measure of the work done per unit charge on the moving charges by forces which are of the nature of friction forces and are directed opposite to the direction of the current.   Hence the expression iR_{ab} is interpreted as the work done per unit charge *against* the resistance forces in moving charges from a to b along the wire, and it is usually called the iR drop along the wire.

A schematic diagram of a simple series circuit is shown in Fig. 35.   Let the battery emf be E, and suppose that the internal resistance of the battery (the resistance of the internal current-carrying path between the terminals) is so small compared to the resistance R of the wire that it can be neglected. The current i in the external circuit is directed from the positive to the negative terminal.   We now compute the work done

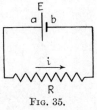

FIG. 35.

by the electrostatic field in moving a charge completely around the closed circuit.   This work must be zero in accordance with Eq. (5.8). We have

$$\underset{\text{(external)}}{V_{ab}} + \underset{\text{(internal)}}{V_{ba}} = 0 \tag{5.11}$$

where the first term is taken along the external circuit and the second inside the seat of emf. From Eq. (5.10) the first term is equal to iR, and the second term is equal to $-E$, the latter equality following from the facts that inside the cell $V_{ba} = V_b - V_a = -(V_a - V_b) = -V_{ab}$, and that there is no internal resistance. Thus Eq. (5.11) becomes

$$iR - E = 0$$

or

$$E = iR \qquad (5.12)$$

Now let us drop the restriction of negligible internal resistance, and let us assume that there is an internal ohmic resistance r between the terminals of the battery. When an electric current is present in the battery, the emf no longer is equal to the potential difference between its terminals. If the direction of the current inside the battery is from the negative to the positive terminal (the case of Fig. 35), then some of the work done per unit charge by the *chemical* or *nonelectrical* forces in driving charge through the battery is expended in overcoming the friction forces (due to ohmic resistance), and the remaining work is available to do work against the electrostatic forces and thus raise the potential energy of the charge. Accordingly, the potential difference between the terminals is less than its value on open circuit by the ir drop through the battery, and we have

$$V_{ab} = E - ir \qquad (5.13)$$

The terminal potential difference is thus the emf minus the ir drop through the battery.

If current is forced through a battery from its positive to its negative terminal (this can be done only with the help of additional seats of emf), then the electrostatic forces inside the battery must be larger than the chemical forces. In fact, the work done by the electric field in moving a charge in this manner between the terminals must be equal and opposite to the sum of the works done by the chemical and friction forces acting on the charge. Expressing this per unit charge, we have, in contrast to Eq. (5.13),

$$V_{ab} = E + ir \qquad (5.14)$$

Equation (5.14) is valid, for example, in the case of charging a storage battery, whereas Eq. (5.13) holds when the same battery is discharging.

Equation (5.12) is no longer correct for the circuit of Fig. 35 when the internal resistance r of the battery is included, but of course Eq. (5.11) is still valid. The second term in Eq. (5.11) which refers to the portion of the closed path lying inside the battery is now

$$V_{ba} = -V_{ab} = -E + ir$$

using Eq. (5.13).   The first term is iR as before, so that we have

$$iR - E + ir = 0$$

or

$$E = i(R + r) \qquad (5.15)$$

as the relation between battery emf, current, and resistances which is to replace (5.12) for a simple series circuit.   We note that (5.15) goes over to (5.12) where $r = 0$.   It is important to remember that Ohm's law in the form of Eq. (5.10) holds only for a portion of a circuit in which there are no seats of emf present.

Equation (5.15) no longer contains any term referring directly to the work done by purely electrostatic forces.   This arises from the

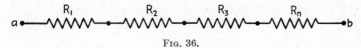

FIG. 36.

fact that this equation refers to a *closed* path, and in accordance with Eq. (5.8) the electrostatic forces yield no contribution.   The emf of the battery (E), which is the work per unit charge done by chemical forces in moving charge through the cell, is equal to the work done per unit charge against the dissipative forces in the conducting circuit. Thus Eq. (5.15) is a particular form of the general principle of conservation of energy (the first law of thermodynamics).

Resistances in Series and in Parallel.   Consider a number n of resistances connected in series (Fig. 36) with a constant potential difference V_{ab} maintained across the terminals.   The equation of continuity requires the steady current i to be the same in all the resistances.   Ohm's law yields

$$V_1 = iR_1; \; V_2 = iR_2; \; \cdots \; ; V_n = iR_n$$

and since

$$V_{ab} = V_1 + V_2 + \cdots + V_n$$

there follows by addition

$$V_{ab} = i(R_1 + R_2 + \cdots + R_n)$$

The series combination of resistances behaves just like a single resistance R, where

$$R = R_1 + R_2 + \cdots + R_n \qquad (5.16)$$

If the resistances are connected in parallel, with a constant potential difference V_{ab} maintained between terminals a and b (Fig. 37), the potential drop across each resistance is equal to V_{ab} by virtue of the electrical connection. Ohm's law then gives

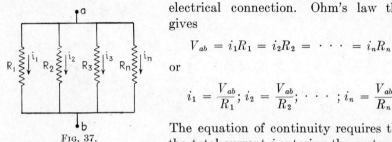

$$V_{ab} = i_1 R_1 = i_2 R_2 = \cdots = i_n R_n$$

or

$$i_1 = \frac{V_{ab}}{R_1}; i_2 = \frac{V_{ab}}{R_2}; \cdots ; i_n = \frac{V_{ab}}{R_n}$$

FIG. 37.

The equation of continuity requires that the total current i entering the system at a be related to the currents in the individual resistances by

$$i = i_1 + i_2 + \cdots + i_n = V_{ab}\left(\frac{1}{R_1} + \frac{1}{R_2} + \cdots + \frac{1}{R_n}\right)$$

Thus the parallel combination behaves like a single resistance R, where

$$\frac{1}{R} = \frac{1}{R_1} + \frac{1}{R_2} + \cdots + \frac{1}{R_n} \tag{5.17}$$

From this we see that the equivalent resistance of a parallel combination of resistances is smaller than the smallest resistance in the combination.

Examples

1. Two batteries of emfs 6 and 8 volts are connected in series as shown in Fig. 38, and a parallel-series combination of resistances is connected to the battery terminals as shown. The internal resistance of the 6-volt battery is 0.4 ohm and that of the 8-volt battery is 0.6 ohm. Required are the currents flowing through the individual resistances, and the potential differences between the battery terminals.

Let the currents be i, i_1, and i_2, as indicated. From the equation of continuity we have, at the junction point a,

$$i = i_1 + i_2$$

We can reduce the problem to that of a simple series circuit by replacing the parallel combination R_1 and R_2 by an equivalent resistance R', where

$$\frac{1}{R'} = \frac{1}{R_1} + \frac{1}{R_2}$$

It is evident that the two batteries have an emf together equal to the sum of the emfs of each, and hence Eq. (5.15) becomes

$$E_1 + E_2 = i(R' + R_3 + r_1 + r_2)$$

or

$$i = \frac{E_1 + E_2}{R' + R_3 + r_1 + r_2}$$

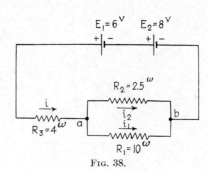

Fig. 38.

For R' we have

$$\frac{1}{R'} = \frac{1}{10} + \frac{1}{2.5} = \frac{5}{10}$$

$$R' = 2 \text{ ohms}$$

so that

$$i = \frac{6 + 8}{2 + 4 + 0.4 + 0.6} = \frac{14}{7} = 2 \text{ amp}$$

To find the currents in R_1 and R_2, we can write

$$V_{ab} = i_1 R_1 = i_2 R_2$$

where V_{ab} is the potential drop between points a and b.   This gives

$$\frac{i_1}{i_2} = \frac{R_2}{R_1} = \frac{2.5}{10} = \frac{1}{4}$$

This, together with the equation of continuity $i = 2 = i_1 + i_2$, gives

$$i_1 = 0.4 \text{ amp}; \qquad i_2 = 1.6 \text{ amp}$$

To find the potential difference across the battery terminals, we may utilize Eq. (5.13), since both batteries are discharging.   For the 6-volt battery,

$$V_6 = E_1 - i r_1 = 6 - 2 \times 0.4 = 5.2 \text{ volts}$$

and for the other,

$$V_8 = E_2 - i r_2 = 8 - 2 \times 0.6 = 6.8 \text{ volts}$$

This problem may also be solved by applying Eq. (5.8), which may be stated in words as follows: the algebraic sum of the potential drops around any closed loop is zero.   In applying this rule, the potential drops iR are positive if one moves *in* the direction of the current, and potential rises are treated as negative potential drops.   The student should work the above problem by this method.   We shall return to a detailed consideration of this scheme in a later section.

2. As a second example, let us consider the problem of determining the value of a resistance by the so-called ammeter-voltmeter method.   For our purposes it is only necessary to state that an ammeter connected in a circuit reads the current through it and acts only as a small resistance.   The voltmeter is a similar instrument which, when connected between any two points of a circuit, reads the potential difference between these points. For reasons which will become evident from our example, voltmeters have relatively high resistances.

One possible method of connection is shown in Fig. 39. The terminals a and b are maintained at a definite potential difference V_{ab} by some sort of

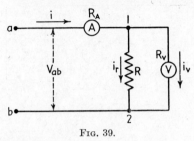

FIG. 39.

battery or d-c generator. The voltmeter of resistance R_v is connected directly across the terminals of the unknown resistance R, and the ammeter A is connected in series with the combination. Let the currents through the ammeter, resistance, and voltmeter be i, i_r and i_v, respectively, as shown. The reading of the ammeter gives i; that of the voltmeter gives V_{12}, the potential drop across the resistor; and let us suppose that R_v is known.

At the junction point 1 we have

$$i = i_r + i_v$$

and from Ohm's law

$$V_{12} = i_r R = i_v R_v$$

or

$$i_r = \frac{V_{12}}{R}; \qquad i_v = \frac{V_{12}}{R_v}$$

so that

$$i = V_{12}\left(\frac{1}{R} + \frac{1}{R_v}\right) \tag{5.18}$$

from which R may be readily found.

If we write the above equation in the form

$$R = \frac{V_{12}}{i}\left(1 + \frac{R}{R_v}\right)$$

we see that if the voltmeter resistance R_v is very large compared to the unknown resistance R, one may obtain the value of R very nearly by writing V_{12}/i. If, however, R_v is not large compared to R, one must use the complete formula and thus correct for the presence of the measuring instrument.

One might suppose that the difficulty might be avoided by connecting the elements as shown in Fig. 40. This does not eliminate the disturbing effect of the instruments. Let the current through the

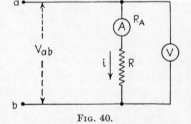

FIG. 40.

resistance R and ammeter be i as shown and the ammeter resistance be R_A. The voltmeter reading is just V_{ab} since its terminals are connected to the points a and b. Since the potential drop across ammeter and resistance in series is also V_{ab}, we have from Ohm's law

$$V_{ab} = i(R + R_A)$$

or

$$R = \frac{V_{ab} - iR_A}{i} \tag{5.19}$$

as the correct formula for R, requiring a knowledge of the ammeter resistance. If we write this relation in the form

$$R = \frac{V_{ab}}{i[1 + (R_A/R)]}$$

we see that again an approximate value of R may be obtained from V_{ab}/i provided $R_A \ll R$. Ammeters are constructed so as to have very small resistances in order that instrument corrections may be neglected in most practical work.

5. Ohm's Law for Extended Media; Conductivity and Resistivity. In the last section we concerned ourselves exclusively with the laws governing the d-c behavior of circuits containing linear conductors such as metallic wires. We now proceed to examine Ohm's law in more detail with the object of formulating it in such a manner that it can be applied at any point of a conducting medium rather than to a section of a linear conductor. As a preliminary step, consider a length l of a wire of uniform cross section A (Fig. 41). It is

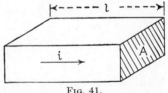

FIG. 41.

found experimentally that the resistance between its end faces is proportional to its length l and inversely proportional to its cross section A. Writing, this as an equation, we have

$$R = \rho \frac{l}{A} = \frac{1}{\sigma} \frac{l}{A} \tag{5.20}$$

where the proportionality constants ρ and σ are called the *resistivity* and *conductivity* of the material of which the conductor is composed, and obviously $\rho = 1/\sigma$.

The unit of resistivity is one ohm-meter, and the corresponding unit of conductivity is called one mho per meter. In engineering practice, however, there has grown a custom of specifying resistivity as "ohms per mil-foot," and this requires a word of explanation. This mixed unit has its origin in the practice of specifying the lengths of wires in feet and their cross sections in so-called "circular mils." *One mil is* $\frac{1}{1000}$ *inch, and 1 circular mil is the area of a circle of diameter 1 mil.*

Thus the cross-sectional area of a wire of diameter d mils is equal to d^2 circular mils. In using the "ohm per mil-foot" units of resistivity, one must be careful in employing Eq. (5.20) to expresss l in feet and A in circular mils to obtain the resistance R in ohms.

The resistivity of copper is about 2×10^{-8} ohm-m, or about 10 "ohms per mil-foot." Table II gives the resistivities of a number of metals. In Table II, the last column specifies the temperature at which the resistivity or conductivity is measured. The resistivity of a metal varies markedly with temperature and increases with increasing temperature. For moderate temperature ranges, the resistivity can

TABLE II

Material	Resistivity, ohm-m	Resistivity, ohms/mil-ft	Conductivity, ohms/m	Temperature, °C
Aluminum............	2.82×10^{-8}	17.0	3.54×10^7	20
Copper, annealed......	1.72×10^{-8}	10.3	5.80×10^7	20
Copper, hard-drawn...	1.77×10^{-8}	10.7	5.65×10^7	20
Gold................	2.44×10^{-8}	14.7	4.10×10^7	20
Iron................	10.0×10^{-8}	60.2	1.0×10^7	20
Steel................	$10\text{--}20 \times 10^{-8}$	60--120	$0.5\text{--}1.0 \times 10^7$	20
Lead................	20×10^{-8}	120	0.48×10^7	20
Mercury.............	95.7×10^{-8}	576	0.1044×10^7	20
Nickel..............	7.81×10^{-8}	47.0	1.28×10^7	20
Silver..............	1.63×10^{-8}	9.81	6.14×10^7	20
Tungsten............	5.52×10^{-8}	33.2	1.81×10^7	20

be represented by a linear function of temperature t (just as for the expansion of solids):

$$\rho = \rho_0(1 + \alpha t) \tag{5.21}$$

where α, the temperature coefficient of resistivity (referred to 0°C) is of the order of magnitude of $\frac{1}{2}$ per cent/°C for ordinary metals. ρ_0 is the resistivity at 0°C. Since the linear coefficient of expansion of solids is extremely small compared to the temperature coefficient of resistivity (of the order of 10^{-5} for most solids), one can write for the temperature variation of the resistance of a metal conductor

$$R = R_0(1 + \alpha t) \tag{5.22}$$

where R and R_0 are the resistances at temperature t°C and 0°C, respectively, and α is the same coefficient as in Eq. (5.21).

Returning now to our original problem, we apply Ohm's law to an infinitesimal volume element inside a conducting medium. At an arbitrary point O we construct a tiny cube $dx \, dy \, dz$, as shown in Fig.

42.   If there is no seat of emf at the point where this volume element is located, Ohm's law in the form of Eq. (5.10) gives

$$V_{x=0} - V_{x=dx} = -dV = iR \qquad (5.23)$$

where $-dV$ is the negative increase (the drop) in potential between the left- and right-hand faces of the volume element, i is the current normal to the faces $dy\,dz$, and R is the resistance between these faces.   From Eq. (5.3), we have $i = J_x\,dy\,dz$, and from Eq. (5.20),

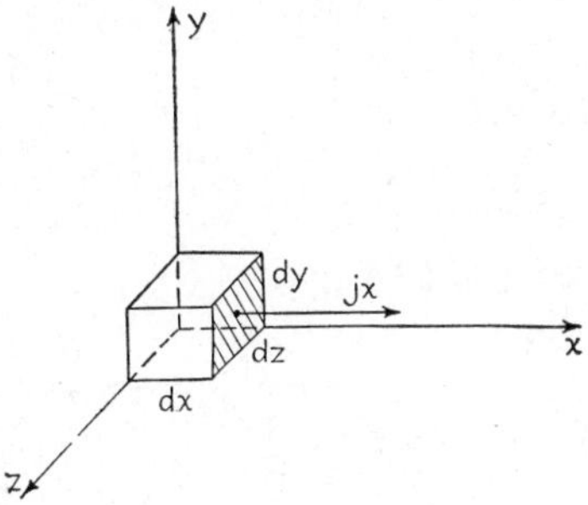

$$R = \frac{dx}{\sigma\,dy\,dz}$$

Fig. 42.

Substituting these values in Eq. (5.23), there follows

$$-dV = J_x\,dy\,dz\,\frac{dx}{\sigma\,dy\,dz} = \frac{J_x}{\sigma}\,dx$$

Now $-dV/dx = \mathcal{E}_x$, the negative x-component of the potential gradient, so that

$$\mathcal{E}_x = \frac{J_x}{\sigma}$$

or

$$J_x = \sigma\mathcal{E}_x \qquad (5.24)$$

In words, the x-component of the current density at a point of a conducting medium is equal to the conductivity of the medium times the x-component of the electric field intensity at that point.   It is clear that Eq. (5.24) holds for any component (x, y, or z), and hence if the medium is isotropic, we can write a single *vector* equation

$$\mathbf{J} = \sigma\boldsymbol{\mathcal{E}} \qquad (5.25)$$

This is Ohm's law in a form which holds at each point of the medium. It must be pointed out that Eq. (5.25) is valid only in the absence of seats of emf.   Since we have no immediate use for the generalization of (5.25) to include seats of emf, we shall not pursue this question at this point.

Equation (5.25) implies that for isotropic media obeying Ohm's law, the direction of the current (for steady currents) coincides with the direction of the electric field intensity at every point.   Thus the lines of flow of the electric current density *coincide* with the lines of electric field intensity and are perpendicular to the equipotential surfaces. This is by no means an evident fact, as one can see by considering the steady current between two electrodes in vacuum where the current is carried by electrons. Here the electron motion is determined by Newton's laws of motion rather than by Ohm's law. In general, the motion of a body is *not* in the direction of the resultant force acting on it. If the lines of $\mathcal{E}$ are not straight lines, then the electron trajectories will certainly not coincide with the lines of $\mathcal{E}$.

6. Joule's Law; Power in D-C Circuits. Let us consider any d-c network S, *i.e.*, any arbitrary combination of resistances and d-c seats of emf, and let a and b represent the terminals of the system across which a definite potential difference V_{ab} is maintained by an external

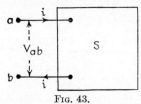

Fig. 43.

seat of emf. Let the steady current into and out of the system be i (Fig. 43). No detailed knowledge is assumed about the structure of the system S. Since by definition $V_{ab} = V_a - V_b$ is the work done by the electrostatic field per unit charge (the drop in potential) in moving a charge from a to b, and since the charge transported per unit time from a to b is i, it follows that the work done per unit time on S (the power absorbed by the system S) is given by

$$P = iV_{ab} \qquad (5.26)$$

This is the general expression for the power input to a d-c system when a current is supplied to it and a potential difference V_{ab} is maintained across its terminals. *Power in our mks system is measured in joules per second, which equal watts (one watt is one volt-ampere).*

Just what happens to the energy absorbed by the system S does depend on its make-up. Let us examine some typical cases. Suppose the system S consists solely of a resistance R obeying Ohm's law (or any combination of resistances which can be replaced by a single equivalent resistance). In this case, Eq. (5.26) can be extended to

$$P = iV_{ab} = i^2R \qquad (5.27)$$

since by Ohm's law $V_{ab} = iR$. The term i^2R is *the rate at which heat is evolved* in the resistance, and the statement that the rate of heating of a conductor is equal to i^2R is known as *Joule's law*. As we see from the foregoing, it is completely equivalent to Ohm's law. The equality between power input and the rate of heating is valid *only* when there are no seats of emf in the system which act as sources or as sinks of energy. As an illustration, suppose the system S consists of a storage battery being charged in series with a resistance (Fig. 44).   Let E be the emf of the battery and R the series resistance (including the internal resistance of the battery).   For this circuit we have

$$V_{ab} = E + iR$$

so that the power input to this system is

$$P = iV_{ab} = Ei + i^2R \qquad (5.28)$$

We see that only a fraction of the input power results in heating, and the remaining term Ei is the power absorbed by the battery, which continually stores up chemical energy (this is the process of charging).   Let us examine this Ei term more closely.   The battery emf E was defined as the work done *by* the chemical forces per unit charge in moving a charge inside the battery from the plate of lower potential to the plate of higher potential.   In our example, charge is forced from the high- to the low-potential terminal inside the battery, so that work is done by the external source *against* the chemical forces.   Hence Ei (the rate of doing work) is the power *absorbed* by the battery.

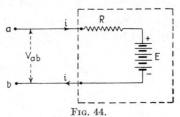

Fig. 44.

If the battery were discharging, the expression Ei would be the power delivered by the battery to the circuit of which it is a part. To clarify this, consider a simple series circuit of a battery of emf E, internal resistance r, and external resistance R.   We have

$$E = i(r + R)$$

as in Eq. (5.15).   Multiplying both sides by i, there follows

$$Ei = i^2R + i^2r \qquad (5.29)$$

The term i^2R is the rate of heating in the external resistance; i^2r is the rate of heating inside the battery, so that Ei represents the total power developed by the battery.   To be sure, only a fraction of this power is delivered to the circuit *external* to the battery, but that is of no import in this argument.

Returning to Eq. (5.28), this can be written in the form

$$(V_{ab} - E)i = i^2R$$

The term $-E$ in the first factor on the left is called the *back emf* in the system S.   One often speaks of the net voltage available for maintaining the current i in the resistance R as the difference between the "applied" voltage V_{ab} and the back emf E. This terminology is common in discussing the action of an electric motor, where the rotating armature becomes a seat of back emf. In such a case the term Ei represents the mechanical power developed by the motor.

In passing, we may point out that we might have logically made Joule's law (rate of heating $= i^2R$) the basis of our discussion of steady currents and derived Ohm's law from it. Had we done so, then resistance would have been defined by the relation

$$R = \frac{\text{power dissipated}}{i^2} \tag{5.30}$$

and for the case of steady direct currents the two definitions are identical. In the case of time-varying currents, and especially for alternating currents, with which we shall be concerned later, the two definitions do not, in general, coincide. It is then usual to refer to resistance as defined by Eq. (5.30) as *effective resistance* (R_{eff}) in contrast to the d-c, or "ohmic," resistance.

7. Kirchhoff's Rules. Problems involving steady electric currents (direct currents) in networks of linear conductors can be solved by straightforward application of the principles expounded in Secs. 2 to 4 of this chapter, but for complex cases it is desirable and convenient to follow a systematic procedure. Of the several schemes which are available we shall present the one embodied in *Kirchhoff's rules.* From the outset we must emphasize the fact that these rules provide no new principle beyond those already presented. By a network one means a system of linear conductors and seats of emf interconnected in some arbitrary fashion.

A typical network is shown in Fig. 45. In this there are four junction points, labeled ①, ②, ③, and ④, at which more than two conductors are joined together.

Kirchhoff's rules are as follows:

1. *The sum of the currents entering any junction point is equal to the sum of the currents leaving this point.*

2. *The algebraic sum of the potential drops around any closed loop of the network equals zero.*

Rule 1 is simply a restatement of the equation of continuity as formulated in Eqs. (5.4) and (5.5). For example, at the junction ① we have

$$i_1 = i_2 + i_3$$

If there are n junction points, there will be $n - 1$ independent current relations of this type.

Rule 2 is a statement of the content of Eq. (5.8). In applying this rule, one must remember that the potential drop across a resistance is positive if one moves *in* the direction of the current in it, and that potential rises are handled as negative potential drops. Thus in the case of Fig. 45, applying this rule to the loop containing E_1, R_1, R_2, R_4, and R_5, we have (starting at point ④ and proceeding in a clockwise direction)

$$-E_1 + R_1 i_1 + R_2 i_2 + R_4 i_4 + R_5 i_5 = 0$$

The current directions are assumed arbitrarily in each of the various

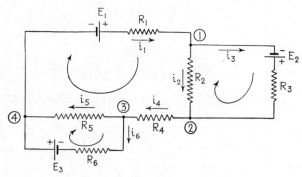

FIG. 45.

branches, and negative answers for these currents indicate that the corresponding directions are to be reversed. In the application of Kirchhoff's rules it is necessary to formulate a number of *independent* equations equal to the number of unknowns. It is a common failing to write a perfectly correct equation which may be obtained, for example, by the addition of two other equations already formulated. Clearly no additional information is obtained thereby, and it is necessary to adopt a systematic procedure. We can best describe this by an example. In Fig. 45 there are four junction points and the equation of continuity requires that

$$
\left.
\begin{array}{ll}
① & i_1 = i_2 + i_3 \\
② & i_2 + i_3 = i_4 \\
③ & i_4 = i_5 + i_6 \\
④ & i_5 + i_6 = i_1
\end{array}
\right\}
\qquad (5.31)
$$

The last equation is not independent of the preceding three, and in fact one can obtain it by adding the first three equations. Thus there are *three* independent current relations. Since there six unknown currents (assuming that the E's and R's are known), we need three more equations to effect a solution. Let us start with the loop equation already written

$$-E_1 + R_1 i_1 + R_2 i_2 + R_4 i_4 + R_5 i_5 = 0 \qquad (5.32)$$

If now we choose a second closed loop not containing E_1, for example, then we are sure that the resulting equation will be independent of Eq. (5.32). Thus in the loop containing E_2, R_2, and R_3, we have

$$-E_2 + R_3 i_3 - R_2 i_2 = 0 \qquad (5.33)$$

Finally, the loop containing E_3, R_5, and R_6 contains neither E_1 nor E_2; hence the equation relating to it must be independent of the two already written. There follows

$$R_6 i_6 - E_3 - R_5 i_5 = 0 \qquad (5.34)$$

This completes the task of finding three independent loop equations and illustrates the procedure to be followed. Other equations can be written, as, for example, the one obtained by proceeding through E_1, R_1, R_2, R_4, R_6, E_3, and back to E_1, which yields

$$-E_1 + R_1 i_1 + R_2 i_2 + R_4 i_4 + R_6 i_6 - E_3 = 0$$

but this is the sum of Eqs. (5.32) and (5.34).

Examples

1. Consider the network of Fig. 46 with $E_1 = 6$ volts, $E_2 = 12$ volts, $R_1 = 10$ ohms, $R_2 = 20$ ohms, and $R_3 = 8$ ohms. Required are the currents i_1, i_2, and i_3. Let the current directions be as shown. Since there are but two junction points, a and b, there is only one current relation, *viz.*,

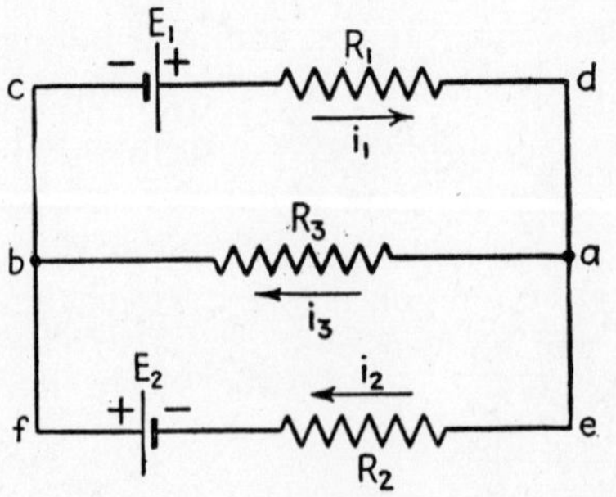

$$i_1 = i_2 + i_3 \qquad (5.35)$$

and we need two loop equations. For the loop *cdabc*, we have

$$-E_1 + R_1 i_1 + R_3 i_3 = 0 \quad (5.36)$$

and for the loop *aefba* (not containing E_1),

$$R_2 i_2 - E_2 - R_3 i_3 = 0 \qquad (5.37)$$

Fig. 46.

Using the value of i_1 from Eq. (5.35) in (5.36), the latter becomes

$$-E_1 + R_1 i_2 + (R_1 + R_3) i_3 = 0$$

Substituting numerical values in this and Eq. (5.37), we obtain

$$10i_2 + 18i_3 = 6$$

and

$$20i_2 - 8i_3 = 12$$

From these one obtains readily $i_3 = 0$, $i_2 = 0.6$ amp, and hence $i_1 = 0.6$ amp.

In this particular example no current is carried by R_3, and points a and b are at the same potential. The removal of R_3 or a short-circuiting wire connected between a and b would thus alter nothing in the other two branches.

2. The Wheatstone Bridge. The Wheatstone bridge is a network utilized to measure unknown resistances and is shown in Fig. 47. M and N are fixed resistances, P a variable resistance, and X the unknown. G represents the

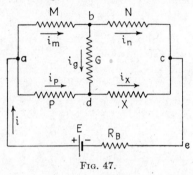

FIG. 47.

resistance of a galvanometer and R a current-limiting resistance, which includes the internal resistance of the battery of emf E. Let the currents be as shown. Three independent current relations are

$$i = i_m + i_p \tag{5.38}$$
$$i_m = i_n + i_g \tag{5.39}$$
$$i_p + i_g = i_x \tag{5.40}$$

Three independent loop equations are

$$Mi_m + Ni_n + iR - E = 0 \qquad \text{(loop } abcea\text{)} \tag{5.41}$$
$$Mi_m + Ni_n - Xi_x - Pi_p = 0 \qquad \text{(loop } abcda\text{)} \tag{5.42}$$
$$Mi_m + Gi_g - Pi_p = 0 \qquad \text{(loop } abda\text{)} \tag{5.43}$$

The solution of these six equations yields the galvanometer current i_g. The bridge is said to be in balance when the current i_g through the galvanometer is zero. Under these conditions Eqs. (5.39) and (5.40) yield

$$i_m = i_n \qquad \text{and} \qquad i_p = i_x$$

so that Eqs. (5.41) to (5.43) become

$$(M + N)i_m + iR - E = 0$$
$$(M + N)i_m - (X + P)i_p = 0$$
$$Mi_m - Pi_p = 0$$

Dividing the second of these equations by the third, one obtains

$$\frac{M + N}{M} = \frac{X + P}{P}; \qquad 1 + \frac{N}{M} = \frac{X}{P} + 1$$

or

$$\frac{X}{P} = \frac{N}{M}; \qquad X = \frac{N}{M}P \tag{5.44}$$

Equation (5.44) is the condition which must be satisfied to balance a Wheatstone bridge. For a fixed ratio of N to M, this may always be accomplished by adjusting P and hence obtaining the value of X.

Problems

1. Sixteen cells, each of emf E and internal resistance r, are connected in series-parallel arrangement (s cells in series and p of these series combinations in parallel). The whole combination is connected in series with a single external resistance $R = r$. Prove that the maximum current which can be sent through the external resistance is four times the current which a single cell will supply to it. How many cells are in series for this to happen?

2. Given two batteries, one of emf 9.0 volts and internal resistance 0.80 ohm, and the other of emf 3.0 volts and internal resistance 0.40 ohm. How must these batteries be connected to give the largest possible current through a resistance R, and what is this current for

a. $R = 0.30$ ohm?

b. $R = 0.40$ ohm?

c. $R = 0.50$ ohm?

3. A storage battery of emf 24.0 volts, internal resistance 0.50 ohm, is to be charged with a current of 10 amp. The battery in series with a resistance R is connected to a 110-volt power line.

a. Draw a diagram showing the proper connections and mark the polarities.

b. What resistance R is needed?

c. What is the potential difference across the battery terminals during the charging process?

4. How large a resistance must be placed in shunt (in parallel) with a resistance of 1,000 ohms to reduce the resistance between its terminals to 50 per cent of its original value?

5. A long uniform wire is cut into n equal lengths which are then used to form an n-strand cable. The resistance of the cable is R. What was the resistance of the original wire?

6. A uniform drop wire of total resistance 1,200 ohms is connected to power mains which maintain a potential difference of 120 volts across it. A voltmeter connected between one end of the drop wire and its mid-point reads 50 volts. What is the resistance of the voltmeter?

7. A drop wire has a total resistance of 55 ohms and has a potential difference of 100 volts maintained across its terminals.

a. What is the potential difference between two points a and b on this wire, if the resistance between these points is 30 ohms?

b. If an external resistance of 60 ohms is connected between a and b, what is the potential difference between these points after the connection has been made?

c. What are the currents in the 30-ohm section before and after the 60-ohm resistance is connected?

8. A closed box has two metal terminals a and b. Inside the box there is a series circuit which may contain resistances obeying Ohm's law and batteries, but nothing else. If a potential difference of 12 volts is maintained between a and b, a positive, a current of 1 amp enters the box at a and emerges at b. If this potential difference is reversed so that b is positive, a current of 2 amp in the reverse direction is observed.

What is the magnitude of the resistance inside the box?

9. In Fig. 48, the current indicated by the ammeter A is the same when both switches are closed as when they are both open. Find the resistance R.

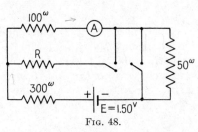

Fig. 48.

10. A resistance of 8 ohms and an unknown resistance R are connected in parallel, and this parallel combination is connected in series with a 72-ohm resistance and a battery of negligible internal resistance. The three resistances are then connected in series with each other and with the same battery. In both connections the current through the 8-ohm resistance is the same. Find the value of the unknown resistance R.

11. Two batteries of emf and internal resistance 2.0 volts, 0.20 ohm and 4.0 volts, 0.40 ohm are connected in series, and the combination is connected to form a simple series circuit with an external resistance of 11.4 ohms.

   a. What is the ratio of currents for the two possible connections?

   b. What is the current for each connection?

12. A uniform drop wire of 10,000 ohms resistance is connected across a 100-volt line, and a voltmeter of 5,000 ohms internal resistance is used to measure the potential difference across a portion of the drop wire of resistance R. Make a plot of the voltmeter reading against R for all possible values of R.

13. A voltmeter is constructed of a galvanometer of 2,000 ohms resistance and two resistances of 2,000 and 6,000 ohms, as shown in Fig. 49. The galvanometer gives full-scale deflection when it carries a current of 2.5 ma. What voltages across the terminals ab, ac, and ad will produce full-scale deflections? Would this instrument serve as a suitable ammeter? Explain.

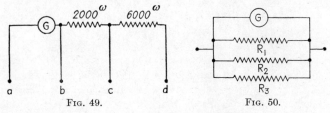

Fig. 49.   Fig. 50.

14. An ammeter consists of an 8-ohm galvanometer and three resistances R_1, R_2, and R_3, all connected in parallel as shown in Fig. 50. By means of a switch, R_2, R_3, or R_2 and R_3 may be disconnected.   Full-scale deflection of the galvanometer occurs for a current of 2.0 ma through it.

What resistances must be used if the ammeter is to have 0.1-, 1-, and 10-amp scales?   Do the shunts change the percentage accuracy of the instrument?

15. A 10-ohm galvanometer with a 90-ohm resistance permanently connected across its terminals is used as a current-measuring device.   The instrument may be used with a choice of connections *ab*, *ac*, *ad*, or *ae*, as shown in Fig. 51.   How should the 90-ohm resistance be divided so that the sensitivity of the instrument (the reciprocal of the current causing full-scale reading) should change by a factor of 10 for each successive connection *ab*, *ac*, *ad*, and *ae*?

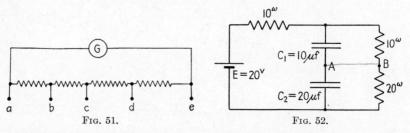

FIG. 51.   FIG. 52.

16. In Fig. 52, find the charges on each of the two condensers, C_1 and C_2, the battery having negligible internal resistance.   If the points A and B are connected by a wire, what are the charges on the condensers?

17. Calculate the resistance of an eight-strand copper cable 2 miles long, each strand being of circular cross section and of diameter 0.020 in.   The resistivity of copper is 10.4 ohms "per mil-foot."

18. A cylindrical rod of copper of diameter 0.20 in. is drawn into a wire 10 mils in diameter.   The resistance of the rod is 0.001 ohm.   Calculate the resistance of the wire, assuming that the drawing has no effect on the resistivity of the copper.

19. A cable consists of a central core of steel wire 500 mils in diameter surrounded by a tightly fitting sheath of copper 0.10 in. thick.   Calculate the resistance of 1 mile of this cable.   What fraction of the current carried in the cable is in the copper?   The resistivities of copper and steel are 10.4 and 90 ohms "per mil-foot," respectively.

20. How constant must the temperature of a coil of wire be maintained if its resistance is to stay constant within 0.1 per cent?   The temperature coefficient of resistivity of the metal is 0.004 per degree centigrade.

21. The resistivity of platinum at 0°C is 54.0 ohms "per mil-foot."   Calculate its conductivity in mhos per meter at 0°C and at 20°C.   The temperature coefficient of resistivity of platinum is 0.00354 per degree centigrade.

22. The electrodes of a cell consist of a metal rod 5.0 cm in diameter and a coaxial hollow cylinder of inside diameter 25 cm.   The electrodes stand on a glass plate in an electrolyte (a conducting solution) which is 20 cm deep over the glass plate.   The cell carries a current of 5.0 amp.

a. Calculate the current density at the surface of each electrode and at any point in the solution.

b. If the electrolyte has a resistivity of 4.8×10^{-2} ohm-m, compute the internal resistance of the cell.

23. A steady current i is carried radially between two concentric spherical electrodes, the radius of the inner electrode being r_1, and that of the surrounding spherical surface being r_2. The medium between the spheres has a conductivity σ.

a. What is the current density at a point at distance r from the common center?

b. Find an expression for the resistance between the electrodes.

24. A pair of metallic electrodes form a condenser of capacity C in vacuum. If these electrodes are embedded in a medium of conductivity σ, the resistance between them is R. Prove that $RC = \epsilon_0/\sigma$, independent of the geometry of the system.

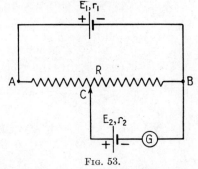

25. The accompanying diagram (Fig. 53) illustrates the essentials of the circuit of a potentiometer. R is a uniform slide-wire. Find the ratio of the length CB to the length AB of the slide-wire in terms of the given data in order that the galvanometer read zero.

Fig. 53.

What is the potential difference between points C and B when this adjustment is made? Which point is at the higher potential?

26. An electric heater has a heating unit of resistance 11 ohms. It is to be operated from a 110-volt d-c power line and must dissipate 550 watts. What additional resistances are needed, and how must they be connected to attain this condition?

27. A battery of emf 20 volts and internal resistance 4.0 ohms is connected to a resistive load of resistance R.

a. For what value of R is the rate of heating in it a maximum? What is this rate in watts?

b. At what efficiency does the seat of emf operate under these conditions?

28. Two batteries of emfs 5.0 and 10 volts and internal resistances of 1.0 and 1.5 ohms, respectively, are connected to a variable resistance R, as shown in Fig. 54.

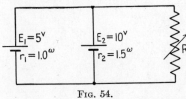

Fig. 54.

a. For what value of R is the rate of heating in it a maximum?

b. What is this maximum rate of heating?

29. Two batteries of emfs 8 and 12 volts and internal resistances 1.0 and 1.5 ohms, respectively, have their positive terminals connected to one end of a variable resistance R and their negative terminals connected to the other end of R.

a. For what value of R will the rate of heating in it be a maximum?

b. What fraction of the power dissipated in R is supplied by the 8-volt battery?

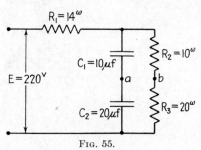

FIG. 55.

30. In the circuit shown in Fig. 55, find the charges on condensers C_1 and C_2 before and after the points a and b have been connected together by a metallic wire. Assume steady-state conditions.

31. Two identical resistors of 60,000 ohms each are connected in series across an 800-volt d-c supply. A voltmeter of internal resistance 30,000 ohms is connected across one resistor.

a. What is the voltmeter reading?

b. What must be the power rating of the resistors if they are not to burn out when the voltmeter is connected?

32. An electric heater immersed in water raises the temperature of 5 kg of water from 0 to 40°C in 5 min when it carries a current of 25 amp. What is the resistance of the heater? $P = \frac{1000}{85} hp$

33. A 10-hp electric motor operates on 110 volts and has an efficiency of 85 per cent. The generator supplying the power has a terminal voltage of 125 volts and is 2,000 ft from the motor. What diameter of copper wire ($\rho = 10.4$ ohms "per mil-foot") is required to deliver current to the motor at its rated voltage?

34. A 72-volt storage battery of 0.33 ohm internal resistance is charged from 110-volt supply mains with a 6-ohm resistance in series with it.

a. How much power is drawn from the mains?

b. What is the rate of heating in the circuit?

c. What is the efficiency of the charging process?

35. Under normal operation on a 110-volt d-c line, the filament of a 1,000-watt incandescent lamp has an absolute temperature of 3000°K. When this lamp is connected to a 2.5-volt battery of internal resistance 0.04 ohm, the filament is at room temperature of 300°K. Assuming the filament resistance is proportional to its absolute temperature, compute:

a. The resistance of the filament when in normal operation.

b. The filament resistance at room temperature.

c. The current drawn from the 2.5-volt battery.

d. The potential difference across the 2.5-volt battery terminals when the lamp is connected to it.

36. A coil of copper wire of mass 60 g and resistance of 0.10 ohm at 0°C is thermally insulated from its surroundings. It is connected across the terminals of a 6-volt storage battery of negligible internal resistance at time $t = 0$. Assume that the steady state is attained in negligible time.

a. Write an expression for the rate of heating in the coil in terms of its resistance and the potential difference across its terminals.

b. How long will it take for the temperature of the coil to rise to 100°C? The temperature coefficient of resistance of copper referred to 0°C is 0.004 per degree centigrade. The heat capacity of copper is 0.40 joule/g- °C.

37. In Fig. 56, $E_1 = 20$ volts, $E_2 = 45$ volts, $R_1 = 5$ ohms, $R_2 = 10$ ohms, $R_3 = 15$ ohms, and $C = 5\mu f$. Find the energy stored in the condenser C.

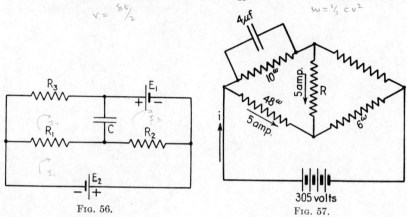

FIG. 56.   FIG. 57.

38. In the steady state, the charge on the 4-μf condenser in the network of Fig. 57 is 800 microcoulombs.

a. Find the battery current i.

b. Find the value of the resistance R.

39. Using Eqs. (5.38) to (5.43), derive an expression for the galvanometer current i_g when the Wheatstone bridge is *not* balanced.

40. In the network shown in Fig. 58, find the current in the three resistances. The internal resistances of the batteries are included in the values of R_1 and R_2.

41. If the 12-volt battery is reversed in Prob. 40, find the currents in R_1, R_2, and R_3.

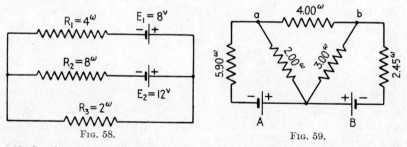

FIG. 58.   FIG. 59.

42. In the circuit of Fig. 59, find the potential difference between points a and b. Which is at the higher potential? Battery A is of emf 12 volts, internal resistance 0.10 ohm, and battery B is of emf 6.0 volts, internal resistance 0.05 ohm.

CHAPTER 6

THE MAGNETIC FIELD OF FORCE

In addition to the heating effects of steady currents which we have studied in the last chapter, there appear mechanical forces on current-carrying conductors or on moving charges which are quite different from electrostatic forces. These are known as *magnetic* forces. It is assumed that the reader is acquainted with the elementary facts concerning the forces which permanent magnets exert on each other. We shall not, however, follow the usual historical treatment of magnetism, which utilizes permanent magnets as the basis for the development. In spite of the apparent simplicity of the idea of magnetic poles, magnetic phenomena are in fact quite different in many respects from electrostatic phenomena, and the usual analogies which are drawn between these subjects, while mathematically convenient, are apt to lead to serious confusion and at best leave much of the fundamental physical interpretation well hidden. In accordance with our program of developing the field concept from the beginning, we delay a detailed discussion of permanent magnets to a later chapter on the magnetic properties of matter and shall introduce the concept of a magnetic field as a field produced by electric currents or by moving charges. It is undeniably convenient to visualize a magnetic field existing in a region of space if a small compass needle freely suspended at its center orients itself in a definite direction (and returns to this orientation if disturbed), and to use this simple experiment as a practical method of determining the field direction at the point where the compass needle is located. Indeed it was as late as 1820 that *Oersted* discovered that an electric current exerts mechanical forces on a magnet. Shortly thereafter *Ampère* observed forces of a similar nature between current-carrying conductors and performed a brilliant series of fundamental experiments from which the laws of force between currents were established. Ampère's experiments were performed with currents in metallic conductors, but it was shown later by *Rowland* that moving charges produce magnetic effects entirely similar to those caused by conduction currents and are acted on by forces when in the vicinity of current-carrying circuits or magnets.

1. The Magnetic Induction Vector B. As stated above, we shall start from the results of the experiments of Ampère, or their equivalent, to develop the concept of a magnetic field. [One of the fundamental observations shows that the force due to the presence of a neighboring current-carrying circuit (or a magnet) acting on an element of length ds of a conductor carrying a current i is directed at *right angles* to the length ds. Stated in terms of moving charges, we can say that such a force acts on a moving charge at right angles to the direction of its motion.] Any region of space in which moving charges (or currents) experience a force of the above type is said to have a *magnetic field* existing in it. This field is produced, of course, by the presence of other currents or of magnets. As in the case of electrostatic fields of force, we shall first examine the nature of the forces exerted by a magnetic field on currents or on moving charges and then, as a second step, concern ourselves with the laws governing the calculation of these fields from the currents giving rise to them. Because these magnetic forces are directed at right angles to the direction of flow of electric charge, they are often referred to as *deflecting* forces or as *side thrusts*.

In order to set up a quantitative description of the field, it will be expedient to introduce the idea of a suitable test body to detect and measure the field, just as we have employed a test charge in the discussion of the electrostatic field. As our test body we can employ an elementary length ds of a current-carrying conductor, or better still, a tiny beam of moving electrons such as one would obtain in a miniature cathode-ray tube. In utilizing such a test body to detect and measure a magnetic field, we encounter immediately a complication relative to the corresponding employment of a test charge in electrostatics. This occurs because the force acting on the test current element depends not only on the position of this element but also on its orientation in space, *i.e.*, on the direction of the test electric current at the point in question. In every case, however, the magnetic force acts at right angles to the current direction. The magnitude of the force depends, among other things, on the direction of the current and vanishes for *one particular direction* of the test current element. *We call this the direction of the magnetic field at the point where the current element is located.* If the current is at right angles to this field direction, the force has a maximum magnitude, and for other orientations the magnitude of the force is proportional to the sine of the angle between the direction of current and the field direction. Furthermore, the force is proportional to the current i carried by the element ds and to the length ds and is always directed at right angles both to the field direction and to the current direction at the point in question. Thus the force is perpendicular to the plane defined by two vectors, one directed along ds and the other in the direction of the field.

At each point of space we now *define* a magnetic field vector, denoted by B and called the *magnetic induction, whose magnitude is the maximum value of the force exerted on a current element divided by the product of the current and the length of the element*, and whose direction has already been specified above. As in the electrostatic case, the test current must be small enough to have no appreciable reaction on the currents or magnets producing the field, and the magnetic induction B is to be defined for the precisionist as the limiting ratio of maximum force to current times element length as the latter approaches zero.

If we denote this maximum force by dF_{max}, we can write

$$B = \frac{dF_{max}}{i \, ds} \tag{6.1}$$

as the magnitude of the magnetic induction vector, the direction of this vector being at right angles to both dF_{max} and ds. As we shall show in a moment, this is entirely equivalent to

$$B = \frac{F_{max}}{qv} \tag{6.2}$$

where F_{max} is now the maximum deflecting force exerted on a charge q moving with a velocity v, and B is perpendicular to both F_{max} and v.

If the direction of the electric current is not perpendicular to B, then the magnitude of the force on a current element is given by

$$dF = i \, ds \, B \sin \theta \tag{6.3}$$

where θ is the angle between ds and B, and dF is at right angles to the plane determined by B and ds. Similarly, the force F acting on a moving charge is

$$F = qvB \sin \theta \tag{6.4}$$

where θ is the angle between v and B.

The directions of the vectors whose magnitudes appear in Eqs. (6.3) and (6.4) are related in the following manner: If one rotates the vector **ds** (in the direction of the current) or **v** through the smallest possible angle so that it lines up with **B**, the force vector points in the direction in which a *right-handed* screw would move when so rotated (Fig. 60). This rule is similar to that determining the direction of the vector moment of a force or of the angular momentum of a particle about a given point. The rather awkward mode of presentation which has just been employed can be avoided by introducing the ideas of vector multiplication, and we shall now digress to define these convenient quantities.

Scalar and Vector Products of Vectors. The scalar, or "dot," product of two vectors **A** and **B** is defined as a scalar of magnitude equal to the product of the magnitudes of A and B and the cosine of the angle between them. It is written in the form

$$\mathbf{A} \cdot \mathbf{B} = AB \cos \theta \qquad (6.5)$$

where θ is the angle between **A** and **B**. It is evident that the scalar product is the magnitude of either one of the vectors multiplied by the projection of the other vector in the direction of the first.

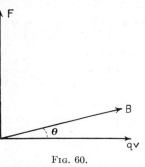

Fig. 60.

As examples, we have the familiar expression for the work done by a force F in moving a particle through a displacement ds. This work dW is

$$dW = \mathbf{F} \cdot \mathbf{ds} = F\,ds \cos \theta = F_s\,ds$$

where θ is the angle between F and ds. Similarly the emf around a closed path can be written as a scalar product in the form

$$\oint \boldsymbol{\varepsilon} \cdot \mathbf{ds} = \oint \varepsilon_s\,ds$$

The second kind of product of two vectors **A** and **B** is called the vector, or "cross," product. It is defined as a vector **C** whose magnitude is the product of the magnitudes of A and B and the sine of the angle between them, and whose direction is perpendicular to the plane of A and B. The sense of the vector C is obtained by rotating A through the smallest angle so that it lines up with B and by taking the direction in which a right-handed screw would move as the direction of C. In symbols, one writes (Fig. 61)

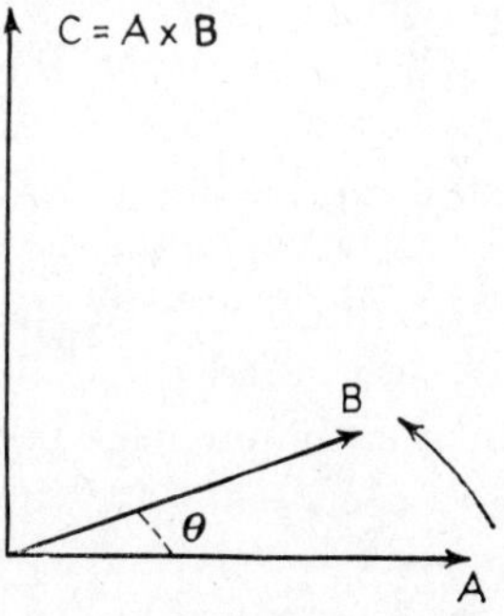

$$\mathbf{C} = \mathbf{A} \times \mathbf{B} \qquad (6.6)$$

Fig. 61.

and the magnitude of C is $AB \sin \theta$. The order of multiplication is important, and we have

$$\mathbf{A} \times \mathbf{B} = -(\mathbf{B} \times \mathbf{A}) \qquad (6.6a)$$

Using this notation, one can write for the torque of a force F about a point O

$$\mathbf{T} = \mathbf{r} \times \mathbf{F}$$

where $\mathbf{r}$ is the vector drawn from O to the point of application of the force $\mathbf{F}$.

Equations (6.3) and (6.4) for the magnetic force on a current element or on a moving charge can be concisely expressed in terms of the vector product. Thus for the current element ds,

$$\mathbf{dF} = i(\mathbf{ds} \times \mathbf{B}) \tag{6.7}$$

and for the moving charge,

$$\mathbf{F} = q(\mathbf{v} \times \mathbf{B}) \tag{6.8}$$

Equations (6.7) and (6.8) are to be regarded as the equations which define the magnetic induction vector B. We still have to examine their equivalence.

Consider a straight metallic conductor of uniform cross section A carrying a steady current i, and let us suppose that the current is due to the steady motion of free electrons inside the conductor. Since the electric current is the rate at which electric charge crosses any cross section A of the conductor, it equals the charge q on each particle times the number of particles crossing A per unit time. Now the particles crossing A in a time interval dt will be found at the end of this interval in a cylinder of base A and altitude $v\,dt$ (Fig. 62), where v is the constant velocity of the charged particles. Thus, if n is the number of such particles per unit volume (a constant for the case of steady flow), the current i may be written as $i = nqvA$. Consider now a length ds of the conductor. The current element

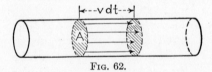

Fig. 62.

$$i\,ds = nqvA\,ds = Nqv$$

where $N = nA\,ds$ is the total number of charged particles in the volume $A\,ds$. The magnetic force acting on these particles is then, in accordance with Eq. (6.7),

$$\mathbf{F} = i(\mathbf{ds} \times \mathbf{B}) = Nq(\mathbf{v} \times \mathbf{B})$$

and the force acting on *one* particle is this expression divided by N, the number of particles in the length element ds. We have thus shown the equivalence between a stream of moving charges and a current element.

The size of the unit of B and its dimensions are determined from the defining equations [(6.7) or (6.8)]. The dimensions of B are thus

$$[B] = \frac{[F]}{[i] \cdot [ds]} = \frac{mlt^{-2}}{qt^{-1}l} = mq^{-1}t^{-1}$$

and the size of the unit of $\underline{B}$ is evidently $\underline{1 \text{ newton/amp-m}}$. This designation is practically never employed, however, and *B is expressed in volt-seconds per square meter, or webers per square meter, where one weber equals one volt-second.* That these two nomenclatures are equivalent can be readily seen as follows: The unit of force (newton) is equal to the unit of electric field intensity (volt per meter) times the unit of charge (coulomb). The unit of current (ampere) is the unit of charge (coulomb) divided by the unit of time (second). Hence

$$1 \text{ unit of } B = 1\,\frac{\text{volt-coulomb}}{\text{meter}} \times \frac{1}{\text{coulomb} \times \text{meter/second}}$$

$$= 1\,\frac{\text{volt-second}}{\text{meter}^2}$$

(*In the electromagnetic absolute system of units, in which centimeter-gram-second mechanical units are employed, the unit current is equal to ten amperes, and the corresponding unit of B is called one gauss. One weber per square meter is equal to* 10,000 *gauss. See Appendix I for further details.*)

2. Magnetic Flux; Solenoidal Nature of the Vector Field of B. At each point of space we can imagine the vector B constructed; the aggregate of these vectors in a given region of space is called the magnetic field there. One can draw lines of B which give the direction of this vector field at each point and can limit the number of lines crossing an elementary area which is normal to the field direction in such a manner that the number of lines per unit area is made equal to the numerical magnitude of B. This is the same convention already employed in our discussion of the electrostatic field. The total number of lines of magnetic induction crossing a surface is called the *magnetic flux* across this area, and one has evidently

$$\Phi = \int B_n \, dS \qquad\qquad (6.9)$$

Φ is the magnetic flux, and B_n is the component of B normal to the surface at the point where the element of area dS is located (Fig. 63.)

From Eq. (6.9) we see that the magnetic induction can be measured in flux units per unit area, and hence B is often called the *magnetic flux density*. *The unit of magnetic flux in the mks system is called one weber, which is equal to one volt-second, so that the unit of B is one weber per square meter or one volt-second per square meter as stated in the previous section.*

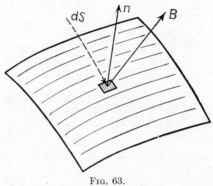

FIG. 63.

The vector field of B is of a *fundamentally different* nature from that of the electrostatic field. In the electrostatic case we have seen that the lines of D or $\mathcal{E}$ (in vacuum) always terminate on charges and hence could never form closed curves. Furthermore, one could introduce a scalar potential having a definite unique value at each point of space, from which the vector field could be obtained by differentiation. These facts are *not* true for the field of B. In contrast, *the lines of B can never start or stop at any point and hence always form closed curves.* A vector field of this sort is called *solenoidal*, or source-free, since no starting points or sources can be assigned to the lines describing the field. We have already encountered one such vector field in our study of steady electric currents, since the conservation of charge requires that the lines of electric current density be closed curves in the steady state (the equation of continuity). Thus one can say that the vector field of the current density J is solenoidal for the steady state.

If we wish to express the above facts concerning the field of B in mathematical form, we note that the *total* magnetic flux crossing any *closed* surface must vanish, since no lines of B can start from or stop at any point inside the volume enclosed by the surface. In symbols we have

$$\int_{\substack{\text{closed}\\\text{surface}}} B_n \, dS = 0 \tag{6.10}$$

Equation (6.10) is one of the fundamental laws of electromagnetic theory.

Furthermore, one cannot introduce a scalar potential which has a unique value at every point of space to describe such a field. It can be shown that it is impossible to find a single-valued scalar function of position such that a purely solenoidal vector field may be obtained from it by differentiation, *i.e.*, by taking the gradient of this scalar function.

3. Motion of Charged Particles in Magnetic Fields.   In this section we shall investigate the motion of charged particles both in magnetic and in combined electric and magnetic fields.   In this study we shall assume that one can neglect the modification of the external field caused by the presence of the moving charges.   This condition is often realized in practice to a high degree of approximation in those cases when the magnetic field produced by the moving charges is negligible compared to the external field in which they move.   The study of the motions of ions or electrons, in particular the determination of the orbits, is of fundamental importance in physics, since the methods of measuring electronic and ionic masses are based on this study.

Since we shall be concerned primarily with the motion of charged elementary particles such as electrons or ions in this section, we shall use e to denote the charge on such a particle rather than q.   From the basic Eq. (6.8) giving the magnetic force acting on such a moving charged particle as $\mathbf{F} = e(\mathbf{v} \times \mathbf{B})$, it follows that, since the force F is perpendicular to the direction of motion, the kinetic energy of the particle is not affected by the magnetic field, and only the direction of the velocity vector v changes during the motion.   It is for this reason that the magnetic force is often called a *deflecting* force.   Consider the problem of the motion of a particle which is projected with an initial velocity v_0 into a region of space where there is present a uniform magnetic field B, the direction of v_0 being at right angles to that of B. The subsequent motion of the particle is one of constant speed v_0 in a curved path, the component of the force tangent to the path being zero.   Normal to this curved orbit, in a direction n, let us say, Newton's second law of motion requires that

$$F_n = ev_0B = \frac{mv_0^2}{r}$$

since the angle between the direction of motion and B is 90° and the component of acceleration normal to the path is v_0^2/r. r is the radius of curvature of the orbit.   Solving for r, we obtain

$$r = \frac{mv_0}{eB} \qquad\qquad (6.11)$$

and as all the quantities on the right-hand side of this equation are constant, the path is a circle of radius r, the circle being a curve of constant radius of curvature (Fig. 64). The direction of rotation is as shown for a positively charged particle; the opposite direction would occur for a negative charge. The angular velocity ω is

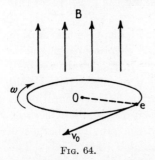

$$\omega = \frac{v_0}{r} = \frac{eB}{m} \qquad (6.12)$$

and hence the period of rotation T becomes

$$T = \frac{2\pi}{\omega} = \frac{2\pi m}{eB} \qquad (6.12a)$$

FIG. 64.

The time for one complete rotation is *independent* of the speed of the particle! This is a very important fact, and much use is made of it in the experimental methods of atomic physics as, for example, in the cyclotron.

If the particle has an initial velocity v_0 not perpendicular to B, we can resolve v_0 into two components, one perpendicular to and one parallel to B. The latter component is not affected by the magnetic induction; hence the motion is a superposition of the circular motion described by Eq. (6.11) in a plane normal to B and a uniform translation parallel to B. The path is a helix of uniform pitch (Fig. 65).

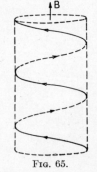

One important application of this result is in its application to magnetic focusing by a longitudinal magnetic field. In Fig. 66 is shown a slit S, through which ions enter a region where there is a uniform magnetic field B. All the ions entering at an angle β, with the magnetic induction B will be brought to a focus at P on a fluorescent screen S located at a distance d from the slit if the time of flight from S to P

FIG. 65.

is just equal to the time of one revolution in the helical path. The time of flight is

$$t = \frac{d}{v_0 \cos \beta}$$

and equating this to the period given by Eq. (6.12a), there follows

$$d = \frac{2\pi m}{eB} v_0 \cos \beta$$

The focal length d thus depends on the initial velocity v_0, the angle β, the induction B, and the ratio of charge to mass of the particles.

The ratio of charge to mass of an ion may be determined for a known initial ion velocity by deflecting the ions in a uniform magnetic field normal to their direction of motion, as shown in Fig. 67. The ions entering through slit S are deflected in a semicircle and impinge on a photographic plate at P. The distance SP is given by

$$SP = \frac{2mv_0}{eB}$$

and v_0 can be determined by allowing the ions to accelerate from rest through a known electrostatic potential difference V prior to entering the slit S. Thus the ratio e/m can be determined, and this is the principle underlying the operation of a mass spectrograph.

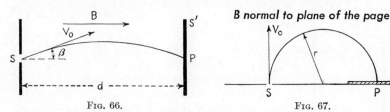

FIG. 66.   FIG. 67.

We now turn to a brief discussion of the motion of a charged particle in combined electric and magnetic fields. As we have already seen, the law of conservation of mechanical energy provides a useful initial step toward the solution of similar problems in purely electrostatic fields. The simultaneous presence of a steady magnetic field does not alter the validity of this law when both electrostatic and magnetic fields are present, since the magnetic force acting at right angles to the motion cannot alter the kinetic energy of the particle. Thus if e is the charge and m the mass of the particle, V the electrostatic potential, and v the velocity, one has

$$\tfrac{1}{2}mv^2 + eV = \text{constant} \tag{6.13}$$

where the constant is the constant total energy of the motion and V is a function of position. Since the law of conservation of energy [Eq. (6.13)] does not completely determine the motion, one must employ additional relations obtained from the use of Newton's second law of motion. The general expression for the vector force acting on a charge in combined electric and magnetic fields is

$$\mathbf{F} = e[\mathbf{\mathcal{E}} + \mathbf{v} \times \mathbf{B}] \tag{6.14}$$

where F is expressed in newtons, e in coulombs, $\mathcal{E}$ in volts per meter, v in meters per second, and B in webers per square meter. Equating this force to the mass of the particle times its vector acceleration then yields three equations of motion, one for each component of force and acceleration. Any two of these and Eq. (6.13) then form the basis for a solution of the problem. Of course, one may use the three equations expressing Newton's second law of motion directly to effect a solution, but in most cases it will be wise to make use of the law of conservation of energy, since it is a partially integrated form of these equations.

4. Side Thrusts on Conductors; the Moving-coil Galvanometer.
The magnetic forces exerted on current-carrying wires are generally

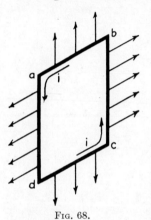

termed "side thrusts" because they act at right angles to the length of the conductor. We have formulated the law for this force in the differential form

$$dF = i(ds \times B)$$

and in order to obtain the resultant force (or torque) acting on any finite length of the conductor, the above expression must be integrated. Since it is a *vector* equation, this must be done, in general, by computing the components of dF before integrating and recombining the integrated components to obtain the resultant force.

Fig. 68.

Steady electric currents always exist in *closed* conducting paths; hence it is important to consider the magnetic force and torque on a closed loop of wire carrying a steady current. For the sake of simplicity we shall employ a rectangular loop, but the results of our analysis will be stated in a form which will be valid for an arbitrary shape of loop. In a uniform field of magnetic induction B, a closed current loop experiences *no* resultant magnetic force. Only if the field is nonuniform, or inhomogeneous, is there a resultant force acting on such a loop. The forces acting on the sides of a rectangular loop whose plane is normal to the direction of a uniform field B are shown in Fig. 68, distributed along the lengths of the conductors. The upward force on side ab is equal to the downward force on side cd. A similar balance occurs for the side thrusts on sides ad and bc, as shown. Evidently this cancellation of forces occurs even when the direction of the uniform field B is not normal to the plane of the loop. In this case the magnitude of the side thrust on side ab would be equal to $iB(ab) \sin \alpha$, where α is the angle between B and the direction of current in the side of length (ab).   The side thrust on side cd is similarly $iB(cd) \sin \alpha$, but of opposite sign since the current direction in this side is opposite to that in side ab.   Since $(ab) = (cd)$, we have a balance between these two forces.   In a nonuniform field of B, however, this cancellation does not occur, since B or $\sin \alpha$ or both will vary from point to point on the loop, and there will then be a resultant force in general.

Next consider the case of a rectangular loop of wire so mounted that it is free to rotate about a horizontal axis OO passing through its center, as shown in Fig. 69.   The width of the loop is w, its length is l, and let the current direction be as shown.   Suppose this loop is in a uniform magnetic field B, which is perpendicular to the axis OO. First we resolve the magnetic induction vector B into two components, one normal to the plane of the loop and of magnitude $B_n = B \cos \theta$, and the other in the plane of the loop and of magnitude $B_t = B \sin \theta$. Consider the forces on the conductors produced by the normal component B_n.   These lie in the plane of the loop (since they must be perpendicular to this component of the magnetic field) and hence

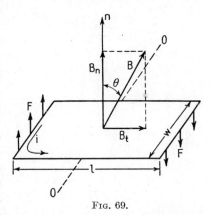

Fig. 69.

contribute nothing to the torque about the axis of rotation OO. Therefore the torque about this axis is due only to the component of B in the plane of the loop.   The two equal and opposite forces on the two conductors of length w are shown as F in the figure, and these give rise to a torque about the axis OO.   The component of B in the plane of the loop B_t does not give rise to any force acting on either side of length l, since the currents in these sides are parallel or antiparallel to this component of the field.   From Fig. 69, we see readily that the torque about this axis is

$$F\frac{l}{2} + F\frac{l}{2} = Fl$$

Since F is the force acting on a conductor of length w and since

$$B_t = B \sin \theta$$

is everywhere constant and at right angles to the current in this conductor, one has

$$F = B \sin \theta \, wi \qquad (6.15)$$

so that the torque becomes

$$T = Bi(wl) \sin \theta$$

and since wl is the area of the loop, this can be written as

$$T = BiA \sin \theta \qquad (6.16)$$

with θ the angle between B and the normal n to the plane of the loop. This torque is a torque tending to rotate the loop into a position in which its plane is normal to the direction of B. In this position $\theta = 0$, and the torque vanishes. It is a position of stable equilibrium. (Note that the direction of the normal is such that a right-handed screw would move in this direction if rotating in the direction of the loop current i.) Equation (6.16) turns out to be valid for a plane loop of arbitrary shape, the torque being proportional to the loop area. The maximum torque occurs when $\theta = \pi/2$, *i.e.*, when the normal to the plane of the loop is perpendicular to B.

Equation (6.16) gives the magnitude of the magnetic torque on a current loop, and it is desirable to generalize this equation to include the direction of the torque. This is along the axis OO perpendicular to the plane formed by the normal n to the plane of the loop and the vector B. For this purpose, we *define* the magnetic moment $\underline{\mathbf{m}}$ of a current loop as a vector of magnitude $\underline{iA}$ (product of current and loop area) and of direction of the positive normal n to the loop. In terms of this magnetic moment, one can write in place of Eq. (6.16) the vector equation

$$\mathbf{T} = \mathbf{m} \times \mathbf{B} \qquad (6.17)$$

which yields both the direction and magnitude of the torque. We note from Fig. 69 that the position of stable equilibrium of the loop is that in which the magnetic field direction coincides with the normal n to the loop. If the magnetic induction B is not uniform over the loop area, one can still apply Eq. (6.17) to a loop of infinitesimal area and then, by a method which will be discussed in Sec. 4 of the next chapter, integrate over the large loop to obtain the resultant torque.

It is found experimentally that the torque exerted by a magnetic field on a small bar magnet, such as a compass needle can be expressed in the form of Eq. (6.17); hence, one can consider such a permanent magnet as describable by a magnetic moment $\mathbf{m}$, directed along its length.   The torque on a small compass needle of magnetic moment **m** when the needle is suspended at its center is given by Eq. (6.17). If the needle is displaced from its equilibrium orientation (in which **m** coincides with **B**) through a small angle θ and released, it will perform angular harmonic motion with a frequency

$$ f = \frac{1}{2\pi} \sqrt{\frac{mB}{I}} \qquad (6.18) $$

where I is the moment of inertia of the compass needle about the rotation axis.   Used in this manner, a small bar magnet serves as a *magnetometer* and is employed to measure weak magnetic fields, such as the magnetic field of the earth. The equivalence of permanent magnets and current loops will be discussed further in Sec. 4 of the next chapter.

One of the most common types of galvanometers, the so-called D'Arsonval, or moving-coil, galvanometer, functions by virtue of the torque action just discussed.   A coil of N turns in series is suspended as a torsion pendulum by wires W, as shown in Fig. 70.   For the uniform field of B indicated in this figure, one side of the coil is pushed toward and the other away from the reader, giving rise to a torque about the axis of suspension

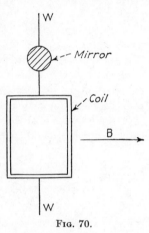

Fig. 70.

$$ T = NBiA \qquad (6.19) $$

where i is the current in the coil and A is its area.   The magnetic field is supplied by a permanent magnet, which is so designed in practice that B lies in the plane of the coil even when the latter is twisted through an angle.   When a current is set up in this coil, it rotates and comes to equilibrium at an angle θ with its original orientation, for which the torsional restoring torque of the suspension is equal and opposite to the magnetic torque.   Since the restoring torque is proportional to θ, we can write for equilibrium

$$ NBiA = k'\theta \qquad (6.20) $$

where k' depends on the torsion modulus, length, and radius of the suspending wires.   Equation (6.18) may be written in the form

$$ \theta = \frac{NBA}{k'} i = \text{constant} \times i \qquad (6.21) $$

so that the angular deflection is proportional to the current. The discussion of the sensitivity of the instrument is left to the problems.

The principle underlying the action of an electric motor is essentially that for the moving-coil galvanometer, the important difference being that the coil (more precisely, the armature carrying the coil) is free to rotate in bearings instead of being subject to a restoring torque.

Problems

1. The magnetic induction in a given region of space is given by

$$B_x = ay; \qquad B_y = -ax; \qquad B_z = 0$$

where a is a constant. Show that the lines of B are concentric circles. How does the magnitude of B vary with distance from the center of such a circle?

2. An electron enters a uniform magnetic field at right angles to the lines of induction and performs circular motion with a period of 10^{-8} sec.

a. Calculate the magnitude of B.

b. If the initial speed of the electron is acquired by accelerating from rest through a potential difference of 3,000 volts, what is the radius of the circular orbit?

3. Carry through the calculations of Prob. 2 for a hydrogen ion (a proton) instead of an electron. The mass of a proton is 1,840 times the electronic mass.

4. A beam of electrons, accelerated from rest by a potential difference of 320 volts, enters a uniform field of magnetic induction of magnitude 6.0×10^{-4} weber/m² at right angles to its initial direction. The radius of the circle in which these electrons move is found to be 10.0 cm. Compute the ratio of charge to mass of an electron.

5. A cloud chamber enables one to observe the tracks of charged elementary particles. When a uniform magnetic field exists in the chamber, the tracks are curved. Suppose that tracks of 104 mm radius are observed for a magnetic field of 0.10 weber/m² and that it is known that the particles have the same charge as an electron and an energy of 5,000 electron-volts. (*One electron-volt is the kinetic energy acquired by an electron in accelerating from rest through a potential difference of one volt.*) What is the mass of the particles?

6. A narrow beam of positively charged particles enters a region in which there is a uniform magnetic field of 0.1015 weber/m² directed at right angles to its direction of motion. The particles enter through a slit with speeds acquired by accelerating from rest through a potential difference of 1,000 volts, move in a semicircular track of 20.0 cm radius, and are collected by a metal plate. If the particles each carry a charge equal to that of an electron, compute:

a. The mass of each particle.

b. The time for a particle to move from the slit to the collecting plate.

7. In Prob. 9, Chap. 2, the two deflecting plates of the cathode-ray tube are replaced by coils producing a uniform transverse magnetic field of

5.3×10^{-4} weber/m^2 in the same region of space in which there was an electric field with the deflecting plates in position. Calculate the ratio e/m for an electron if the beam is deflected 3.10 cm.

8. Referring to Fig. 67 of the text, show that all electrons with the same speed v_0, leaving the slit S at small angles with the normal, will be brought to a focus at P.

9. *a.* What is the velocity of a beam of electrons which move undeflected in a region of space in which there exist both a uniform electric field $\mathcal{E}$ of 3.4×10^5 volts/m and a uniform magnetic field B of 2.0×10^{-3} weber/m^2, both fields being normal to the beam and at right angles to each other?

b. Show the orientation of the vectors v, $\mathcal{E}$, and B in a diagram.

c. What is the radius of the electron orbit when the electric field is removed and only the magnetic field is applied?

10. Electrons are emitted normally from the negative plate of a parallel-plate condenser of plate separation d with negligible speeds under the action of ultraviolet light. The condenser is situated in a uniform magnetic field with the lines of B parallel to the plates, and a potential difference V is maintained between the plates. Show that no electrons will reach the positive plate if $V < \frac{1}{2} (e/m)d^2B^2$.

Use Newton's second law for the motion parallel to the plates and the conservation of mechanical energy.

11. A magnetron consists of a grounded cylindrical cathode of 1.0 cm radius surrounded by a coaxial cylindrical plate of inner radius 5.0 cm. When the tube is placed in a uniform magnetic field with its axis parallel to the lines of B, it is observed that the electron current from cathode to plate is zero for plate potentials less than 10.2 volts. Calculate the magnitude of B. Assume the electrons leave the cathode with negligible initial velocities.

HINT: Set up the equation for conservation of mechanical energy, and set the torque about the axis equal to the rate of change of angular momentum. Use polar coordinates.

12. A charged particle of charge e and mass m starts from rest at the origin of a coordinate system and moves under the action of a uniform electric field $\mathcal{E}$ directed parallel to the y-axis and of a uniform magnetic field B parallel to the z-axis.

a. Show that the equations of motion are

$$m \frac{dv_x}{dt} = eBv_y$$

$$m \frac{dv_y}{dt} = e\mathcal{E} - eBv_x$$

$$m \frac{dv_z}{dt} = 0$$

b. Find x and y as functions of the time from these equations, and show that the particle moves along the x-axis with an *average* speed equal to $\mathcal{E}/B$. (Integrate the first equation, using $v_y = dy/dt$, to find v_x in terms of y, and substitute in the second.)

13. A thin, rigid, metallic rod of length 7.0 cm and mass 20 g is free to rotate in a vertical plane about an axis through one of its ends. The other end of the rod can slide without friction on a vertical circular metallic track of radius 7.0 cm with its center at the rotation axis. A steady current of 20 amp is carried by the rod from the track to the axis. If the system is in a uniform horizontal magnetic field, $B = 7.0 \times 10^{-2}$ weber/m², what angle does the rod make with the vertical when in equilibrium?

14. A 60-mil-diameter rigid copper wire (specific gravity = 8.9) 1 ft long is pivoted at A and rests lightly against a horizontal wire passing through B, as shown in Fig. 71. A current of 1 amp is sent through the wires from A to C, and a uniform magnetic field of 0.10 weber/m² is applied normal to the plane of the wires. What angle θ with the vertical will the hanging wire make in equilibrium?

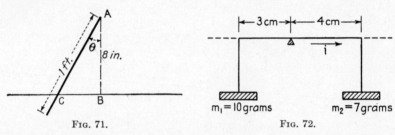

Fig. 71.   Fig. 72.

15. The horizontal arm of the balance shown in Fig. 72 carries a steady current of 10 amp. Find the direction and magnitude of the magnetic field necessary to bring this balance into equilibrium.

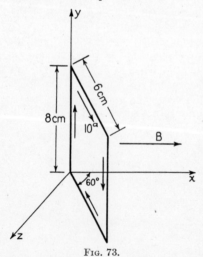

Fig. 73.

16. The rectangular loop carrying a steady current of 10 amp as shown in Fig. 73 is hinged along the y-axis. The loop is in a uniform magnetic field of 0.20 weber/m² parallel to the x-axis. The plane of the loop makes an angle of 60° with the x-y plane.

a. Find the force exerted by the magnetic field on each side of the loop.

b. Find the torque required to hold the loop in equilibrium in the position shown.

17. A copper bar weighing 100 g rests on two rails 20 cm apart and carries a current of 20 amp from one rail to the other. The coefficient of friction is 0.60. What is the smallest magnetic field that would cause the bar to slide, and what is its direction?

18. A very thin wooden block, 25 by 40 cm, has 10 turns of wire wound around its edge, and the block is suspended in equilibrium with its plane horizontal on an east-west axis with its 40-cm edges pointing north and south. Using very flexible leads, a current of 28 amp is sent through the coil. How far from the axis of suspension must a 1-g body be hung so that the coil remains in equilibrium in the earth's magnetic field? The horizontal and vertical components of the earth's field are 0.21×10^{-4} and 0.48×10^{-4} weber/m², respectively.

19. An equilateral triangular loop of wire, of side a and weight W, is suspended from one vertex so as to turn freely in all directions. A current i is sent around the loop, and it is placed in a uniform magnetic field B.

a. The field is normal to the loop. Draw the forces acting on the wires and find the tension in the bottom wire.

b. The field is horizontal and in the plane of the loop. What is the torque tending to rotate the loop?

c. The field is vertical. What is the equilibrium position of the loop?

20. A circular loop of wire of area A, carrying a current i, is placed in a uniform magnetic field B parallel to the plane of the loop. Show that the torque on the loop is BiA.

21. A uniform magnetic field is applied normal to a rigid circular loop of wire carrying a current. Find the tension in the wire.

22. The coil of a D'Arsonval galvanometer has 100 turns and encloses an area of 5.0 cm². The magnetic induction in the region where the coil is located is 0.10 weber/m², and the torsional constant of the suspension is 10^{-9} m-newton /deg.

a. Find the angular deflection of the instrument per microampere in the coil.

b. If the angular deflection is measured by reflecting a beam of light from a mirror on the suspension, what current would cause a deflection of 1 mm of the light spot on a scale 1 m distant from the mirror?

23. How will the sensitivity of a galvanometer change if the number of turns of wire on the coil is doubled, the diameter of the wire being correspondingly reduced so as to keep the weight constant? Consider both the ampere and volt sensitivities.

24. Discuss how the sensitivity of a D'Arsonval galvanometer depends on the magnetic induction B, the coil area, and the length and radius of the suspending fiber. What practical limitations can you give for the design of the instrument, if one desires maximum sensitivity?

25. Calculate the period of a moving-coil galvanometer for torsional oscillations, neglecting friction. Derive a formula for the angular deflection of such an instrument in terms of the current, magnetic induction B, number of turns N, coil area A, the period calculated above, and the moment of inertia of the instrument about the axis of suspension.

26. A large current is sent through the coil of a D'Arsonval galvanometer for a very short time. Neglecting friction, prove that the maximum angle of deflection is proportional to the total charge passing through the coil. Derive a formula for the porportionality constant.   When a galvanometer is used in the manner described, it is called a *ballistic galvanometer*.   Why should a ballistic galvanometer have a relatively large moment of inertia about its suspension axis?

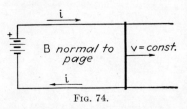

B *normal to page*   v = *const.*

Fig. 74.

27. A metal bar slides on two conducting rails carrying a steady current i. Under the influence of a magnetic field B and a suitable external force, it moves with a constant velocity (Fig. 74).   Calculate the rate at which the external force does work on the system.   Compare this result with the rate of change of magnetic flux through the circuit behind the wire.

28. The armature of an electric motor is a cylinder 25 cm in diameter and rotates with an angular velocity of 1,200 rpm.   The armature carries 100 conductors, each 40 cm long and each carrying 15 amp at right angles to a magnetic field of flux density 0.85 weber/m². Compute the torque and horsepower developed by the motor.

CHAPTER 7

THE MAGNETIC FIELD OF STEADY CURRENTS

In this chapter, we continue our study of magnetic fields and turn our attention to the question of the laws governing the production of magnetic fields by electric currents. Although Biot and Savart made contemporary important contributions, these laws are due principally to Ampère, who inferred them from his experiments on the forces exerted by one current-carrying circuit on another. Just as in the case of electrostatics, one finds that these magnetic forces depend not only on the currents but also on the material bodies which are present. Once again we postpone a detailed treatment of the effects of such material bodies of finite size and confine our attention almost entirely to the case of empty space. We shall, however, include the case of infinite, homogeneous isotropic media, since in this *special* case the separation of the effects of matter from those of the electric currents can be obtained in an extremely simple and straightforward manner.

1. Ampère's Rule; the Magnetic Intensity H. The conclusions drawn by Ampère may be stated as follows: The magnetic induction vector **B** at a given point of space may be considered as the vector sum of infinitesimal vectors **dB**, each of the latter being due to a current element i **ds** of the circuit producing the field. Let **r** be the radius vector from the current element i **ds** at O to the field point P where the magnetic field is to be calculated (Fig. 75). The magnitude of **dB** due to this current element is proportional to the magnitude of i **ds**, to the sine of the angle α between i **ds** and **r**, and inversely proportional to the square of the distance r. In symbols,

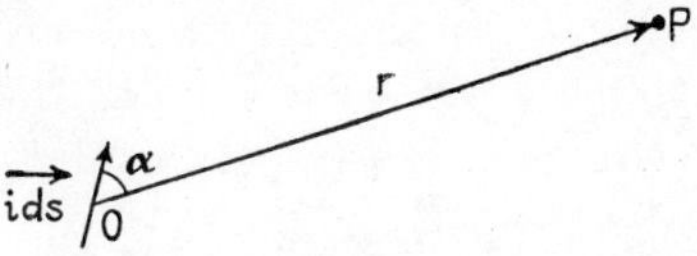

FIG. 75.

$$dB \sim \frac{i \, ds \, \sin \alpha}{r^2}$$

The direction of **dB** is at right angles to the plane containing i **ds** and **r**, and if the vector **ds** is rotated through the smallest possible angle so that it lines up with **r**, the direction in which a right-handed screw would move is the direction of **dB**. Thus in Fig. 75, the vector **dB** at

123

P is directed into the plane of the page.   Using vector-product notation, the above proportionality may be written in the form

$$dB \sim \frac{i(ds \times r)}{r^{\circ}}$$

If there is another current element at P, let us say $i'\,ds'$, the force acting on it is, according to Eq. (6.7),

$$dF = i'(ds' \times dB) \sim \frac{ii'}{r^3}[ds' \times (ds \times r)] \tag{7.1}$$

The proportionality expressed by (7.1) summarizes Ampère's law for the force exerted on a current element $i'\,ds'$ by another current element $i\,ds$ separated from it by a distance r.   If we write the proportionality factor as $\mu_0/4\pi$ (the subscript zero on μ_0 is to remind us that we are concerned with a problem in empty space), the relation (7.1) may be written as an equation,

$$dF = \frac{\mu_0}{4\pi}\frac{ii'}{r^3}[ds' \times (ds \times r)] \tag{7.2}$$

The factor μ_0 is called the magnetic permeability of empty space. In the case where the conductors are embedded in an infinite homogeneous and isotropic material medium, the above relations are still valid if one replaces μ_0 by μ, with μ the magnetic permeability of the medium.   This is a special case, however, and, in general, for finite material bodies, the effect of these media cannot be divorced from the currents giving rise to the field in any such simple manner.

Reverting to the case of empty space (or, for all practical purposes, air), we can write for dB, the magnetic induction due to the current element $i\,ds$ (Ampère's rule),

$$dB = \frac{\mu_0}{4\pi}i(ds \times r) \tag{7.3}$$

Just as in the electrostatic case, even though our principal concern is with problems in empty space, it is desirable to introduce a second magnetic vector so that the basic laws which we develop will be written in such a manner as to have unrestricted validity.   This vector (the analogue of D in electrostatics) is called the *magnetic field intensity* and is denoted by H.   *For the case of empty space, H is defined by*

$$H = \frac{B}{\mu_0}; \qquad B = \mu_0 H \tag{7.4}$$

In the more general case of isotropic homogeneous material media, H is defined by

$$H = \frac{B}{\mu}; \qquad B = \mu H \tag{7.4a}$$

with μ the magnetic permeability of the medium. More detailed discussion of the physical interpretation of Eq. (7.4a) and an alternative general definition of H will be given in Chap. 14. In empty space, or in isotropic material bodies, B and H are identical in direction (so that a single field plot maps a magnetic field no matter which vector one employs) but differ in magnitude and dimensions. The contribution to H at a given point of space due to a current element i ds is then, using (7.3) and (7.4),

$$\mathbf{dH} = \frac{i}{4\pi} \frac{(\mathbf{ds} \times \mathbf{r})}{r^3} \tag{7.5}$$

and the vector $\mathbf{H}$ is obtained by a vector summation of the elementary vectors $\mathbf{dH}$ produced by all the current elements. The magnitude of the elementary vector $\mathbf{dH}$ is accordingly

$$dH = \frac{i\, ds \sin \alpha}{4\pi r^2} \tag{7.6}$$

Equation (7.2) provides the basis for the definition of the *ampere*, the unit current in the mks system of units, and from this the definition of the unit charge, the coulomb. For simplicity, let us suppose that the two current elements are parallel to each other and carry the same current i. Equation (7.2) then becomes

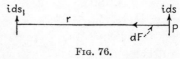

Fig. 76.

$$dF = \frac{\mu_0}{4\pi} \frac{i^2\, ds\, ds'}{r^2} \tag{7.7}$$

and dF is a force of attraction acting along r (Fig. 76). The element i ds' produces a field at P normal to and into the page,

$$dB = \frac{\mu_0}{4\pi} \frac{i\, ds'}{r^2} \tag{7.8}$$

and hence the force on i ds is as shown and is of magnitude

$$dF = i\, ds\, dB = \frac{\mu_0}{4\pi} \frac{i^2\, ds\, ds'}{r^2}$$

The ampere is now defined as follows: *If two parallel current elements of equal length ds carrying equal currents attract each other with a force of*

10^{-7} *newton per unit length (per meter) of each element when separated by a distance of 1 meter, the current i in each is 1 ampere.* The choice of the force as 10^{-7} newton is *arbitrary* and characteristic of the mks system. The above definition is not a convenient working definition, although logically correct, since one always is concerned with closed circuits rather than current elements; hence we shall give an equivalent, more convenient definition later.

From Eq. (7.2) or (7.8) we see that the dimensions of μ_0 are given by

$$[\mu_0] = \frac{ml}{q^2}$$

and from the definition of the unit current, the ampere, its numerical value is $4\pi \times 10^{-7}$, so that we have

$$\mu_0 = 4\pi \times 10^{-7} \text{ kg-m/coulomb}^2 \tag{7.9}$$

It is customary to express μ_0 in terms of the equivalent units of henrys per meter, where *one henry is used to denote one weber per ampere.* To see that these two units are identical, we note that

$$1 \frac{\text{kilogram-meter}}{\text{coulomb}^2} = 1 \frac{\text{newton-second}^2}{\text{coulomb}^2} = 1 \frac{\text{volt-second}^2}{\text{meter-coulomb}}$$

$$= 1 \frac{\text{volt-second}}{\text{meter-ampere}} = 1 \frac{\text{henry}}{\text{meter}}$$

Thus we usually write

$$\mu_0 = 4\pi \times 10^{-7} \text{ henry/m} \tag{7.9a}$$

From Eq. (7.5) we have directly the dimensions of H as a current per unit length, $[H] = q/lt$, so that the magnetic intensity H is expressed in amperes per meter.

We recall that ϵ_0, the permittivity of empty space, has the value 8.85×10^{-12} farad/m and that this value is determined by experiment, not by definition, as is μ_0. From Coulomb's law,

$$F = \frac{q_1 q_2}{4\pi \epsilon_0 r^2}$$

we see that the dimensions of ϵ_0 are $q^2 m^{-1} l^{-3} t^2$, and since the dimensions of μ_0 are mlq^{-2}, we have for the dimensions of the product $\epsilon_0 \mu_0$

$$[\epsilon_0 \mu_0] = l^{-2} t^2$$

the reciprocal of the square of a velocity. Denoting this velocity by c, we have

$$c = \frac{1}{\sqrt{\epsilon_0 \mu_0}} = \frac{1}{\sqrt{(8.85 \times 10^{-12})(4\pi \times 10^{-7})}} = 3.00 \times 10^8 \text{ m/sec}$$

$$(7.10)$$

and this characteristic velocity will play an important role in our future development.

There is an older system of electromagnetic units, the so-called absolute electromagnetic system of units, which is closely related to the mks system which we are employing. In it the mechanical units are centimeters, grams, and seconds, and the proportionality constant in relation (7.1) is set equal to unity for empty space, a pure number with no dimensions. Thus all quantities are expressed dimensionally in terms of mass, length, and time. The unit current is called the *abampere* and is defined by a scheme similar to the one employed to define the ampere, using Eq. (7.8) with the factor $\mu_0/4\pi$ replaced by unity and an attractive force of 1 dyne per cm length of each current element when the elements are separated by 1 cm. *One abampere is equal to ten amperes.* Further details will be found in Appendix I.

Let us now summarize the discussion of this section. Suppose we have the problem of calculating the force exerted by one current-carrying circuit on another. The following procedure is to be used:

1. Calculate the vector **H,** due to the second circuit at a point where an element of the first circuit is located, by applying Eq. (7.5) and integrating over all the current elements of the second circuit. Since the magnetic intensity **H** is a vector, one must first resolve **dH** into components, integrate separately for each component, and then find the resultant **H**.

2. Find the vector **B** from $\mathbf{B} = \mu_0\mathbf{H}$ (or $\mathbf{B} = \mu\mathbf{H}$ for infinite homogeneous isotropic media).

3. Calculate the force on the element of this first circuit due to this magnetic induction **B** from Eq. (6.7).

4. Integrate over all the elements of the first circuit to find the resultant force on it. This calculation is performed by first taking components of **dF** and then integrating as in step 1.

In the following sections we shall be concerned principally with the first step of the foregoing procedure.

2. Examples; the Biot-Savart Law. As a first example of the application of the relations of the preceding section, let us consider the magnetic field of a very long straight wire carrying a steady current i (Fig. 77). From the symmetry of the problem we see that the magnetic field intensity H can depend only on the distance a of the field P from the wire and not on its other coordinates. The contribution to

H from any current element $i\,dx$ is a vector pointing straight into the page at P, at right angles to the element $i\,dx$ and to r.   Since all the vectors $\mathbf{dH}$ due to the elements which comprise the wire have the same

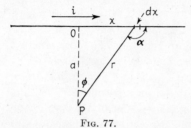

FIG. 77.

direction (only one component of $\mathbf{H}$ is different from zero), we may integrate directly and have from Eq. (7.5) or (7.6)

$$H = \frac{i}{4\pi} \int \frac{dx\,\sin\alpha}{r^2} \quad (7.11)$$

To evaluate this integral, it is simplest to use the angle ϕ of Fig. 77 as the integration variable.   From the figure it is evident that

$$\sin\alpha = \sin(\pi - \alpha) = \cos\phi$$

$x = a\tan\phi$; $dx = a\sec^2\phi\,d\phi$; $1/r^2 = (1/a^2)\cos^2\phi$; $dx/r^2 = d\phi/a$; so that Eq. (7.11) becomes

$$H = \frac{i}{4\pi a} \int_{-\pi/2}^{+\pi/2} \cos\phi\,d\phi = \frac{i}{4\pi a} \left[\sin\phi \right]_{-\pi/2}^{+\pi/2} = \frac{i}{2\pi a}$$

We thus find for the magnetic intensity H due to a long straight wire at a point P a vector of magnitude

$$H = \frac{i}{2\pi a} \quad (7.12)$$

which is directed at right angles to the plane of the wire and a.   This result, known as the Biot-Savart law, is of great importance, since it gives the field near a straight wire of finite length if the distance a is small compared to the length of the wire.

Suppose the point P of Fig. 77 describes a circle of radius a about the wire with the center at O.   At every point of this circle, the vector H (and also B) is tangent to it, and hence the circle is one of the lines of H or of B.   Thus we see that the lines of magnetic intensity or induction are circles with their centers at the wire (Fig. 78).   Note that if one moves around a line of magnetic intensity in the direction of H, the current producing the field is in the direction in which a right-handed screw would move if so rotated.

Let us now examine the magnetic field produced by a circular loop of wire carrying a steady current i.   First we calculate the field intensity H at the center of the loop (Fig. 79).   The vector H is normal to the plane of the loop and points out at the reader.   For all the elements of arc ds of the circle, the angle between ds and r is $\pi/2$, so that Eq. (7.6) becomes simply

$$dH = \frac{i\,ds}{4\pi r^2}$$

and since r is the constant radius of the circle, we have

$$H = \frac{i}{4\pi r^2} \int ds = \frac{i}{2r} \tag{7.13}$$

We can extend this result immediately to calculate the magnetic intensity at any point on the axis of the current loop (Fig. 80). The

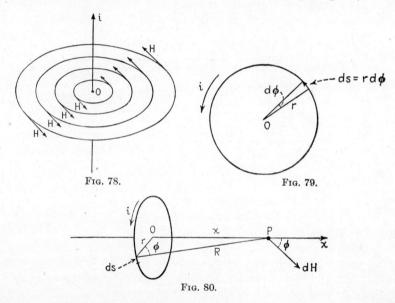

FIG. 78.   FIG. 79.

FIG. 80.

distance R from any element ds of the loop to P is constant, independent of the location of ds on the loop, and is given by $R = \sqrt{x^2 + r^2}$. Furthermore, ds is perpendicular to R for every element ds of the loop, so that $\sin \alpha = 1$ in Eq. (7.6).   Hence

$$dH = \frac{i}{4\pi} \frac{ds}{(x^2 + r^2)}$$

Before integrating we must resolve dH into components, one along the x-axis and the other perpendicular to it.   By symmetry, the latter will vanish when the integration is carried out for the whole loop, and $H = H_x$.   Thus we have

$$dH_x = dH \cos \phi = dH \frac{r}{R}$$

and hence

$$H = H_x = \frac{i}{4\pi} \int \frac{r\,ds}{(x^2 + r^2)^{\frac{3}{2}}} = \frac{ir}{4\pi(x^2 + r^2)^{\frac{3}{2}}} \int ds = \frac{ir^2}{2(x^2 + r^2)^{\frac{3}{2}}} \quad (7.14)$$

This expression for the axial field of a circular current loop is useful for calculating the axial field of any number of coaxial circular loops. As an example, we consider the case of a *solenoid*, which is a closely wound helical coil of conducting wire. We can obtain the axial field by integrating the contributions from the individual turns as given by Eq. (7.13), since for very close winding each turn may be considered as circular to a good degree of approximation.

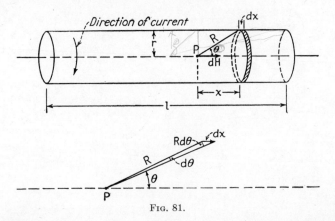

FIG. 81.

We replace the solenoid by a steady current directed circumferentially around a hollow cylinder of radius r (everywhere perpendicular to the axis). If there are n turns per unit length of the solenoid, each carrying a current i, then the current per unit length is ni, and the current carried in a circular ring of thickness dx is $ni\,dx$ (Fig. 81). The contribution dH of this ring to the field intensity at P is, according to Eq. (7.14),

$$dH = \frac{nir^2\,dx}{2(x^2 + r^2)^{\frac{3}{2}}} = \frac{ni\,dx\,r^2}{2R^3}$$

where x is the distance from P to the plane of the disk. This expression must be integrated over the whole length l of the solenoid to find the axial field H at P. From the lower sketch in Fig. 81 we see that

$$R\,d\theta = \sin\theta\,dx; \qquad dx = R\,d\theta/\sin\theta$$

and since $r/R = \sin \theta$, the expression for dH becomes

$$dH = \frac{ni}{2R} \frac{R\, d\theta}{\sin \theta} \sin^2 \theta = \frac{ni}{2} \sin \theta \, d\theta$$

The integration then yields immediately

$$H = \frac{ni}{2} \int_{\theta_1}^{\theta_2} \sin \theta \, d\theta = \frac{ni}{2} (\cos \theta_1 - \cos \theta_2) \qquad (7.15)$$

where θ_1 and θ_2 are the values of θ (the angle with the positive x-axis) when dx is at the right-hand and left-hand end of the solenoid, respectively.

When the solenoid is of infinite length, $\theta_1 = 0$ and $\theta_2 = \pi$, so that

$$H = ni \qquad (7.16)$$

gives the magnetic intensity on the axis of an infinitely long solenoid wound with n turns per unit length, each turn carrying a steady current i. Equation (7.15) can be used to find the axial magnetic field of a solenoid of finite length. Further discussion is left to the problems.

3. The Ampère Circuital Law for H. There is a more general relation (also due to Ampère) than Eq. (7.5) between the magnetic intensity H and the steady current i which produces it, and this relation is known as the *circuital law.* In fact, we have introduced the magnetic intensity H in order to state this law in a *form* which has unrestricted validity. To formulate this circuital law, we must introduce the idea of *magnetomotive force* (mmf) along a path. This is defined as $\int H_s \, ds = \int \mathbf{H} \cdot \mathbf{ds}$ taken along the given path. If the path is closed, we write it as $\oint H_s \, ds$, the circle on the integral sign indicating the fact that a closed path is employed. *The integral is always to be evaluated by traversing the path in such a direction that the enclosed area is kept on the left.*

Let us consider the expression for the mmf around a closed path in the magnetic field of a long straight wire, given by the Biot-Savart law [Eq. (7.12)]. First, we take the closed path as one of the closed lines of H (a circular path), as shown in Fig. 82a. Since H is everywhere tangential to this circular path, we have

$$\text{mmf} = \oint H_s \, ds = \oint H \, ds = \oint Ha \, d\psi$$

If now from Eq. (7.12) we insert the value $H = i/2\pi a$ into this integral, there follows

$$\oint H_s \, ds = \oint \frac{i}{2\pi a} a \, d\psi = \frac{i}{2\pi} \oint d\psi = i \qquad (7.17)$$

since the integral of $d\psi$ around the circle is 2π. [It can be shown in general that the mmf $\oint H_s\, ds$ around *any* closed path which encloses the wire has the value i.] [On the other hand, if the closed path does not enclose the wire, the integral is zero.] We can readily check this

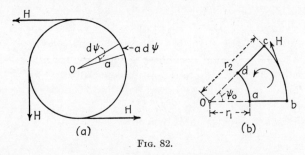

(a)   (b)

FIG. 82.

last statement for a closed path such as that of Fig. 82b, consisting of two radial segments and two arcs of circles of radii r_1 and r_2. We have

$$\oint H_s\, ds = \int_a^b H_s\, ds + \int_b^c H_s\, ds + \int_c^d H_s\, ds + \int_d^a H_s\, ds$$

The first and third terms are zero, since H is everywhere at right angles to a radius vector. The second integral is

$$\int_b^c H_s\, ds = \int_0^{\psi_0} \frac{i}{2\pi r_2} r_2\, d\psi = \frac{i\psi_0}{2}$$

and the fourth one is

$$\int_d^a H_s\, ds = \int_{\psi_0}^0 \frac{i}{2\pi r_1} r_1\, d\psi = -\frac{i\psi_0}{2}$$

Thus we see that $\oint H_s\, ds = 0$ for this path which encloses no current.

The results obtained above for the special case of a straight wire turn out to be true in general and hold not only for steady currents in wires but also for currents distributed in space. This is the essence of *Ampère's circuital law*, one of the fundamental laws of electromagnetic theory. The formal statement of this law is as follows:

[*The mmf around any closed path is equal to the current crossing any surface of which this closed path is a boundary.*]

This law has unrestricted validity [with suitable generalization of the definition of H, such as Eq. (7.4a)], and the fundamental general character of the circuital law as contrasted with the Ampère rule [Eq. (7.5)] will become evident when we study the magnetic behavior of matter and investigate the effects of boundaries between magnetic media.

In symbols we write the circuital law in the form

$$\oint H_s \, ds = i \tag{7.18}$$

with H in amperes per meter, ds in meters, and i in amperes in the mks system. One must not lose sight of the fact that this law as written holds *only* for steady currents, since in this case the lines of electric current are closed curves, and hence the current crossing any surfaces having a common perimeter is the same for all such surfaces.

If the currents are distributed in space, we have for the current across any surface

$$i = \int J_n \, dS$$

and the Ampère circuital law takes the more general form

$$\oint H_s \, ds = \int J_n \, dS \tag{7.19}$$

where the surface integral is evaluated over *any surface having the closed path as a boundary.* $\Phi = \int B_n \, ds$

In general, the problem of the complete determination of the magnetic field of electric currents can be solved by the simultaneous use of Eqs. (6.10) and (7.19) together with $B = \mu_0 H$, and this is a relatively difficult task.   In certain special cases, where because of the symmetry of the situation one knows the direction of the magnetic lines of force, one can determine the field from the circuital law alone.   This is analogous to the corresponding use of Gauss's law in electrostatics.

As an example of this procedure, let us consider the magnetic field *inside* a long straight circular conductor of radius R carrying a steady current i uniformly distributed over its cross section.   The lines of H inside the conductor will be circles concentric with those outside the wire, by virtue of the cylindrical symmetry, but the magnitude of H will not vary as $1/r$, r being the distance from the axis of the conductor to the field point.   To find the correct variation, we evaluate the mmf around a circle of radius r less than R and have

$$\oint H_s \, ds = 2\pi r H$$

since H can vary only with r and hence is constant at all points of the circle and tangent to it at every point.   This must be equal to the current crossing the area enclosed by the circle.   If the uniform current density is $J = i/\pi R^2$, this enclosed current is simply $J\pi r^2$, so that

$$2\pi r H = J\pi r^2 = i \frac{r^2}{R^2}$$

and this yields for H the value

$$H = \frac{ir}{2\pi R^2} \qquad (r \leq R) \qquad (7.20)$$

For $r > R$, we still have the value $H = i/2\pi r$, and we note that there is no discontinuity in H as one moves across the surface of the conductor, since at the surface both Eqs. (7.20) and (7.12) yield the same value, $i/2\pi R$.

The calculation of the magnetic intensity inside a *very long* closely wound solenoid can be accomplished readily with the help of the circuital law.

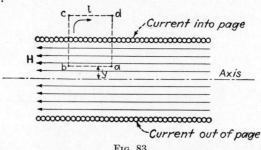

FIG. 83.

Figure 83 shows a portion of a section of the infinitely long solenoid through its axis. From the symmetry we see that the lines of H and B must be straight lines parallel to the solenoid axis in the space inside the winding. (These lines will, of course, emerge from the solenoid in the regions near its ends and close on themselves. If the solenoid is long enough compared to its radius, however, the lines of H and B outside the central part of the solenoid will be far from it.) H can depend only on the distance y from the axis. Let us evaluate the mmf around the dotted path. For the portion of the path outside the solenoid, H is practically zero, and the two portions normal to the axis yield no contribution to the mmf, since H is at right angles to them. Thus the whole integral takes its value from the portion ab of the closed path. If the length of this latter portion is l, we have

$$\oint H_s \, ds = Hl$$

where H is the magnitude of the magnetic intensity at a distance y from the axis. The current crossing the area enclosed by this path is nli, with n the number of turns per unit length and i the current carried by each turn. Thus we have

$$\oint H_s \, ds = Hl = nli$$

so that

$$H = ni \tag{7.21}$$

and is constant, independent of position inside the solenoid. This result is in accord with Eq. (7.16) for the field at points on the solenoid axis, but we now see that the result holds for points other than those on the axis. The corresponding value of B is

$$B = \mu_0 ni \tag{7.22}$$

in vacuum, and here we have an example of a uniform field of magnetic induction in a limited region of space. In practice, one never has an infinitely long solenoid, but if the solenoid diameter is very small compared with its length, Eqs. (7.21) and (7.22) are excellent approximations for the field in the central portion of the solenoid. As one nears the ends, the lines start to curve, and in these regions the above equations no longer hold.

4. Magnetic Moment of a Current Loop; Scalar Magnetic Potential. Let us return to the problem of the magnetic field produced by a circular current-carrying loop. In Sec. 3 of this chapter, we have derived the expression [Eq. (7.14)] for the magnetic intensity H at any point on the axis of such a loop. It is

$$H = \frac{ir^2}{2(x^2 + r^2)^{\frac{3}{2}}}$$

with r the loop radius and x the distance from the center of the loop to the field point on its axis where H is calculated. If the radius r of the loop is very small compared to x, the above equation becomes, very nearly,

$$H = \frac{ir^2}{2x^3} = \frac{iA}{2\pi x^3} \tag{7.23}$$

where A is the area of the loop.

This expression is just like the corresponding expression for the electrostatic field on the axis of an electric dipole at distances large compared with the dimensions of the dipole. The correspondence between the magnetic intensity at large distances from a small current loop and the electric field intensity or displacement at large distances from a small dipole is also true for points not on the axis. Therefore it is very convenient to describe the magnetic field of a small current loop in terms of an equivalent *magnetic dipole*. For an electric dipole of dipole moment p, the expression for D, let us say, corresponding to Eq. (7.23) is

$$D = \frac{p}{2\pi x^3} \tag{7.23a}$$

and D has the same direction as the vector p, from the negative to the positive charge of the dipole.

We now recall the definition of the *magnetic moment* **m** of a small

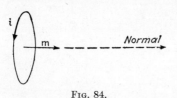

FIG. 84.

current loop as a vector of magnitude iA (product of current and loop area) directed along the normal to the plane of the loop. The sense of the vector **m** is such that a right-handed screw rotated in the direction of the current will move in the direction of **m** (Fig. 84).

In terms of the magnetic moment of the current loop, Eq. (7.23) takes the form

$$H = \frac{m}{2\pi x^3} \qquad (7.23b)$$

It must always be kept in mind that this expression for the axial magnetic field is valid *only* at points x which are far from the loop $(x \gg r)$. Furthermore, in the electrostatic case, the dipole field at large distances can be obtained by taking the gradient of the scalar potential V given by Eq. (3.22). The convenience of using a scalar potential has also been carried over to the case of a magnetic dipole, and we define the *scalar magnetic potential* of a dipole at large distances from it by (Fig. 85)

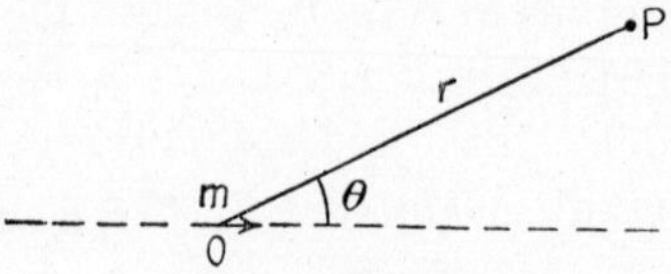

FIG. 85.

$$V_m = \frac{m \cos \theta}{4\pi r^2} \qquad (7.24)$$

and from this the magnetic intensity H can be obtained as

$$H = - \operatorname{grad} V_m \qquad (7.25)$$

It is found experimentally that the magnetic field produced by a small bar magnet is identical at large distances with that produced by a small current loop; hence one can consider such a permanent magnet as describable by a magnetic moment. This equivalence between permanent magnets and current loops is valid also for large bar magnets and solenoids, provided one restricts one's attention to the field *outside* the bar magnet or solenoid. In fact, from measurements of the external field produced by a bar magnet or by a solenoid, one cannot distinguish between them. The scalar potential is particularly convenient for describing the magnetic field of permanent magnets. We recall that the condition for the existence of a scalar potential (for magnetic fields) is that the mmf around a closed path be zero

$$\left(\oint \mathbf{H} \cdot \mathbf{ds} = 0\right)$$

We have seen that this is true for paths not enclosing a current. In the case of permanent magnets there are certainly no measurable currents at any point, and hence the scalar magnetic potential has all the convenience and utility in this case that the electrostatic potential

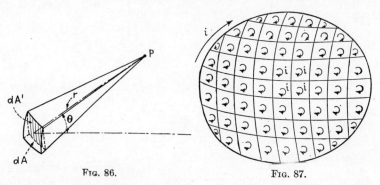

Fig. 86.   Fig. 87.

possesses for electrostatic problems. If, however, we consider a region of space in which distributed electric currents exist (such as the interior of a current-carrying conductor), the mmf around a closed path is certainly not zero, and hence *no* scalar potential exists.

Equation (7.24) for the scalar magnetic potential of an infinitesimal current loop can be put into an interesting and useful form. Writing it as

$$V_m = \frac{i \, dA \, \cos \theta}{4\pi r^2}$$

we see from Fig. 86 that the elementary area dA' normal to r is related to dA by

$$dA' = dA \, \cos \theta$$

and that the solid angle $d\Omega$ subtended at P by dA is therefore

$$d\Omega = \frac{dA'}{r^2} = \frac{dA \, \cos \theta}{r^2}$$

Hence the potential V_m can be written simply as

$$V_m = \frac{i \, d\Omega}{4\pi} \tag{7.26}$$

Having written the equation in this form, one can deduce the corresponding potential for a finite current-carrying loop of any shape whatsoever.   If we have a large loop carrying a current i, we can imagine it built up by superposing a huge number of tiny loops, each carrying the same current i, as shown in Fig. 87.   Any part of a loop not on the perimeter carries two equal and opposite currents (hence zero current), so that the large single loop is equivalent to the sum of the small ones. This construction bears the name of Ampère.   At a point P the large loop subtends a solid angle which is evidently the sum of the solid angles subtended by the tiny loops.   Hence, using Eq. (7.26), the scalar magnetic potential due to any loop of current at a point P is

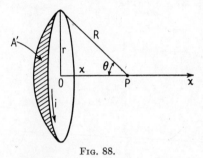

FIG. 88.

$$V_m = \frac{i\Omega}{4\pi} \qquad (7.27)$$

where i is the loop current and Ω the solid angle subtended by the loop at P.

As an illustration of the use of Eq. (7.27), we calculate the scalar magnetic potential of a circular loop of radius r at a point on the axis of the loop.   The solid angle Ω subtended at P by the circular loop is equal, by definition, to the area of the portion A' of a spherical surface of radius R divided by R^2 (Fig. 88). The area A' is readily found to be

$$A' = 2\pi R^2 (1 - \cos \theta)$$

where θ is the angle between the radius R to a point of the loop and the x-axis, as shown.   Thus

$$\Omega = \frac{A'}{R^2} = 2\pi(1 - \cos \theta) = 2\pi \left(1 - \frac{x}{R} \right) = 2\pi \left(1 - \frac{x}{\sqrt{x^2 + r^2}} \right)$$

and from Eq. (7.27)

$$V_m = \frac{i}{2} \left(1 - \frac{x}{\sqrt{x^2 + r^2}} \right) \qquad (7.28)$$

This gives the potential at points on the x-axis, and we can obtain the axial field intensity H, according to Eq. (7.25), as

$$H = -\frac{dV_m}{dx} = \frac{i}{2} \left[\frac{1}{\sqrt{x^2 + r^2}} - \frac{x^2}{(x^2 + r^2)^{\frac{3}{2}}} \right] = \frac{ir^2}{2(x^2 + r^2)^{\frac{3}{2}}}$$

and this is identical with Eq. (7.14).

We have already pointed out the equivalence of a small bar magnet, such as a small compass needle, and a small current loop with respect to the external field produced by each. This equivalence is also true with respect to the torque exerted on each by a magnetic field, as discussed in Sec. 4, Chap. 7.

There is a simple current-measuring instrument, *the tangent galvanometer*, which operates with the aid of a suspended compass needle. Suppose the needle is free to rotate about a vertical axis through its center, which is located at the center of a large vertical circular coil of wire of N turns and radius R. The plane of the coil is perpendicular to the east-west direction. When there is no current in the coil, the compass needle points north. If

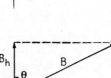

Fig. 89.

a steady current i is set up in the coil, it produces a field B_c at its center in an east-west direction (Fig. 89) of magnitude [see Eq. (7.13)]

$$B_c = \mu_0 \frac{Ni}{2R}$$

The compass needle now comes to equilibrium in the direction of the resultant of this field and the horizontal component of the earth's magnetic field, B_h. The tangent of the angle between the direction of the compass needle and north is given by (Fig. 89)

$$\tan \theta = \frac{B_c}{B_h} = \frac{\mu_0 N}{2RB_h} i$$

or

$$\tan \theta = \text{constant} \times i \qquad (7.29)$$

Thus one has a simple and relatively cheap ammeter which can be used to determine the absolute value of the current i if B_h is known.

If one were to mount a small current-carrying coil at the center of a large vertical coil so that the small coil is free to rotate about a vertical axis through its center, it would behave just like the compass needle. It is, of course, more convenient to use the small permanent magnet. If we hold the small coil so that its plane is normal to that of the large coil and send the same current i through both (series connection), we must exert a torque on the small coil equal to

$$T = \mu_0 \frac{Ni}{2R} ni\pi r^2$$

where N, R and n, r are the number of turns and radius of the large and small coils, respectively. This can be written as

$$T = \frac{\pi \mu_0 N n r^2}{2R} i^2 \qquad (7.30)$$

and this equation can be used as a basis for the definition of the ampere.

In conclusion, we should mention that the definition of magnetic moment of a current loop $(m = iA)$ which we have adopted is at variance with that adopted by a number of writers. The alternative definition, viz., $m' = \mu_0 iA$, has enjoyed considerable popularity and, when used, leads to equations differing somewhat from those we have obtained. For example, Eq. (7.24) for the scalar magnetic potential becomes

$$V_m = \frac{m' \cos \theta}{4\pi \mu_0 r^2}$$

and Eq. (6.17) for the torque on a current loop takes the form

$$\mathbf{T} = \mathbf{m'} \times \mathbf{H}$$

One cannot refute this choice of definition of magnetic moment on purely logical grounds, but in view of the fact that B and not H is the fundamental magnetic force vector, the last relation seems forced and unnatural. We return to a more critical discussion of this point in connection with the study of the magnetic behavior of ferromagnetic bodies.

Problems

1. Two long straight parallel wires carry equal and opposite currents. The wires are separated by a distance of 10 cm, and each carries a current of 20 amp.

   a. Calculate an expression for the magnetic intensity H at any point (outside the wires) in the plane of the wires.

   b. Plot to scale the magnitude of H as a function of distance along a line perpendicular to both wires, using the mid-point between the wires as an origin.

2. Solve Prob. 1 for the case that the currents in the two wires are in the same direction.

3. A long straight wire of circular cross section and radius 0.20 cm carries a steady current of 50 amp. Calculate the total flux of B inside a cylinder coaxial with the wire of radius 2.0 cm and altitude 1 m. Neglect the flux *inside* the wire.

4. Calculate the attractive force per foot of length between two long parallel wires 5.0 in. apart when each carries a current of 50 amp. Express your answer in pounds per foot.

5. Calculate the magnetic intensity due to two long parallel conductors separated by a distance $2d$ and carrying equal currents in opposite directions

at any point of a plane bisecting a line joining the two wires and perpendicular to the plane of the conductors. Where is this intensity a maximum?

6. Derive an expression for the magnetic induction at the center of a square loop of wire of side a, if the loop carries a steady current i.

7. A 6.0- by 6.0-m square current loop carries a steady current of 5.83 amp. Compute the magnetic field intensity at a point 4.0 m from the center of the square on the axis passing through this center normal to the plane of the loop.

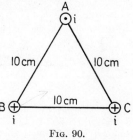

FIG. 90.

8. Three long parallel straight wires pass through the corners of an equilateral triangle of side 10 cm and are perpendicular to the plane of the triangle. Each wire carries a current of 15 amp, the current being into the page (Fig. 90) for wires B and C and out of the page for A.

Find the force per unit length acting on the wire A and on the wire B. Indicate the directions of these resultant forces on a diagram.

9. The circuit of Fig. 91 carries a steady current of 5.0 amp. Find the magnetic intensity at the center O of the semicircular portion

    a. Due to the curved wire.

    b. Due to the straight wires.

    c. Due to the entire circuit.

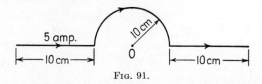

FIG. 91.

10. A long thin straight metallic strip of width b carries a steady, uniformly distributed current i along its length. Find an expression for the magnetic induction B at an external point P in the plane of the strip at a distance d from one of the strip edges.

11. In Prob. 10, find the magnitude and direction of the magnetic induction B at a point P in a plane perpendicular to the metal strip and containing the center line of the strip, the point P lying at a distance d from the strip. What limiting value does B approach as the point P approaches the plane of the metallic strip?

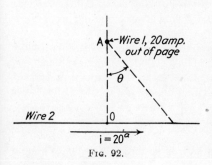

FIG. 92.

12. Two long straight wires are mutually perpendicular and carry equal currents of 20 amp, as shown in Fig. 92. Compute the torque on wire 2 about the axis OA due to the current in wire 1, using the angle θ as an integration variable.

13. The bent wire shown in Fig. 93 carries a steady current of 28 amp. Find the magnitude and direction of the magnetic intensity H at the point P of the figure.

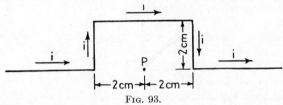

FIG. 93.

14. A solenoid of 1,000 turns is wound uniformly on a cylindrical tube 40 cm long and 8.0 cm in radius. The winding carries a steady current of 3.0 amp. Calculate the axial magnetic intensity at the center of the solenoid and in the plane at one end of the solenoid.

15. Derive a formula for the magnetic intensity at points on the axis of a solenoid of length l in terms of the distance x from the center of the solenoid. Plot the magnitude of H against x for points both inside and outside the solenoid.

16. A uniformly charged circular ring of radius R carries a total charge q and is rotated about its axis with a constant angular velocity ω. Calculate the magnetic field intensity at the center of the circle and at any point on the axis.

17. A uniformly charged disk of radius R, carrying a charge q, rotates about its axis of symmetry with a constant angular velocity ω. Using the results of Prob. 16, calculate:

a. The magnetic field intensity at the center of the disk.

b. The magnetic field intensity at any point on the axis of symmetry.

18. A sphere carries a charge q uniformly distributed over its surface and is rotated about a diameter with constant angular velocity ω. Using the results of Prob. 16, calculate the magnetic induction B at the center of the sphere.

19. Calculate and plot the magnetic induction as a function of distance from the central axis of a long cylindrical conductor of radius 2.0 cm carrying a steady current of 100 amp. What is the flux of B per meter of length *inside* the wire?

20. A long straight cylindrical wire of radius a carries a steady current i, and this current returns along a coaxial hollow cylinder of inner radius b and outer radius c. Assuming uniform current density in the conductors, find the magnetic intensity (with the help of the circuital law) as a function of distance from the axis of the system.

21. In Prob. 20 calculate the ratio of the flux of B outside the conductors to that inside both conductors.

22. A toroid of inner radius 9.0 cm and outer radius 10.0 cm is wound

uniformly with 2,000 turns of wire (Fig. 94). If a current of 4.0 amp is maintained in the winding, what is the mag-
netic induction at a point 9.2 cm from
the axis of the toroid? What is the
maximum percentage variation in the
magnitude of B between points inside
the winding?

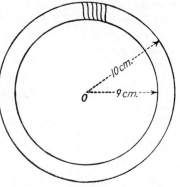

23. A brass rod of square cross section
(2 by 2 cm) is bent to form a ring of inner radius 5.0 cm, and the ends are
welded together. The ring is wound
toroidially with 500 turns of wire, and a
current of 2.0 amp is maintained in the
winding. Taking the magnetic permeability of brass to be that of empty

Fig. 94.

space, compute the total magnetic flux (of B) inside the brass. (Note that B
varies from point to point in the brass.)

$$\frac{dH}{dx} = \frac{i R^2}{2(x^2 + R^2)^{3/2}}$$

$$\frac{d^2 H}{dx^2}$$

24. Calculate an expression for the rate of change of the axial magnetic
field intensity along the axis of a circular turn of radius R, carrying a steady
current i. Show that the above expression is zero at a point on the axis at a
distance $R/2$ from the center of the turn. What is the value of H at this point?

25. The results of Prob. 24 are used in the design of *Helmholtz coils*, used to
produce a uniform magnetic field in a small region of space. Two coils, each
of N turns and radius R, are mounted coaxially at a separation equal to R.
The field due to equal currents in both coils is nearly uniform in the neighborhood of the point on the axis midway between them.

Calculate and plot the resultant axial field due to both coils as a function
of position along the common axis of the coils.

26. Two vertical turns of wire, each of radius 20 cm, are mounted coaxially
at a separation of 20 cm. Each turn carries a steady current of 10 amp, and
this device is used as a tangent galvanometer. A compass needle is mounted
at a point on the axis midway between the turns, and the common axis lies
along the east-west direction. If the horizontal component of the earth's
magnetic field is 2.0×10^{-5} weber/m², calculate the angle between the needle
and the axis of the system.

27. Show by Ampère's circuital law that the magnetic intensity on either
side of a plane sheet of current is equal to $J_s/2$, where J_s is the surface current
density and is directed parallel to the plane.

28. Two long parallel metal strips, each of width b, carry equal and opposite
steady currents i uniformly distributed over their *inner* surfaces. The separation of the strips is very small compared to their width.

a. Using the Ampère circuital law, find an expression for the magnetic field
intensity H at a point between the conductors in terms of i and b.

b. What is the value of H at points just outside either conductor?

29. A long thin strip of metal, of width b and negligible thickness, carries a steady current i uniformly distributed across its width. It is placed in an external uniform magnetic field of intensity $i/2b$ directed parallel to the strip and at right angles to the current.

 a. Show that the resultant field H is zero on one side of the strip and i/b on the other.

 b. Show that the force on the metal strip is equivalent to a pressure equal to $\mu_0 H^2/2$ acting on the side of the strip where there is the resultant field H.

 30. Coils are frequently wound in "pancake" sections, each section being a closely wound, plane spiral of wire.   Find the force between two neighboring sections if they are wound of 3.0-mm-diameter wire, if the inside diameter of the section is 9 cm, the outside diameter 18 cm, and if the wire carries a steady current of 30 amp.   Consider a section as equivalent to a current distribution on a plane, the lines of flow being circles, the surface current density being constant, and the lines of B being approximately radial just outside the plane.

 31. Find the force with which two magnetic dipoles of magnetic moments m_1 and m_2 attract or repel each other when separated by a distance r which is large compared to the size of the dipoles and when the axes of the dipoles (the magnetic moments) are collinear.

 32. Find an expression for the resultant force between two very long straight wires carrying equal currents if the wires do not lie in the same plane and form an angle θ with each other.

CHAPTER 8

INDUCED ELECTROMOTIVE FORCES AND INDUCTANCE

In the preceding chapters we have considered the magnetic fields produced by steady electric currents and the forces which these fields exert on current-carrying conductors and on moving charges. The magnetic field produced by a distribution of steady currents is a stationary or static field, the value of B, for example, being constant at a given point of space. Stationary magnetic fields exert no forces on conductors at rest if the latter carry no current, nor do they give rise to electric currents in conducting bodies at rest. If, however, a stationary conducting circuit is placed in a region of space where a magnetic field *varies with the time*, an electric current is observed in the circuit, a so-called *induced current*, and the current persists as long as there is a time variation of the magnetic field. One interprets this current as being caused by an emf induced in the circuit, and these induced emfs and currents were discovered by Faraday in 1831 and

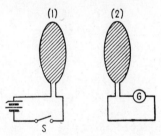

Fig. 95.

also independently by Henry. Consider two fixed conducting loops placed near together with the planes of the loops parallel to each other as shown in Fig. 95. If the switch S is closed, a momentary deflection of the galvanometer G is observed, ceasing as the current in circuit (1) attains a steady value. If the switch is then opened, the galvanometer deflects in the opposite direction. Thus we see that while the current in circuit (1) is increasing or decreasing, with a consequent increase or decrease of the magnetic field, an emf is induced in circuit (2). Faraday also discovered that if circuit (2) is moved relative to circuit (1), while the latter carries a *steady* current, an emf is also induced in circuit (2). This motion may be such that circuit (2) remains rigidly undeformed or may consist of a geometrical deformation of the circuit. The emfs induced in conductors which move relative to a stationary magnetic field are often called *motional* emfs, and these are the emfs induced in many types of rotating electrical machines. In the follow-

145

ing sections we shall formulate the laws governing these induced voltages and examine some of their consequences.

1. The Faraday Induction Law for Stationary Circuits; Lenz's Law.
We start our discussion with the emf induced in a stationary circuit, which we take for simplicity as a single loop of metallic wire. If the magnetic field in the region of space occupied by the loop is changed in any manner, *e.g.*, by changing the current in neighboring circuits or by moving the latter when they carry steady currents or by moving a permanent magnet near the loop, *the induced emf is found to be equal to the time rate of change of the magnetic flux which crosses any area of which the loop is a boundary.* The magnetic flux crossing such a surface is said to *link* the circuit.

Denoting the induced emf by $E = \oint \mathcal{E}_s \, ds$ and the flux linking the circuit by $\Phi = \int B_n \, dS$, the Faraday induction law is written as

$$E = -\frac{d\Phi}{dt} \tag{8.1}$$

The negative algebraic sign occurring in Eq. (8.1) is to indicate the direction of the induced emf and hence that of the induced current. The convention for the sign of the emf $E = \oint \mathcal{E}_s \, ds$ around a closed path is the following: We construct a vector normal to a surface bounded by the closed path. Then the emf is positive for that direction of traversal of the closed path such that a right-handed screw moves along the direction of this normal. The induced current is always established, according to Eq. (8.1), in such a direction that its magnetic field tends to *oppose the change* in the magnetic field which produces it. Thus, if we try to increase the magnetic flux through the loop ($d\Phi/dt$ positive), the induced current is in such a direction that its field tends to decrease the flux and opposes the *change*. Hence the minus sign indicates that the induced voltage establishes a current tending to decrease the magnetic flux in this example.

This law concerning the direction of induced emfs is perfectly general, holding equally well for induced emfs in moving circuits, and bears the name of *Lenz's law*. It follows directly from the law of conservation of energy, since otherwise an induced emf once started would increase indefinitely and be self-sustaining. If, instead of a single conducting loop, one considers a coil of N turns in series, Eq. (8.1) becomes

$$E = -\sum_{k=1}^{N} \frac{d\Phi_k}{dt} \tag{8.2}$$

where Φ_k is the magnetic flux linking the kth turn. An important special case occurs when all the Φ_k's are equal (or very nearly so), the same flux linking each turn of the coil. Equation (8.2) then becomes

$$E = -N \frac{d\Phi}{dt} = -\frac{d}{dt}(N\Phi) \qquad (8.3)$$

and the product $N\Phi$ is called the number of flux linkages. In our mks system of units, Φ is expressed in webers, t in seconds, and E in volts.

The Faraday induction law holds equally well for extended conducting bodies at rest. In this case it is more convenient to write Eq. (8.1) in the equivalent form

$$\oint \mathcal{E}_s \, ds = -\frac{\partial}{\partial t} \int B_n \, dS = -\int \frac{\partial B_n}{\partial t} \, dS \qquad (8.4)$$

Here the emf is taken around *any* closed path in the conducting medium, and the integral $\int B_n \, dS$ is the flux linking this path. The spatially distributed currents which are set up under such conditions are called *eddy* currents. There is a further generalization of the induction law which we shall require later. *We postulate that an electric field is established in any region of space where a magnetic field changes with time, and that Eq. (8.4) is valid whether the closed path is in a conducting or nonconducting material medium or in empty space.*[1] In this connection it must be emphasized that the electric field so generated is of a nature quite different from that produced by stationary electric charges. In fact, Eq. (8.4) shows clearly that $\int \mathcal{E}_s \, ds$ is not zero, and hence that no scalar potential for $\mathcal{E}$ exists. One can no longer obtain the electric field intensity $\mathcal{E}$ as the negative gradient of a scalar potential when discussing the electric field generated by changing magnetic fields. This is, of course, in sharp contrast to the electrostatic case.

2. Motional Electromotive Forces. We now turn our attention to the case of induced emfs caused by the motion of conductors relative to a magnetic field. An exact analysis of this situation requires the theory of relativity and lies beyond the scope of this book; hence we must content ourselves with an approximate method which gives excellent results provided the velocities encountered are small compared with $c = 1/\sqrt{\epsilon_0\mu_0} = 3 \times 10^8$ m/sec. For most practical problems this condition is extraordinarily well satisfied. We shall approach the question from the law giving the force exerted by a magnetic field

---

[1] One of the striking modern examples of the existence of this field is the electron accelerator known as the betatron, which operates on this induction principle.

on a moving charge, the so-called *Lorentz* force.   This force is

$$F = q(v \times B)$$

where v is the vector velocity of the charge q.   If we now imagine a metallic circuit moving in a stationary magnetic field, the conduction electrons in it will be acted on by a force per unit charge equal to $v \times B$ and, being free to move, will set up an induced current.   Treating this force per unit charge as an equivalent electric field intensity $\mathcal{E}'$ from the standpoint of an observer moving with the circuit, we should expect the magnitude of the induced emf around the circuit to be given by the formula

$$E = \oint \mathcal{E}'_s \, ds = \oint (v \times B)_s \, ds \qquad (8.5)$$

Equation (8.5) is the correct formula for low velocities, and the induced emf as given by this equation sets up a current which, in accordance with Lenz's law, tends to oppose the motion producing it. There will be a force exerted on the moving conductors tending to slow them down, and this force action is usually termed *electromagnetic reaction*.   In many applications of Eq. (8.5) it is convenient to visualize an emf induced in each element of length ds of the circuit

$$dE = \mathcal{E}'_s \, ds = (v \times B)_s \, ds \qquad (8.6)$$

and the emf along any path becomes the sum of these infinitesimal emfs.   Viewed in this manner, one can state

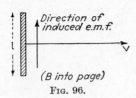

Direction of induced e.m.f.

l

v

(B into page)

Fig. 96.

that *the emf induced in a conductor is equal to the rate at which this conductor cuts lines of B*.   This can be seen readily with the help of a simple example.   Consider a metal bar moved at constant velocity in a direction perpendicular to its length in a uniform field of magnetic induction directed normal to the plane of the conductor length and the velocity vector, as shown in Fig. 96.   In time dt, the conductor sweeps out an area equal to $lv \, dt$ and cuts all the lines of B which cross this area.   Thus the number of lines cut is

$$d\Phi = Blv \, dt$$

so that the induced emf has a magnitude given by

$$E = \frac{d\Phi}{dt} = Blv \qquad (8.7)$$

This is just the result obtained by using Eq. (8.6), if we remember that v is normal to B and that $v \times B$ is directed along the length of the conductor.   Furthermore, both **v** and **B** have the same magnitudes and directions at all points of the metal bar.   Other cases will be taken up in the problems.

If we apply Eq. (8.5) to a moving closed circuit or to a closed path in an extended conductor in motion, we can, under certain conditions, find a simple relation between the rate of change of magnetic flux through the moving circuit and the induced emf as given by this equation.   *If the circuit moves as a rigid body*, undeformed during its motion, *the induced emf as given by Eq. (8.5) is just equal to the rate of change of flux through the circuit.*   This is true if the magnetic field is stationary.   If the magnetic field varies with time, one obtains the induced emf by computing the total time rate of change of flux linking the circuit.   This now consists of the sum of two terms, one the rate of flux change due to the time-varying field and the other the rate of flux change due to the motion of the circuit in the magnetic field.

We shall not attempt a general proof of the above statement but shall content ourselves with a simple, but important, example.   Consider a rigid rectangular coil of width d and length l which is rotated with constant angular velocity ω about an axis perpendicular to a

uniform field of magnetic induction B, as shown in Fig. 97.   The angle θ between the direction of B and that of the normal n to the plane of the loop varies uniformly with the time, so that $\theta = \omega t$.   Let us first evaluate the induced emf in the coil with the help of Eq. (8.5).   We note that the vector $\mathbf{v} \times \mathbf{B}$ is directed parallel to the rotation axis for all the length elements ds comprising the circuit, and hence the induced emf may be considered as generated in the sides l only.

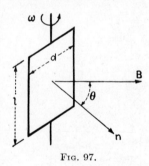

Fig. 97.

This is in accord with the idea of cutting lines of B, and the two emfs thus induced add as one moves around the loop.   For each side l we have

$$|\mathbf{v} \times \mathbf{B}| = vB \sin \theta$$

and the vector is directed along l; hence

$$E = \oint (\mathbf{v} \times \mathbf{B})_s \, ds = 2vlB \sin \theta = 2vlB \sin \omega t$$

The speed v of any point of either side l is related to the angular velocity ω by $v = \omega d/2$, so that the induced emf is

$$E = \omega Bld \sin \omega t = \omega BA \sin \omega t \tag{8.8}$$

Now let us calculate this emf by evaluating the rate of change of flux through the coil. When in the position shown in Fig. 97, the magnetic flux Φ linking the circuit is

$$\Phi = \int B_n \, dS = BA \cos \theta = BA \cos \omega t$$

and differentiating with respect to the time, we find

$$E = \omega BA \sin \omega t$$

which is identical with Eq. (8.8). Writing Φ_m for the maximum flux linking the coil, and assuming the coil to consist of N turns in series, we have an induced voltage equal to

$$E = N\omega\Phi_m \sin \omega t \qquad (8.9)$$

where $\Phi_m = BA$. Equation (8.9) is the fundamental formula underlying the action of both a-c and d-c generators. If the coil terminals are brought out to slip rings on the rotation axis, we have the case of an a-c generator for which the induced emf varies sinusoidally with the time. In the case of d-c generators, a commutator, which reverses the direction of current in opposite sides l (relative to a fixed external circuit) every half cycle, takes the place of the slip rings.

The situation for induced emfs in circuits which are deformed and do not move as rigid bodies is more complicated, and in general it is safest to employ Eq. (8.5). Only in special cases is it true that the induced emf is equal to the rate of change of flux through the circuit. One such special case is shown in Fig. 98, in which a metal rod ab, of

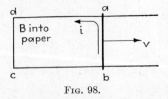

FIG. 98.

length l, is moved with constant velocity v and slides along conducting rails ad and bc. The induced voltage around the circuit $adcb$ is $E = Blv$, and this is equal to the magnitude of the time rate of change of flux through the circuit $adcb$. Since B is assumed uniform, the rate of increase of flux equals the flux density B times the rate of increase of area. The latter is lv. The steady induced current, which has the direction shown in Fig. 98, has a magnitude

$$i = \frac{E}{R} = \frac{Blv}{R} \qquad (8.10)$$

where R is the resistance of the rod, assuming the conducting rails to be of negligible resistance. Since the conducting rod ab carries this current, there is a side thrust on it equal to $F = Bli = B^2 l^2 v / R$, which is directed opposite to the direction of v. This is the electromagnetic reaction, and one must exert a force on the conductor equal to and opposite to this reaction to maintain the constant velocity v. The power required is

$$P = Fv = \frac{B^2 l^2 v^2}{R} = \frac{E^2}{R} = i^2 R \tag{8.11}$$

and we see that the law of conservation of energy is satisfied, the mechanical work done per unit time by external forces being just equal to the rate of heating in the circuit. When one moves an extended metallic conducting body in a magnetic field, there is an electromagnetic reaction similar to that just discussed, and the conductor moves as if in a viscous medium, the force being proportional to and directed opposite to the velocity of the body. This is the principle of the eddy-current brake.

In all the applications with which we shall be concerned, we shall deal with either stationary circuits in varying magnetic fields or moving circuits which are *not* deformed during the motion. In both these cases we may use the Faraday induction law as expressed in Eq. (8.1) to compute induced emfs.

3. Self- and Mutual Inductance. In the preceding sections we have been concerned primarily with the formulation of the Faraday induction law for stationary and moving circuits. This has been done in terms of induced emfs generated by magnetic fields which are produced by currents or magnets *external* to the system under consideration. If one now inquires into the currents which are set up as a consequence of these induced voltages (induced currents in circuits or eddy currents in extended conducting bodies), one must investigate the magnetic fields produced by these currents and the so-called *self-induced* emfs which they generate. The total emf induced is to be calculated from the resultant of the external field and the magnetic field produced by the induced currents themselves in accordance with Faraday's law. Thus one must solve simultaneously for the induced currents and the resultant magnetic field which gives rise to them. In the case of circuits consisting of linear conductors, the problem is considerably simplified because the current directions are prescribed by the geometry of the circuit. For extended conducting bodies, however, one is confronted by a calculation of considerable complexity to determine both the directions and magnitudes of the eddy currents and simultaneously the magnetic fields and induced voltages produced by them. In the case of fixed, rigid circuits—and we shall restrict our attention to this case—one can attack the problem with the help of an approxi-

mate method which is extremely useful and of a high degree of validity
for magnetic fields which vary slowly with time.   A more exact mean-

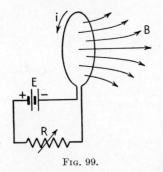

FIG. 99.

ing of the expression "slowly varying" must
be delayed to a later point in our study.

First we examine the induced voltages
generated in circuits by the currents which
they carry, these currents varying with
time.   To start with, consider a simple
circuit as shown in Fig. 99, carrying a
steady current i.   The magnetic field set up
by this current is a static field, and some
of the lines of B are indicated in the figure.   There is a definite magnetic flux linking the coil, and the number of flux linkages is given by

$$N\Phi = N \int B_n \, dS$$

where N is the number of turns of the coil and the integral extends
over an area bounded by the loop.   The exact evaluation of this
integral is exceedingly difficult in all but a few simple geometrical
shapes of the circuit; but no matter what the geometry, the results of
Chap. 7 require that Φ be proportional to the steady current i carried
by the circuit (H and hence B at any point of space are proportional
to i).   If we denote the proportionality factor by L, we can write
for the flux linkages

$$N\Phi = Li \tag{8.12}$$

where L, called the *self-inductance* of the circuit, depends only on the
geometry of the circuit and not on the current, at least in empty space.

If we now vary the current in the circuit by changing the variable
resistance, and if we *assume that while the current is changing, $N\Phi$ is
proportional to the instantaneous value of the current*, an induced emf
will be generated in the circuit according to Eq. (8.1), and its magnitude is

$$E = N \frac{d\Phi}{dt} = L \frac{di}{dt} \tag{8.13}$$

The direction of this emf is such as to oppose the change in current,
by Lenz's law.   This emf is often called a *back* emf.   Our assumption
concerning the validity of the proportionality $\Phi \sim i$ (this is the approximation referred to in the opening paragraph of this section) turns out
to be very accurately true for slow rates of change of i with time, and
for the present we shall accept it as true for all the cases we shall

examine.   A more exact criterion for its validity will appear in Chap. 10.

According to Eq. (8.12) the self-inductance L of a circuit equals the number of flux linkages set up in the circuit per unit current in it. *In the mks system, the unit inductance is called one henry, and this is one weber per ampere, or, as is evident from Eq. (8.13), one volt-second per ampere.*

In general, whenever one causes the current in a circuit to change (by the application of external emfs), there will be induced in it a back emf given by Eq. (8.13), which tends to prevent the change.   Thus, when one closes a switch in a circuit fed by a d-c seat of emf, the current will attain its final steady-state value only after some time has elapsed.   While the current is increasing, the total emf around the circuit is $E - L(di/dt)$, where E is the external emf.   Similarly, a steady current cannot be reduced instantaneously to zero.

We shall now calculate the inductance of two simple but important circuits.   First, consider a solenoid of length l (large compared to its radius r), n turns per unit length, N total turns carrying a steady current i.   From Eqs. (7.21) and (7.22) we have for H and B at all points inside the solenoid

$$H = ni$$

and

$$B = \mu_0 ni$$

These formulas are, strictly speaking, valid only for an infinitely long solenoid but are good approximations when l is large compared to the radius.   This is equivalent to neglecting end effects in a manner similar to the treatment of a parallel-plate condenser in electrostatics.   The total flux Φ inside the solenoid is accordingly

$$\Phi = BA = \pi r^2 B$$

and the total number of flux linkages is

$$N\Phi = N\pi r^2 B = \pi r^2 N \left(\frac{\mu_0 Ni}{l} \right)$$

where we have written

$$N = nl$$

Thus we obtain from Eq. (8.12) a formula for the inductance of a long solenoid in air:

$$L = \frac{N\Phi}{i} = \frac{\mu_0 N^2 \pi r^2}{l} \tag{8.14}$$

or, written in terms of the number of turns per unit length,

$$L = \mu_0 n^2 \pi r^2 l \tag{8.14a}$$

As a second example, consider a long coaxial cable consisting of a central cylindrical conductor of radius a and an outer thin hollow cylinder of radius b, shown in cross section containing the axis in Fig. 100. We shall assume that $(b - a) \gg a$, so that we can neglect the magnetic flux inside the conductors. Since the magnetic induction B

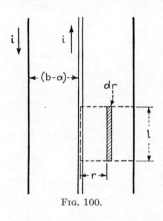

FIG. 100.

has the value $B = \mu_0 i / 2\pi r$ at points in space between the two conductors, the total flux linking a length l of the circuit can be obtained by a simple integration. Consider an element of area $l\,dr$ as shown in the figure. Since B is normal to this area, the flux across it is evidently

$$d\Phi = Bl\,dr = \frac{\mu_0 li}{2\pi r}\,dr$$

and the total flux linking the length l is

$$\Phi = \frac{\mu_0 il}{2\pi} \int_a^b \frac{dr}{r} = \frac{\mu_0 li}{2\pi} \ln \left(\frac{b}{a}\right) \quad (8.15)$$

This gives for the *inductance per unit length* of the cable the value

$$L' = \frac{L}{l} = \frac{\Phi}{il} = \frac{\mu_0}{2\pi} \ln \left(\frac{b}{a}\right) \quad (8.16)$$

From this we see immediately that μ_0 is expressed in henrys per meter.

Mutual Inductance. Now let us consider the case of two circuits such as those shown in Fig. 101. If the current in circuit I is changed, a voltage is induced in circuit II, and conversely a changing current in circuit II induces a voltage in circuit I. First suppose there is a steady current i_1 in circuit I. This sets up a stationary magnetic field, as indicated in the figure, and a fraction of the flux produced by i_1 links circuit

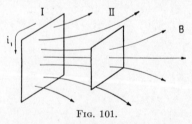

FIG. 101.

II. Let the flux linking circuit II due to i_1 be denoted by Φ_{21}, the first subscript indicating the circuit linked and the second the circuit or current giving rise to the magnetic flux. Φ_{21} is proportional to i_1, to N_1, the number of turns in circuit I, and the proportionality constant depends only on the geometry of the system, *i.e.*, on the relative positions, shapes, and dimensions of both circuits. In symbols, we have

$$\Phi_{21} = KN_1 i_1 \quad (8.17)$$

Now consider a steady current i_2 in circuit II, and let us call the flux linking circuit I due to this current Φ_{12}. This flux is proportional to the number of turns N_2 of circuit II and to i_2. The proportionality constant depends only on the dimensions and shapes of the two circuits and on their relative positions, and it can be shown that it is the same as K in Eq. (8.17). Thus we can write

$$\Phi_{12} = KN_2 i_2 \tag{8.18}$$

We now define the *coefficient of mutual inductance M* of the system as the number of flux linkages of either circuit per unit current in the other. Hence

$$M = \frac{N_2\Phi_{21}}{i_1} = \frac{N_1\Phi_{12}}{i_2} = KN_1N_2 \tag{8.19}$$

Now suppose the current i_1 in circuit I changes with time. There will be an emf E_2 induced in circuit II given by

$$E_2 = -N_2\frac{d\Phi_{21}}{dt} = -M\frac{di_1}{dt} \tag{8.20}$$

and if the current i_2 in circuit II varies with time, an emf is induced in circuit I given by

$$E_1 = -N_1\frac{d\Phi_{12}}{dt} = -M\frac{di_2}{dt} \tag{8.21}$$

In addition to these induced emfs, there will be also the self-induced emfs in each circuit. Thus in circuit I, the total emf induced around the circuit is

$$-M\frac{di_2}{dt} - L_1\frac{di_1}{dt}$$

with L_1 the self-inductance of circuit I; and similarly for circuit II the total induced emf is equal to

$$-M\frac{di_1}{dt} - L_2\frac{di_2}{dt}$$

In both these expressions, the first term is the induced emf due to an external magnetic field and the second that due to the magnetic field produced by the current in the circuit under consideration. Thus, for simple circuits such as those treated here, the problem is reduced to that of computing self- and mutual inductances, or to their experimental determination.

Any two circuits so arranged that an appreciable fraction of the flux due to one links the other are said to be *coupled*, and any change in the current in one induces a voltage in the other as well as in itself. The maximum mutual inductance occurs when all the flux produced by either circuit links the other. Let us now calculate the mutual inductance of two long coaxial solenoids. Suppose the length of each is l, the numbers of turns N_1 and N_2, and the radii r_1 and r_2, respectively. For the sake of definiteness, let us take $r_1 > r_2$. The induction B produced by a current i_1 in the outer solenoid is

$$B = \frac{\mu_0 N_1 i_1}{l}$$

and the flux linking the inner solenoid is

$$\Phi_{21} = B\pi r_2^2 = \frac{\mu_0 N_1 i_1}{l} \pi r_2^2$$

The mutual inductance is then, according to Eq. (8.19),

$$M = \frac{\mu_0 N_1 N_2}{l} \pi r_2^2 \tag{8.22}$$

The same result is obtained by considering a current in the inner solenoid and calculating the flux linkages with the outer solenoid. This is left as an exercise for the reader. With the help of Eq. (8.14), we have for the self-inductances of the two solenoids

$$L_1 = \frac{\mu_0 N_1^2}{l} \pi r_1^2 \tag{8.23}$$

and

$$L_2 = \frac{\mu_0 N_2^2}{l} \pi r_2^2 \tag{8.24}$$

Comparing Eqs. (8.22), (8.23), and (8.24), one finds readily that

$$M = \frac{r_2}{r_1}\sqrt{L_1 L_2} \qquad r_1 > r_2 \tag{8.25}$$

This is a special case of the general relation between the mutual inductance and the self-inductances for coupled circuits. In general, one has

$$M = k \sqrt{L_1 L_2} \qquad k \le 1 \tag{8.26}$$

where k is called the coefficient of coupling and is less than or at most equal to unity. If $k = 1$, $M = \sqrt{L_1 L_2}$, and this is the maximum mutual inductance possible. In our case of the two long solenoids we see that this happens for $r_1 = r_2$, in which case all the flux produced by one evidently links the other.

4. Energy Stored in the Magnetic Field of an Inductance; Energy Density. In setting up a steady distribution of electric currents, a definite amount of work must be done by the external sources of emf against the self-induced voltages which exist while the currents are being built up. We think of this work as being stored in the magnetic field, and it can be regained by allowing the currents to vanish. To investigate these relations quantitatively, consider a simple series circuit formed by connecting a coil

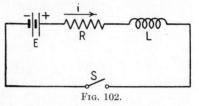

Fig. 102.

of inductance L and a resistance to a battery as shown in Fig. 102. When the switch S is closed, a current i starts to build up in the circuit, with a consequent increase of the magnetic field produced by this current. At any instant of time the Faraday induction law applied to the circuit gives

$$\oint \mathcal{E}_s \, ds = -N \frac{d\Phi}{dt} = -L \frac{di}{dt} = emf.$$

where L, strictly speaking, refers to the self-inductance of the whole circuit. We shall, however, assume that the flux linkages other than those of the coil are negligible compared to the latter, so that L is to be taken as the coil inductance. If we assume now that Ohm's law is valid for time-varying currents, the left-hand side of the above equation has the value

$$\oint \mathcal{E}_s \, ds = -E + iR$$

just as for steady currents, with E the emf of the battery. Thus we have

$$E = iR + L \frac{di}{dt} \tag{8.27}$$

as the differential equation for the current in this series circuit. The work done by the battery per unit time, *i.e.*, the power input to the system consisting of the resistance and inductance, is Ei. Using Eq. (8.27), there follows

$$Ei = i^2 R + Li \frac{di}{dt} = i^2 R + \frac{d}{dt} \left(\tfrac{1}{2} L i^2 \right) \tag{8.28}$$

The first term on the right-hand side is the rate of heating in the resistance, and we interpret the second term as the rate of increase of magnetic energy. The total energy stored in the magnetic field produced by the inductance L after a time interval t, when the current has attained a value I, is accordingly

$$U_m = \int_0^t \frac{d}{dt}\left(\frac{1}{2}Li^2\right) dt = \int_0^I d\left(\frac{1}{2}Li^2\right) = \frac{1}{2}LI^2 \qquad (8.29)$$

Just as in the case of electrostatic energy, and for similar reasons, we can think of this energy as distributed throughout the region of space where the magnetic field is present and introduce the concept of *magnetic energy density*, the magnetic energy stored per unit volume of space. We can obtain a formula for this energy density by considering the magnetic field of an infinitely long solenoid carrying a steady current i. Consider a section of the solenoid of length l. Its inductance is, according to Eq. (8.14a),

$$L = \mu_0 n^2 A l$$

where n is the number of turns per unit length and A the cross section. The current is related to the magnetic induction B inside the solenoid by

$$B = \mu_0 n i$$

so that

$$i^2 = \frac{B^2}{\mu_0^2 n^2}$$

Hence the magnetic energy $\frac{1}{2}Li^2$ is

$$U_m = \frac{1}{2}\mu_0 n^2 A l \frac{B^2}{\mu_0^2 n^2} = \frac{B^2}{2\mu_0}(Al)$$

Now Al is just the volume of that region of space enclosed by a length l of the solenoid, so that the energy per unit volume of the space where the magnetic field is present is

$$u_m = \frac{B^2}{2\mu_0} = \frac{1}{2}\mu_0 H^2 \qquad (8.30)$$

This formula, although derived here for a simple special case, turns out to be correct in general and is valid even when B varies from point to point of space. From the derivation it is evident that the magnetic energy as calculated represents the work done against induced emfs in establishing the field with the help of electric currents. The total magnetic energy can be calculated from

$$U_m = \int \frac{B^2}{2\mu_0}\,dv = \int \frac{1}{2}\mu_0 H^2\,dv \qquad (8.31)$$

if the spatial dependence of B or H is known, the integration extending over all space.

Problems

1. The magnetic flux linking a fixed coil of 1,000 turns is varied so that its value at any time t is given by

$$\Phi = \Phi_m \sin (120\pi t)$$

where $\Phi_m = 3.0 \times 10^{-5}$ weber and t is in seconds. Derive an expression for the induced emf E in the coil. What is the maximum value of this emf? On the same graph, plot Φ and E as functions of the time.

2. A long straight wire carries a current i varying with time as

$$i = I_0 \sin \omega t$$

$\frac{10^f}{2300}$

A fixed rectangular loop 100 cm long and 9.0 cm wide has its long sides parallel to the straight wire, and these sides lie at distances of 1.0 and 10 cm from the straight wire. If the angular frequency ω is 500 radians/sec, what must be the value of I_0 if a maximum emf of 1 mv is induced in the rectangular loop?

3. A tightly wound circular coil of 1 cm radius and of 100 turns is placed with its axis parallel to the direction of a homogeneous magnetic field. The coil is rotated about a diameter through 180° in 0.1 sec, and the average emf induced in the coil is observed to be 0.001 volt. What is the magnitude of the magnetic induction B?

4. A long solenoid, 20 cm in diameter, is wound with 2,000 turns per meter, and the winding carries a current given by

$$i = 10 \sin 120\pi t$$

with i in amperes and t in seconds. A square coil of 100 turns, 5.0 cm on an edge, is placed inside the solenoid with its plane perpendicular to the solenoid axis and its center on this axis. Find the emf induced in this square coil as a function of the time. What is its maximum value?

5. A long straight wire carries a steady current of 40 amp. A slender metal rod 9.0 cm long is moved with a constant velocity of 2.0 m/sec parallel to the wire, the length of the rod being perpendicular to the wire and the center of the rod lying at a distance of 5.5 cm from the wire. Calculate the emf induced in this rod. What is the direction of this induced emf if the velocity vector is parallel to the direction of the current in the wire?

6. A slender metallic rod of length $2l$ rotates about an axis through its center with an angular velocity of n rps. If the rod is placed in a uniform magnetic field B directed parallel to the axis of rotation, show that the magnitude of the emf induced between the axis and either end of the rod is given by

$$E = \pi l^2 B n$$

7. A copper disk of 10.0 cm radius is rotated about its axis of symmetry with an angular velocity of 3,600 rpm. The disk is in a uniform field of magni-

tude 2.0×10^{-2} weber/m² whose direction makes an angle of 30° with the plane of the disk.

1.88×10^{-2} volt

a. Calculate the induced voltage between the axis and rim of the disk.

b. Draw a diagram indicating the directions of magnetic field, rotation, and induced emf.

8. A copper disk 10.0 cm in radius is placed inside a long solenoid of radius 11.0 cm with its axis coincident with that of the solenoid.   The solenoid is 1 m long, has 1,000 turns, and carries a steady current of 8.0 amp.   The copper disk is rotated about its axis with a constant angular velocity of 1,200 rpm. Calculate the emf induced between slip rings connected to the rim and to the axis.

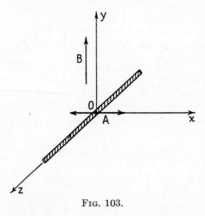

Fig. 103.

9. A long straight conducting wire of conductivity σ parallel to the z-axis and in a uniform magnetic field B directed along the y-axis performs simple harmonic translational motion of amplitude A and frequency f parallel to the x-axis, as shown in Fig. 103.

a. Find the electric field intensity induced in the wire as a function of time.

b. Derive an expression for the average rate of heating per unit volume in the wire.

✓ **10.** A square wire of length 15 cm, mass 10 g, and resistance of 0.20 ohm slides without friction down two parallel conducting rails inclined at an angle of 30° with the horizontal, as shown in Fig. 104.   The rails are of negligible resistance and are short-circuited at the bottom.

Find the steady-state velocity v of the wire in a uniform magnetic field of 0.50 weber/m² directed vertically downward.

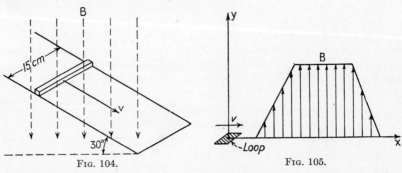

Fig. 104.   Fig. 105.

11. With the help of a magnet, a field of magnetic induction is established with the lines of B parallel to the y-axis, and the variation of the magnitude of

B with x is shown in Fig. 105. The rectangular conducting loop shown in the figure has its plane perpendicular to the y-axis and is moved in translation with a constant velocity v parallel to the x-axis.

Plot the emf induced in this loop as a function of its position along the x-axis. How does the size of the loop affect your plot?

12. The flux linking a 100-turn coil connected to a ballistic galvanometer is changed suddenly, and the maximum angular deflection of the galvanometer is 0.01 radian. The sensitivity of the galvanometer is 10 radians/coulomb, and the resistance of the circuit is 10 ohms. Find the change in magnetic flux through the coil.

13. A large circular coil of N turns and radius b carries a steady current i and is rotated at constant angular velocity about a horizontal diameter. At the center of this coil is a small fixed horizontal circular turn of radius a. Calculate the emf induced in the small loop as a function of the time. What is the angle between the planes of the coils when this emf is a maximum?

14. Given N turns of wire connected in series. Under what conditions would you expect the inductance of such a coil to be proportional to the number of turns? How should the turns be arranged to obtain the maximum inductance?

15. A solenoid 3.0 cm in radius and 90 cm long is wound closely and uniformly with 20 turns per centimeter of length. What is its self-inductance?

16. A closely wound circular coil of 60 turns is wound around the central portion of the solenoid of Prob. 15. Assuming that all the flux produced by the solenoid links this coil, calculate the mutual inductance of the system. Would this be altered if the 60-turn coil is short-circuited by connecting its ends together?

17. In Prob. 16, suppose the solenoid carries a current given by

$$i = 2.0 \sin 2\pi f t$$

where $f = 60$ cycles/sec, i is in amperes, and t in seconds. Compute the emf induced in the 60-turn coil as a function of time when this coil is on open circuit.

18. Given two concentric coplanar coils A and B of N_1 and N_2 turns, respectively. Let r_1 be the radius of coil A and r_2 that of coil B, and suppose $r_1 \gg r_2$, so that one may assume the magnetic field produced by coil A to be uniform over the area of coil B. Find an expression for the mutual inductance of the system.

19. Solve Prob. 18 for the case where the two coils are coaxial, their planes separated by a distance R, which is much larger than r_1.

20. A transmission line consists of two long straight parallel wires, each of radius a, separated by a distance $d \gg a$, and the wires carry equal currents in opposite directions. Neglecting the magnetic flux *inside* the conducting wires, derive an expression for the self-inductance per unit length of this part of the circuit.

21. Two telephone circuits A and B each consist of a pair of parallel conductors 10 km long.   The four conductors lie in the same plane, are mutually parallel, and are equally spaced, as shown in Fig. 106.   Compute the mutual inductance of these two circuits, neglecting the small end effects.

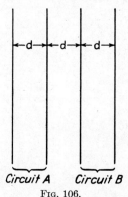

22. A toroidal coil of N turns has a square cross section, each side of the square being of length a, and is of inner radius b.

a. Find an expression for its self-inductance in terms of N, a, and b.

b. Express in similar terms the mutual inductance of the system formed by the coil and a long, straight wire along the axis of symmetry of the toroidal coil. Assume the conductors closing the circuit of which the long straight wire is a part are situated far from the coil, so that their influence may be neglected.

Circuit A   Circuit B

Fig. 106.

c. Find the ratio of the self-inductance of the coil to the mutual inductance of the system.

23. A coil carrying a steady current i is moved from a position where there is no external magnetic field to a position where an external flux Φ links the coil.   During this process the current is maintained constant by the use of suitable seats of emf.   Show that the work done by these seats of emf against induced emf is given by $i\Phi$.

24. Starting from the expression for the energy density in a magnetic field, compute the magnetic energy stored per unit length *inside* a long circular metallic wire of radius a when it carries a steady current i.   From this find an expression for the contribution to the inductance of a circuit (per unit length) of the flux inside the conductor.

25. Proceeding according to the scheme of Prob. 24, derive an exact formula for the inductance per unit length of a coaxial cable, with radius of the inner conductor a, inner and outer radii of the outer conductor equal to b and c, respectively.   Compare your result with that given by Eq. (8.16), and state the conditions under which Eq. (8.16) is a good approximation.

26. Prove that, if two coils are connected in series, the inductance of the system is given by $L_1 + L_2 \pm 2M$, where L_1 and L_2 are the self-inductances of the two coils and M is the mutual inductance of the system.   Under what conditions is the plus sign valid?

27. A rectangular coil of width a and length l having N turns is placed between two very long parallel conductors of separation $3a$ forming part of a circuit.   The coil is centered between the conductors, the long sides l being parallel to the conductors and the plane of the coil lying in the plane of the parallel conductors.

Derive an expression for the mutual inductance of the system.

28. Solve Prob. 27 if the parallel conductors are of separation $4a$ and the coil, instead of being centered between the conductors, has one of the long sides l halfway between the conductors.

29. Two fixed coils of self-inductances L_1 and L_2 and mutual inductance M carry steady currents i_1 and i_2, respectively. Show that the energy stored in the magnetic field is given by

$$U_m = \tfrac{1}{2} L_1 i_1^2 + \tfrac{1}{2} L_2 i_2^2 \pm M i_1 i_2$$

the sign of the last term depending on the relative directions of the two currents.

Using the fact that this expression must be independent of the manner and order in which the two currents i_1 and i_2 are established, prove that the proportionality constants K in Eqs. (8.17) and (8.18) are equal.

CHAPTER 9

ELEMENTARY ALTERNATING-CURRENT CIRCUITS

In this chapter we shall investigate the behavior of simple circuits in which there are time-varying emfs and currents, and in particular we shall consider the case of sinusoidal time variations. We have seen in the last chapter that one can generate a sinusoidally varying emf in a coil by rotating it with constant angular velocity in a uniform magnetic field, and we shall study the steady-state behavior of simple circuits connected to the terminals of such an a-c generator. We shall assume that the generators employed are sufficiently large so that their terminal voltage may be taken as independent of the current drawn from them.

The theory of a-c circuits is based on the application of the Faraday induction law, which provides the extension of the Kirchhoff rules employed in the case of steady currents. In the latter case the statement that the sum of the voltage drops around a closed circuit equals zero is equivalent to the fundamental law of electrostatics,

$$\oint \mathcal{E}_s \, ds = 0$$

and the evaluation of this integral in terms of iR drops and impressed emfs leads to the d-c circuit equations. For the case of currents varying with time, this equation takes the more general form given by Faraday's law, *viz.*,

$$\oint \mathcal{E}_s \, ds = -\frac{d}{dt}(N\Phi) = -L\frac{di}{dt}$$

where the evaluation of the integral leads to the sum of the *instantaneous* voltage drops around the circuit. Thus we shall be led to circuit equations which are entirely similar to those for steady currents, differing essentially in the presence of the $L(di/dt)$ term. There are two common methods of dealing with this term: (1) One puts it on the left-hand side of the equation and treats it as additional voltage drop in the circuit. In so doing, one retains the original form of the Kirchhoff rule for the a-c case. (2) One can interpret this term as a "back" emf which is to be subtracted from the impressed emfs to obtain the net emf acting around the circuit.   Both procedures lead, of course, to identical equations.

The basic assumption which is made in applying the above reasoning to actual circuits is *that the current variations are sufficiently slow that, at a given instant of time, the electric and magnetic fields are essentially the same as would be produced by the corresponding steady-state currents and charges.*   Thus, for example, we take the current at a given instant of time to be the same at all points of an a-c series circuit, so that the concept of inductance may be employed to describe the time rate of change of magnetic flux through the circuit.   An exact criterion for the range of validity of the above assumption must be delayed to a later chapter, and the phenomena for which this assumption is valid are called *quasi-stationary.*

1. The Simplest A-C Circuits.   First consider the simplest possible case, a noninductive resistance R connected across the terminals of a generator whose terminal voltage is given by $E = E_0 \sin \omega t$, with $\omega = 2\pi f$, f being the frequency of the impressed sinusoidal emf. Assuming the validity of Ohm's law for time-varying currents, we have for the sum of the voltage drops around the series circuit

$$-E + iR = 0$$

or

$$E = iR \qquad (9.1)$$

In this equation, which is identical in form with that employed to describe a similar d-c circuit, both E and i vary with the time, so that Eq. (9.1) gives the relation between *instantaneous current* and *instantaneous* generator emf.   There follows for the current i as a function of time,

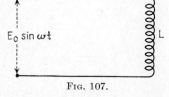

$$i = \frac{E}{R} = \frac{E_0}{R} \sin \omega t = I_0 \sin \omega t \qquad (9.2)$$

Fig. 107.

where $I_0 = E_0/R$ is the maximum value of the current.   Equation (9.2) shows that the sinusoidal current in the circuit is in phase with the sinusoidal voltage drop across the resistance.

Now consider a coil of self-inductance L and of negligible resistance connected to the terminals of the same generator (Fig. 107).   At any instant of time there is an induced emf in the coil equal to $-L \, di/dt$, so that Kirchhoff's rule gives

$$E - L\frac{di}{dt} = 0$$

or

$$E = L \frac{di}{dt} \tag{9.3}$$

The time rate of change of current at any instant is proportional to the instantaneous voltage impressed on the coil. Writing Eq. (9.3) in the form

$$\frac{di}{dt} = \frac{E}{L} = \frac{E_0}{L} \sin \omega t$$

a direct integration yields for the current

$$i = - \frac{E_0}{\omega L} \cos \omega t = \frac{E_0}{\omega L} \sin \left(\omega t - \frac{\pi}{2} \right) \tag{9.4}$$

where we have used the identity $\sin [\omega t - (\pi/2)] = - \cos \omega t$. Again we find an alternating current of the same frequency as the generator voltage, but in this case the current is not in phase with the voltage, lagging it by $\pi/2$ radians $= 90°$. In Fig. 108 are plotted the voltage

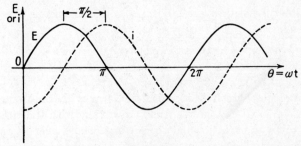

FIG. 108.

drop E across the inductance and the current carried by it as functions of the angle $\theta = \omega t$. From the figure one sees readily that the current reaches its maximum value at a later time than does the voltage. Since the phase lag is $\pi/2$, the time lag Δt is given by $\omega \Delta t = \pi/2$, or, since $\omega = 2\pi f$, $\Delta t = 1/4f$. The quantity $\omega L = 2\pi fL$ is known as the *inductive reactance* of the coil at the frequency f and is usually denoted by X_L. Thus we can write Eq. (9.4) as

$$i = \frac{E_0}{X_L} \sin \left(\omega t - \frac{\pi}{2} \right) = I_0 \sin \left(\omega t - \frac{\pi}{2} \right) \tag{9.5}$$

where the maximum current $I_0 = E_0/X_L$.

As a third and final example, consider the case of a condenser of capacity C connected to the generator terminals (Fig. 109). The charge on both plates of the condenser will now vary with time, and hence the electric field between the condenser plates will also vary with the time.   The flow of charge to and away from the condenser plates constitutes an alternating electric current in the wires connecting the condenser plates to the generator, and this current is related to the charge q by $i = dq/dt$.   This follows from the law of conservation of charge.   We now assume that as the charge on the plates varies, the electric field in the condenser at any instant of time is the same as would be produced by the same *static* charge on the plates.   Thus we can think of the potential difference between the condenser plates varying with time, and the static relation

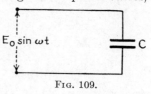

FIG. 109.

$V = q/C$ is assumed valid even when q varies with time.   This is our quasi-stationary assumption and is true as long as the time required for the charge to distribute itself over the plates is very small compared to the period of the alternating current and voltage.

According to the above, we write for the charge on the condenser at any time

$$q = CE_0 \sin \omega t \tag{9.6}$$

and hence the current in the circuit is

$$i = \frac{dq}{dt} = \omega CE_0 \cos \omega t = \omega CE_0 \sin \left(\omega t + \frac{\pi}{2} \right) \tag{9.7}$$

Consequently, the sinusoidally alternating current is of the same frequency as the generator voltage but is not in phase with it, the current leading the voltage by $\pi/2$ radians $= 90°$.

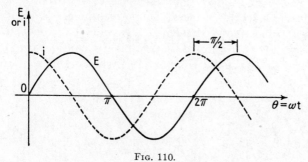

FIG. 110.

In Fig. 110 are plotted the voltage drop E across the condenser and the current i in the circuit as functions of the angle $\theta = \omega t$.   One sees that the current attains its maximum value before the voltage reaches its maximum.   The time lead is $\Delta t = 1/4f$.   The quantity

$$\frac{1}{\omega C} = \frac{1}{2\pi f C}$$

is known as the *capacitive reactance* of the condenser at the frequency f and is denoted by X_c.   Thus Eq. (9.7) may be written in the form

$$i = \frac{E_0}{X_c} \sin\left(\omega t + \frac{\pi}{2}\right) = I_0 \sin\left(\omega t + \frac{\pi}{2}\right) \qquad (9.8)$$

with $I_0 = E_0/X_c$ being the maximum value of the current.

Summarizing, we have the following important results relating the voltage drops across the three circuit elements—resistance, inductance, and capacity—when they carry an alternating current of maximum value I and of angular frequency ω:

1. The voltage drop across a noninductive resistance R has an amplitude equal to IR, and the current is in phase with this voltage drop.

2. The voltage drop across an inductance L is of amplitude

$$I\omega L = IX_L,$$

and the current *lags* this voltage drop by 90°.

3. The voltage drop across a condenser of capacity C which is connected in an a-c circuit has an amplitude of $I/\omega C = IX_c$, and the current *leads* the voltage drop by 90°.

2. Vector Representation of Sinusoidal Functions.   If we now wish to apply the results of the preceding section to series or parallel a-c circuits, the application of Kirchhoff's laws will require the addition of two or more sinusoidally varying voltages or currents of the same frequency.   Since these sinusoidal functions possess both amplitudes and phases, one cannot add them as algebraic quantities, and we now look into the law of addition.   For simplicity, consider the sum of two alternating voltages of the same frequency but of different amplitudes and phases:

$$\left.\begin{aligned} E_1 &= A \sin \omega t \\ E_2 &= B \sin (\omega t + \delta) \end{aligned}\right\} \qquad (9.9)$$

Here A and B are the maximum values or amplitudes of E_1 and E_2, respectively, and δ is the phase difference between them.   The sum of these terms will be a sine function of the same frequency, but this sum will not be in phase with either E_1 or E_2.   Let this sum E be

$$E = E_1 + E_2 = C \sin (\omega t + \epsilon) \qquad (9.10)$$

and our problem is that of finding the amplitude and initial phase C and ϵ in terms of A, B, and δ. We have

$$E = E_1 + E_2 = A \sin \omega t + B \sin (\omega t + \delta)$$

or

$$E = A \sin \omega t + B \sin \omega t \cos \delta + B \cos \omega t \sin \delta \qquad (9.11)$$

since $\sin (\alpha + \beta) = \sin \alpha \cos \beta + \cos \alpha \sin \beta$. Equation (9.11) can be written as

$$E = (A + B \cos \delta) \sin \omega t + (B \sin \delta) \cos \omega t \qquad (9.12)$$

and we must identify this with Eq. (9.10). Equation (9.10) can be written as

$$E = C \sin (\omega t + \epsilon) = (C \cos \epsilon) \sin \omega t + (C \sin \epsilon) \cos \omega t \quad (9.13)$$

and a comparison of Eqs. (9.12) and (9.13) shows that

$$\begin{aligned} C \sin \epsilon &= B \sin \delta \\ C \cos \epsilon &= A + B \cos \delta \end{aligned} \qquad (9.14)$$

from which we can calculate C and ϵ. Squaring and adding these equations, there follows

$$C^2 = (A + B \cos \delta)^2 + B^2 \sin^2 \delta = A^2 + B^2 + 2AB \cos \delta \quad (9.15)$$

and dividing the first by the second

$$\tan \epsilon = \frac{B \sin \delta}{A + B \cos \delta} \qquad (9.16)$$

This completes our task. Now Eqs. (9.15) and (9.16) are *exactly* the formulas for the sum of two vectors A and B which make an angle δ with each other (Fig. 111). Thus we have the important result: *The sum of two sinusoidal functions of the same frequency is a sinusoidal function of the same frequency, and the amplitude and phase of the sum can be obtained from those of the two given*

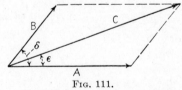

FIG. 111.

functions by vector addition.   We can therefore represent sine functions of the same frequency by vectors, the lengths of these vectors being the amplitudes of the sine functions and the fixed angles between the vectors being the constant phase differences between the corresponding sine functions.   It follows readily that the addition of more than two such sine functions is also equivalent to adding the same number of vectors.

The results just obtained can be given a simple geometrical interpretation. Consider a vector A rotating with a constant angular velocity ω about an axis through one end as shown in Fig. 112. The y-component

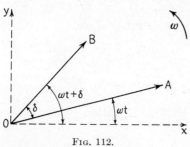

FIG. 112.

of this vector is evidently given by $A_y = A \sin \omega t$, and thus a sinusoidal function can be regarded as the projection of a rotating vector. In the same figure is shown another vector B rotating with the same angular velocity ω. We have $B_y = B \sin (\omega t + \delta)$. We note that the phase difference between A_y and B_y is equal to the angle between the two rotating vectors and does not vary with time, since both vectors rotate with the same angular velocity. This is equivalent to stating that the two sinusoidal functions have the same frequency. Our theorem then is a statement of the fact that the sum of the y-components of the two rotating vectors A and B is equal to the y-component of the resultant vector obtained by vector addition of A and B.

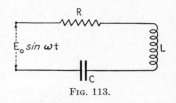

FIG. 113.

3. The Simple Series Circuit. Consider a simple series circuit consisting of resistance R, inductance L, and capacity C, connected to the terminals of an a-c generator as shown in Fig. 113. Applying Kirchhoff's laws to this circuit (the sum of the instantaneous voltage drops around the circuit must vanish), we have

$$-E_0 \sin \omega t + iR + L\frac{di}{dt} + \frac{q}{C} = 0$$

or

$$L\frac{di}{dt} + Ri + \frac{1}{C}q = E_0 \sin \omega t \tag{9.17}$$

and the solution of this equation, along with $i = dq/dt$, yields the current i in the circuit and the charge q on the condenser as functions of the time. The complete solution of this equation contains two terms: one is a transient current which depends on the initial conditions and soon dies out, and the other is a steady-state current which persists as long as the external emf E is impressed on the circuit. We shall confine our attention to the *steady-state* behavior in this section, and since the steady-state current is of the same frequency as the applied voltage, we can apply the results of the previous sections to obtain this solution.

Equation (9.17) states that the applied or impressed voltage ($E_0 \sin \omega t$) is the sum of the voltage drops across inductance, resistance, and condenser, and we shall add these with the help of a vector representation. We can write symbolically,

$$\mathbf{E} = \mathbf{V}_L + \mathbf{V}_R + \mathbf{V}_C$$

where the $\mathbf{V}$'s are the vectors representing the drops across the individual circuit elements. From the results of Sec. 1 of this chapter, we have for the magnitudes of these vectors:

$$V_L = \omega L I; \qquad V_R = RI; \qquad V_C = \frac{I}{\omega C}$$

where I is the amplitude of the alternating current i. Figure 114 shows the *vector diagram* of the circuit. The vector I represents the common current in the circuit; the vector $V_R = IR$ is in phase with I; the vector $V_L = \omega L I$ leads I by 90° (taking the counterclockwise direction of rotation as positive), and $V_C = I/\omega C$ lags 90° behind I according to our previous results. Since V_R is perpendicular to V_L and V_C, we have evidently

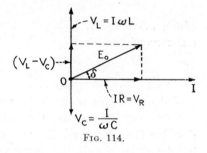

Fig. 114.

$$E_0 = \sqrt{V_R^2 + (V_L - V_C)^2} = I \sqrt{R^2 + \left(\omega L - \frac{1}{\omega C}\right)^2}$$

$$= I \sqrt{R^2 + (X_L - X_C)^2}$$

and

$$\tan \delta = \frac{\omega L - (1/\omega C)}{R} = \frac{X_L - X_C}{R}$$

(9.18)

The first of these equations relates the amplitudes of the current I and of the applied voltage E_0. The second gives the *phase angle δ* of the applied emf relative to the current. This is a positive angle when the current lags the voltage (the case shown in Fig. 114) and is negative when the current leads the voltage. The ratio of E_0 to I is called the *impedance* of the circuit and is denoted by the letter Z. We have

$$Z = \sqrt{R^2 + \left(\omega L - \frac{1}{\omega C}\right)^2} \qquad (9.19)$$

From Eqs. (9.18) we see that the instantaneous current i is given by

$$i = \frac{E_0}{Z} \sin (\omega t - \delta) \qquad (9.20)$$

if $E = E_0 \sin \omega t$. Z is given by Eq. (9.19) and δ by the second of Eqs. (9.18). *Equation (9.20) is the steady-state solution of Eq. (9.17).* Note that impedance and reactance are measured in ohms, just as is resistance, but that they depend on the frequency. From the expression for tan δ we see that the current will be in phase with the applied voltage if $X_L = X_C$. When this condition is satisfied, the series circuit is said to be in *resonance,* and the current (considered as a function of frequency) has the maximum value possible (Z is a minimum). At resonance then, Eq. (9.20) becomes

$$i = \frac{E_0}{R} \sin \omega t \qquad \text{(at resonance)} \qquad (9.21)$$

where $\omega L = 1/\omega C$. This resonance condition written in terms of frequency f becomes

$$f = \frac{1}{2\pi} \sqrt{\frac{1}{LC}} \qquad (9.22)$$

Further discussion of the series-resonant circuit is left to the problems.

4. Energy Considerations for the Series Circuit. Now let us examine the energy relations in a series a-c circuit. First, the power input to the circuit, Ei, is not constant but varies with the time. There will be, however, an average rate of doing work which must be computed. In the resistance R the dissipated power $i^2 R$ will vary with time so that the rate of heating is not constant, and we must calculate the average rate of heating. In the inductance L there will be an instantaneous power consumption $Li \, (di/dt)$, which represents the rate at which the magnetic field energy increases or decreases. As we shall see directly, this averages to zero over a cycle. Finally, there will be an instantaneous power consumption by the condenser equal to $(q/C)i$ representing the rate of change of electric field energy of the electric field in the condenser. As in the case of the magnetic energy, this also averages to zero over a cycle.

The instantaneous rate of heating in the resistance is

$$i^2 R = I^2 R \sin^2 (\omega t - \delta) = I^2 R \sin^2 \theta \qquad (9.23)$$

utilizing Eq. (9.20) with $I = E_0/Z$ and $\theta = \omega t - \delta$. The average rate of heating (averaged over one period of oscillation) is accordingly

$$\overline{i^2R} = I^2R \left(\frac{1}{2\pi} \int_0^{2\pi} \sin^2 \theta \, d\theta \right) \qquad (9.24)$$

since, in one period, θ increases by 2π, and the definition of the average value of any function $f(x)$ over an interval $x = 0$ to $x = a$ is defined by

$$\overline{f(x)} = \frac{1}{a} \int_0^a f(x) \, dx$$

Now since $\sin^2 \theta = \frac{1}{2}(1 - \cos 2\theta)$, the integral in Eq. (9.24) can be written as

$$\int_0^{2\pi} \sin^2 \theta \, d\theta = \frac{1}{2} \int_0^{2\pi} (1 - \cos 2\theta) \, d\theta = \pi - \frac{1}{4} \int_0^{2\pi} \cos 2\theta \, d(2\theta) = \pi$$

Inserting this value into Eq. (9.24), there follows for the average rate of heating

$$P_R = \overline{i^2R} = \tfrac{1}{2}I^2R \qquad (9.25)$$

or one-half the maximum rate. From this we see that the average value of the square of the alternating current i is $I^2/2$. The square root of this average square of the current $\sqrt{\overline{i^2}}$ is called the *root-mean-square* (rms) value of the current, or the *effective* current, and this is the value which would be read on an a-c ammeter. Thus we can write

$$i_{\text{eff}} = \sqrt{\overline{i^2}} = \frac{1}{\sqrt{2}} I = 0.707I \qquad (9.26)$$

The effective value of a sinusoidally varying current is $1/\sqrt{2}$ times the maximum value of the current. A similar relation holds for the effective value E_{eff} of a sinusoidally varying emf. In terms of effective current, the average rate of heating is $i_{\text{eff}}^2 R$.

The rate of increase of magnetic field energy in the inductance has the instantaneous value

$$Li\frac{di}{dt} = \omega L I^2 \sin (\omega t - \delta) \cos (\omega t - \delta) = \omega L \frac{I^2}{2} \sin 2(\omega t - \delta)$$

or, in terms of the effective current,

$$P_L = \omega L i_{\text{eff}}^2 \sin 2(\omega t - \delta) = i_{\text{eff}}^2 X_L \sin 2(\omega t - \delta) \qquad (9.27)$$

The average power input to the inductance is thus zero, since the average value of $\sin 2(\omega t - \delta)$ is zero. Energy is alternately stored up in the magnetic field and returned to the generator.

A similar state of affairs exists in the condenser. The power input to the condenser is

$$P_C = \frac{qi}{C} = -\frac{I^2}{\omega C} \sin(\omega t - \delta) \cos(\omega t - \delta) = -\frac{I^2}{2\omega C} \sin 2(\omega t - \delta)$$

or

$$P_C = -\frac{i_{\text{eff}}^2}{\omega C} \sin 2(\omega t - \delta) = -i_{\text{eff}}^2 X_C \sin 2(\omega t - \delta) \qquad (9.28)$$

Energy is alternately stored up in the condenser while it is charging and returned to the generator during discharge. The average power consumption is zero.

The instantaneous power input to the whole circuit from the generator is

$$P = Ei = E_0 I \sin \omega t \sin(\omega t - \delta)$$
$$= E_0 I \cos \delta \sin^2 \omega t - E_0 I \sin \delta \sin \omega t \cos \omega t \qquad (9.29)$$

The average power input is therefore

$$\bar{P} = \frac{E_0 I}{2} \cos \delta = E_{\text{eff}} i_{\text{eff}} \cos \delta \qquad (9.30)$$

since the average value of the last term in (9.29) is zero. Since $\tan \delta = (X_L - X_C)/R$, $\cos \delta = R/\sqrt{R^2 + (X_L - X_C)^2} = R/Z$, and $E_0 = IZ$, Eq. (9.30) can be written as $P = (I^2/2)R = i_{\text{eff}}^2 R$, the average rate of heating in the resistance.

The ratio of the average power input to a system to the product of the effective voltage impressed on it and the effective current delivered to it is called the *power factor* of the system. For the case of sinusoidal alternating currents, Eq. (9.30) shows that

$$\text{pf} = \cos \delta \qquad (9.31)$$

The relations just derived allow a simple interpretation based on a vector diagram, as shown in Fig. 115. Here we show the effective rather than maximum values of impressed emf and current and the phase difference δ between them. The average power input, as given by Eq. (9.30), is clearly the product of the rms voltage and the component of rms current in phase with this voltage. The second term in Eq. (9.29) for the instantaneous power can be written as

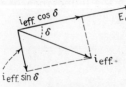

FIG. 115.

$$(E_{\text{eff}} i_{\text{eff}} \sin \delta) \sin 2\omega t$$

and this quantity is often referred to as the "wattless," or "reactive," power.   For certain values of t, Eq. (9.29) gives negative values of the power input, and at these times energy flows from the circuit to the external seat of emf.

5. The Simple Parallel Circuit. Consider a simple parallel combination of resistance, inductance, and capacity, connected to the terminals of an a-c generator as shown in Fig. 116.   At any instant

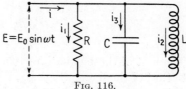

Fig. 116.

of time, by virtue of the parallel connection, the voltage drops across R, L, and C are equal to each other and to the impressed emf

$$E = E_0 \sin \omega t$$

The equation of continuity further requires that

$$i = i_1 + i_2 + i_3 \tag{9.32}$$

where the currents i, i_1, i_2, and i_3 are instantaneous values.   Since

$$
\left.
\begin{aligned}
i_1 &= \frac{E_0}{R} \sin \omega t = I_1 \sin \omega t \\[2mm]
i_2 &= \frac{E_0}{\omega L} \sin \left(\omega t - \frac{\pi}{2} \right) = I_2 \sin \left(\omega t - \frac{\pi}{2} \right) \\[2mm]
i_3 &= E_0 \omega C \sin \left(\omega t + \frac{\pi}{2} \right) = I_3 \sin \left(\omega t + \frac{\pi}{2} \right)
\end{aligned}
\right\} \tag{9.33}
$$

and

according to Eqs. (9.2), (9.4), and (9.7), Eq. (9.32) calls for the addition of three sinusoidally varying currents of different amplitudes and phases, and we shall perform this addition with the help of a vector diagram as shown in Fig. 117.   The vector E_0 represents the common voltage across the parallel circuit; the vector $I_1 = E_0/R$ is in phase with E_0; the vector $I_2 = E_0/\omega L$ lags E_0 by 90°; and $I_3 = E_0\omega C$ leads E_0 by 90° in accordance with Eqs. (9.33). I is the maximum value of the line current delivered by the generator $[i = I \sin (\omega t - \delta)]$, and δ is the phase difference between line voltage and line current.   From the figure it is evident that

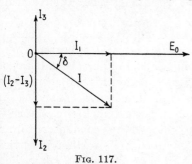

Fig. 117.

$$I = \sqrt{I_1^2 + (I_2 - I_3)^2} = E_0 \sqrt{\left(\frac{1}{R}\right)^2 + \left(\frac{1}{\omega L} - \omega C\right)^2}$$

and

$$\tan \delta = \frac{R}{\omega L} - \omega R C$$

$$(9.34)$$

The first of these equations relates the amplitude of the line current I to that of the line voltage E_0, and the second gives the phase difference δ between them. The ratio of maximum current to maximum impressed emf is called the *admittance* of the circuit and is denoted by the letter Y. We have

$$Y = \sqrt{\left(\frac{1}{R}\right)^2 + \left(\frac{1}{\omega L} - \omega C\right)^2}$$

$$(9.35)$$

and from Eqs. (9.34) we can write for the instantaneous line current i

$$i = E_0 Y \sin (\omega t - \delta)$$

$$(9.36)$$

Once again the line current and line voltage are in phase if $\omega L = 1/\omega C$, and when this occurs, we have the case of *parallel resonance*. (Note that the resonance condition $\omega L = 1/\omega C$ is the same as for series resonance.) At resonance, Y has a minimum value, and hence the line current also becomes a minimum. The instantaneous currents in the condenser and inductance branches of the circuit become equal in magnitude but are opposite in phase and thus add up to zero, and the generator current is just that drawn by the noninductive resistance R. The current in the LC loop may attain a very large amplitude in parallel resonance, and this current is often called a *circulating current*.

6. Free Oscillations of an LC Circuit; Simple Transients. There is a simple important case in which steady-state alternating currents may be set up without the aid of an external seat of emf. Consider the circuit of Fig. 118, consisting of a condenser and inductance connected as shown, and let us suppose that the resistance is negligible. We charge the condenser to an initial potential difference V_0 so that it carries

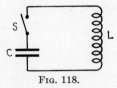

FIG. 118.

an initial charge q_0, and close the switch S. Kirchhoff's law then requires that

$$L \frac{di}{dt} + \frac{q}{C} = 0$$

or, since $i = dq/dt$,

$$\frac{d^2q}{dt^2} + \frac{1}{LC}\, q = 0 \tag{9.37}$$

This is the equation for simple harmonic motion, and the solution is

$$q = q_0 \cos \omega_0 t \tag{9.38}$$

and

$$i = \frac{dq}{dt} = -\omega_0 q_0 \sin \omega_0 t = -\omega_0 C V_0 \sin \omega_0 t \tag{9.39}$$

since at $t = 0$, $q = q_0$ and $i = 0$. $\omega_0 = \sqrt{1/LC}$, so that one obtains free oscillations of the system with a frequency f given by

$$f = \frac{1}{2\pi} \sqrt{\frac{1}{LC}} \tag{9.40}$$

We note that this is just the relation for parallel or series resonance when a circuit is driven by an external emf [cf. Eq. (9.22)], and in fact the circuit of Fig. 118 behaves just like the LC loop in Fig. 116 in the limiting case of $R \to \infty$ at resonance.   In the latter case the line current is zero, and the circulating current in the LC loop is independent of the presence of the generator for the steady state.   The generator would serve the purpose of starting the oscillations (the transient part of the solution which we have not discussed), just as charging the condenser in our present case supplies the requisite initial conditions that such an oscillation exist.

While the system is oscillating, there is a continuous interchange of energy between the electric field of the condenser and the magnetic field of the inductance, the total energy remaining constant.   At any instant of time this total energy is

$$\frac{1}{2} L i^2 + \frac{1}{2} \frac{q^2}{C}$$

and, using Eqs. (9.38), (9.39), and (9.40), this is

$$\frac{L}{2} \left(\omega_0^2 q_0^2 \sin^2 \omega_0 t \right) + \frac{q_0^2}{2C} \cos^2 \omega_0 t = \frac{q_0^2}{2C} \left(\sin^2 \omega_0 t + \cos^2 \omega_0 t \right) = \frac{q_0^2}{2C}$$

Thus the total constant energy is the energy stored initially in the condenser.   This oscillation is analogous to the case of a mechanical oscillation with the corresponding interchange of potential and kinetic energy.   If resistance is present, the oscillations die out, as they do when friction is present in the mechanical case.

Thus far we have considered only steady-state solutions of the circuit equations, and we now turn to two simple cases of nonsteady, or transient, currents. Consider first the circuit shown in Fig. 119. At any instant of time we have

$$L \frac{di}{dt} + Ri = E \qquad (9.41)$$

as the differential equation for the current as a function of time. To integrate this equation, we set $i = i' + (E/R)$, and substituting in Eq. (9.41), the latter becomes

$$L \frac{di'}{dt} + Ri' = 0 \qquad (9.42)$$

so that the constant term E has been eliminated. Equation (9.42) can now be integrated directly, yielding

$$i' = ce^{-(R/L)t}$$

where c is an arbitrary constant, and the complete solution of Eq. (9.41) becomes

$$i = \frac{E}{R} + ce^{-(R/L)t} \qquad (9.43)$$

Equation (9.43) shows that the current is the sum of a steady-state current E/R (Ohm's law) and a transient term $ce^{-(R/L)t}$, which depends on the initial conditions and eventually vanishes. This is an example of the general case that the circuit equations have solutions which can be represented as the sum of a steady-state and a transient solution. Suppose that the initial conditions are that a switch is closed at $t = 0$ to establish the closed circuit. Then $i = 0$ for $t = 0$, and Eq. (9.43) gives for the integration constant c,

$$c = -\frac{E}{R}$$

so that in this case

$$i = \frac{E}{R} (1 - e^{-(R/L)t}) \qquad (9.43a)$$

A plot of current versus time is shown in Fig. 120. Now consider the case in which a steady current is present in the circuit of Fig. 119, and suppose that at $t = 0$, the d-c battery is short-circuited. At all subsequent times there is no external emf acting in the circuit; consequently we set $E = 0$ in Eq. (9.41), obtaining

$$L \frac{di}{dt} + Ri = 0$$

which has the solution

$$i = i_0 e^{-(R/L)t} \tag{9.43b}$$

where i_0 is the steady current in the circuit at the instant when the battery is removed.   A plot of i versus t is shown in Fig. 121.   The

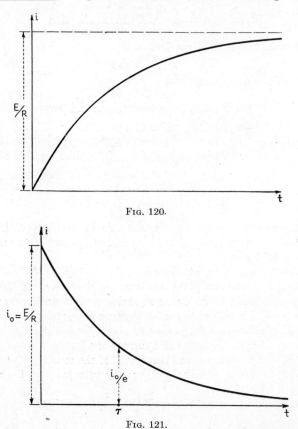

Fig. 120.

Fig. 121.

time required for the current to drop to $1/e$ of its initial value is called the *time constant* of the circuit.   Denoting this by τ, we have

$$\tau = \frac{L}{R} \tag{9.44}$$

As a second and final example of transient currents, let us consider the discharge of a condenser through a noninductive resistance (Fig.

122).   Suppose the condenser initially carries a charge q_0, so that the initial potential difference between its plates is $V_0 = q_0/C$, and that at $t = 0$ a switch is closed establishing the circuit shown.   The discharge is given by the equation

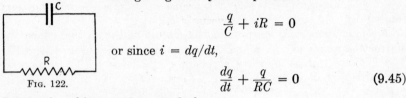

$$\frac{q}{C} + iR = 0$$

or since $i = dq/dt$,

FIG. 122.

$$\frac{dq}{dt} + \frac{q}{RC} = 0 \qquad (9.45)$$

Integrating this equation, we find

$$q = q_0 e^{-t/RC} \qquad (9.46)$$

and from this the current

$$i = \frac{dq}{dt} = -\frac{q}{RC} e^{-t/RC} = -\frac{V_0}{R} e^{-t/RC} \qquad (9.47)$$

Both current and condenser charge decay exponentially with time, the plots being similar to that of Fig. 121.   The time constant of such an RC circuit is

$$\tau = RC \qquad (9.48)$$

Problems

All voltages and currents are rms values unless otherwise stated.

1. A 1,000-turn solenoid, 50 cm long and of 2.0 cm² cross section, has a resistance of 1.20 ohms.

a. What is its impedance at a frequency $f = 500$ cycles/sec?   *1.99 Ω*

b. If a second solenoid of 500 turns is wound closely around the first, what emf will be induced in this 500-turn solenoid on open circuit when a 24-volt, 500 cycles/sec emf is applied to the 1,000-turn winding?   *9.5 co Q*

2. A coil of unknown inductance and of resistance 37.7 ohms is connected to a 230-volt, 60-cycle a-c line, and a current of 4.7 amp is drawn by the coil.

a. Calculate the reactance and inductance of the coil.   *31.5 Ω*

b. What is the phase difference between the voltage across the coil and the current carried by it?   *39.6°.*

c. What would be the coil current if the frequency of the applied emf were 30 cycles/sec?   *5.64 amp*

3. A coil takes a current of 25 amp when connected to 220-volt, 60-cycle mains.   If this same coil in series with a 5-ohm resistance is connected to a 110-volt d-c line, the current is 17 amp.   Compute the resistance and inductance of the coil.   *1.48 ; 23 mh*

4. A resistance draws 10 amp when connected to a 110-volt, 60-cycle line. How big a condenser must be connected in series with the resistance so that the current drops to 5.0 amp?   What are the voltage drops across the condenser and across the resistance for this connection?

1.39 uF $V_c = 95.4$

$V_R = 55$

5. A series circuit consists of a 50-ohm resistance, an inductance of 0.1 henry, and a condenser of capacity of 10μf.   A 60 cycles/sec emf of 100 volts is impressed on the circuit.

a. Find the current in the circuit.   0.424 amp

b. Find the voltage drops across the resistance, inductance, and condenser, respectively, and show these on a vector diagram. V_R=21,2 V_L=16 V_c=113.5

6. A coil is connected to a 60-cycle, 100-volt a-c generator.   Its impedance and reactance at 60 cycles/sec are 4.0 and 2.0 ohms, respectively.

a. Find the current drawn by the coil and the phase angle between this current and the applied voltage.   25 ; 30°

b. What capacitance should be added in series if the current is to lead the applied voltage by 30°?   What are then the voltage drops across coil and condenser?   0.667 mh ; V_L=V_c=100 V.

7. A series circuit consists of a 300-ohm resistance, an inductance whose reactance at 60 cycles/sec is 400 ohms, and a condenser of 500 ohms reactance at 60 cycles/sec.   A 60 cycles/sec emf of 500 volts is impressed on this circuit.

a. Calculate the inductance in henrys and the condenser capacity in microfarads.   —1.06 h   5.30 uf

b. What is the impedance of the circuit?   3.16 Ω

c. What is the steady-state current in the circuit?   1.58 amp

d. What is the phase angle between the current and the applied voltage?   —18.4°

e. What size condenser would be needed to produce series resonance? What would the current be under these conditions?   —6.65 uf   1.16 amps

8. An a-c series circuit has an emf of 100 volts of angular frequency $\omega = 2\pi f = 500$ radians/sec impressed on it, and it contains a resistance of 3.0 ohms, a condenser of capacity 50 μf, and a self-inductance which can be varied from 10 to 80 millihenrys.   The condenser is rated to stand an effective voltage of 800 volts.

a. What is the largest current possible without damaging the condenser?   2.0 amp

b. To what value can the inductance be safely increased?   72 mh

9. A condenser of capacity 6.67 μf is connected in series with a coil to an a-c supply of 1.20 volts emf and of variable frequency.   By varying the frequency it is observed that the current reaches a largest effective value of 0.20 amp when the angular frequency ω equals 50,000 radians/sec.

a. What are the resistance and self-inductance of the coil?   +.4 ; 0.06 mh

b. What is the current when the angular frequency is $\omega = 150,000$?   .0935 amp

c. What is the peak voltage across the condenser at this frequency?   0.132 V.

10. A series circuit consisting of a resistance R, an inductance L, and a capacitance C is connected to an a-c generator of variable frequency so that the impressed voltage is given by $E = E_0 \sin 2\pi f t$, where E_0 is constant at all frequencies.

a. Calculate expressions for the circuit impedance as a function of frequency f if $L = 0.10$ henry and $C = 1.0$ μf for the following values of resistance: $R = 100$ ohms; $R = 10$ ohms; $R = 1.0$ ohm.   503 cycles

b. Plot the current as a function of frequency for those values of resistance.

14.14 amp.

c. What is the resonant frequency?   If $R = 1.0$ ohm, $E_0 = 10\sqrt{2}$ volts, what is the current at resonance?   For what values of frequency is the current one-half its value at resonance?

11. A coil of resistance 2.0 ohms and inductance 0.10 henry is used in series with a condenser to show resonance.   The only available source of emf is a 110-volt, 60-cycle line.   What is the necessary condenser capacity?

If the condenser is designed to stand an effective voltage of 500 volts, what resistance must be inserted in the circuit to limit the drop across the condenser to this value?

12. An alternating voltage of constant amplitude and variable frequency is applied to a series R, L, C circuit.   Deduce an expression for the frequency at which the voltage drop across the condenser is a maximum.   Is this higher or lower than the resonance frequency of the circuit?

13. For the circuit of Prob. 12, deduce an expression for the frequency at which the voltage drop across the inductance is a maximum.

14. The equations of two alternating emfs are $E_1 = 150 \sin 377t$ and $E_2 = 150 \sin (377t + 60°)$.   If these emfs are in series, what is the equation of their resultant?   What is the phase angle between the resultant and each of the two emfs?   At the instant of time when the resultant is zero, what are the values of E_1 and E_2?

15. An alternating current of amplitude 10.0 amp is rectified so that current flows only during the positive half cycles (half-wave rectification).   Calculate the average and rms values of the current.

16. A series circuit consists of a d-c battery of emf 110 volts, an a-c generator of rms terminal voltage 110 volts at 25 cycles/sec, a coil, an a-c ammeter (reading rms values of current), and a d-c ammeter (reading average values of current).   The internal resistances of the battery, generator, and ammeters are negligible.

The d-c ammeter reads 2.5 amp, and the a-c ammeter reads 3.2 amp.   Find the resistance and inductance of the coil.

17. A coil has a power factor of 0.866 at a frequency of 60 cycles/sec.   What is its power factor at 180 cycles/sec?

18. A series circuit consists of a variable resistance R and a reactance $X = 10$ ohms at 60 cycles/sec.   It is connected to a 220-volt, 60-cycle generator, and the power absorbed by the circuit is read on a wattmeter.   (A wattmeter reads average power.)

a. What value of R will give the maximum wattmeter reading?

b. What is this maximum reading in watts?

19. A 100-volt power line is supplied by a 60-volt a-c generator in series with an 80-volt a-c generator of the same frequency.

a. What is the phase difference between the generator voltages?

b. A coil absorbs 300 watts and draws a current of 5.0 amp when connected to this 100-volt line.   Find the resistance, reactance, impedance, and power factor of the coil.

20. Two coils have resistances of 10 and 16 ohms and inductances of 0.02

and 0.40 henry, respectively.   If connected in series across 220-volt, 60-cycle mains, what current will they take?   What is the power factor of the circuit? What is the phase difference between the voltage drops across the two coils?

21. A coil of 2.7 ohms resistance and of variable inductance is connected in series with a noninductive resistance across a 220-volt, 60-cycle line.   The circuit is so adjusted that the drop across the coil is 150 volts and the power it absorbs is 250 watts.

What is the value of the noninductive resistance?

22. A noninductive resistance of 25 ohms in series with a condenser absorbs 968 watts when connected to a 220-volt, 60-cycle line.   What current will this circuit take when connected to a 110-volt, 25-cycle line?   What power will it absorb?

23. A coil is connected in series with a condenser across 220-volt, 60-cycle mains.   The circuit absorbs 650 watts at a power factor of 0.87 and is so adjusted that the voltage drops across coil and condenser are equal.   What are these voltages?

24. A coil takes 250 watts at a power factor of 0.10 when connected to a 220-volt, 60-cycle line.   What capacity must be connected in series with this coil so that it takes the same power from a 110-volt, 60-cycle line?   What is the power factor of the latter circuit?

25. A series circuit with $R = 10$ ohms, $L = 0.10$ henry, and $C = 30$ μf is connected to 110-volt, 60-cycle mains.   At the instant at which the impressed emf is zero, what is the energy in the condenser?   When there is no energy in the condenser, what is the energy in the magnetic field of the inductance?

26. A 120-volt, 60-cycle a-c generator is connected to a series circuit containing a resistance R, a capacitance C, and a variable inductance L.   It is found that the circuit absorbs maximum power of 1,440 watts when $L = 0.10$ henry.   What are the values of R and C?

27. A coil of resistance 20 ohms and self-inductance 0.10 henry is connected to a 110-volt, 60-cycle a-c line.

   a. Find the power factor of the coil at 60 cycles.

   b. What size condenser must be connected in series with the coil to make the power factor of the circuit equal to unity?

   c. Find the ratio of the current when the condenser is in the circuit to the current when the coil alone is connected to the line.

28. Given a series circuit with a resistance of 20 ohms, a coil of inductive reactance of 30 ohms at the operating frequency, and a variable condenser. For a certain value C_1 of the condenser capacity, the circuit takes a current from an a-c line such that the product of line voltage and current is 400 volt-amp.   Under these conditions the circuit dissipates 320 watts.   The condenser capacity is then *increased* to a value C_2, for which the circuit again absorbs 320 watts.   The line voltage is maintained constant throughout.

   a. Find the power factor for the two cases.

   b. Find the line voltage.

   c. Construct a vector diagram for each of the two cases.

29. An alternating emf of 110 volts and 60 cycles/sec is impressed on a circuit containing a resistance of 153 ohms and a condenser of capacity 10 μf in parallel.

a. What are the currents in the line, in the condenser branch, and in the resistance? $I_R = 0.719$ $I_C = 0.415$ $I_L = 0.826$

b. What are the phase differences between these three currents and the line voltage?

c. What is the power factor of the circuit?

30. Two noninductive resistances of 10 and 20 ohms, respectively, are connected in parallel across the terminals of a 1,000-cycle/sec a-c generator. A variable condenser is inserted in series with one of these resistances and adjusted so that the two resistances absorb equal amounts of power. In series with which resistance is the condenser placed, and what is its capacity?

31. When a noninductive resistance of 10 ohms is connected in parallel with a coil across a 100-volt, 60-cycle line, the total current drawn from the line is 27.2 amp. When the resistance and coil are connected in series across the same line, the current drawn is 7.35 amp. What are the resistance and reactance of the coil at 60 cycles/sec?

$I_R = 2$
$I_L = 9.81$

32. A noninductive resistance and a condenser are connected in parallel across 220-volt, 60-cycle power mains and take a total current of 10 amp at a power factor of 0.20. What are the currents in the parallel branches?

33. A resistance $R = 33.3$ ohms, an inductance whose reactance is 20 ohms at 60 cycles, and a condenser of reactance 100 ohms at 60 cycles are connected in parallel across a 110-volt, 60-cycle line. Find the line current, the current in each branch, and the power factor of the system. 5.5; 3.3; 5.5; 1.1   0.6

34. A coil of resistance 12 ohms takes a current of 11 amp from a 220-volt, 60-cycle line. If a condenser of reactance 32 ohms at 60 cycles is connected in parallel with the coil, what is the total current drawn by the parallel combination?   6.16 $\checkmark$

35. A long single-layer solenoid has a circular cross section of 4.0 cm radius and is wound with 800 turns per meter. The winding is made of copper wire 1.0 mm in diameter, of resistivity 2.0×10^{-8} ohm-m. What is the time constant of the coil?   0.89 m sec.

36. A coil has a resistance of 1 ohm and an inductance of 0.10 henry.

a. What is the time constant of the coil?   0.1

b. Plot the current as a function of time during the first second after an emf of 10 volts is impressed on the coil.

c. Plot the rate at which energy is supplied to the coil during this second.

d. What is the magnetic field energy 0.1 sec after the switch is closed?

37. A coil has a resistance of 5.0 ohms and an inductance of 0.15 henry. With the coil carrying a steady current of 25 amp, the impressed emf is suddenly replaced by a noninductive resistance of 10 ohms.

a. What fraction of the initial magnetic energy is ultimately dissipated in the 10-ohm resistance?

b. What is the initial voltage across the 10-ohm resistance?

38. A 10-μf condenser which has been charged to a potential difference of 200 volts is discharged by connecting a 1,000-ohm resistance across its terminals.

a. What is the initial energy stored in the condenser?

b. What is the current when the charge on the condenser has fallen to one-half its initial value?

c. By evaluating $\int_0^\infty i^2R\ dt$, compute the total heat generated in the resistance, and compare with the answer to part *a*.

39. A 300-volt voltmeter of resistance 300,000 ohms is permanently connected to the terminals of a 10-μf condenser. The condenser is charged to a potential difference of 270 volts and then disconnected from the charging source, discharging through the voltmeter. What is the voltmeter reading 3 sec after the discharge begins?

40. A condenser of capacity C is charged through a resistance R by connecting the two in series to the terminals of a battery of constant emf E.

Derive formulas for the charge in the condenser and for the charging current as functions of the time.

41. In Prob. 40 the condenser has a capacitance of 10 μf, the resistance R = 100 ohms, and the battery emf is 200 volts.

a. Compute the total work done by the battery during the charging process.

b. What fraction of this work is dissipated in heating the resistance?

CHAPTER 10

DISPLACEMENT CURRENT AND ELECTROMAGNETIC WAVES

In Chaps. 6 and 7 we have formulated the laws of the stationary magnetic field produced by steady electric currents, and now we must extend these laws to cover nonsteady, or transient, phenomena. The concept of inductance and the circuit laws discussed in the last chapter have been based on the assumption that the Ampère circuital law for steady currents was also valid for time-varying currents. We are now ready to investigate the range of validity of this assumption. From the fundamental law of the conservation of electric charge, expressed as the equation of continuity, we have seen that the flow of lines of *steady* electric currents always close on themselves; consequently one has to deal exclusively with closed circuits in the case of steady currents. For nonsteady, transient currents this is no longer necessarily the case, and one may have currents in *open circuits* as, for example, in the case of a condenser being charged or discharged. Our first task is to formulate the equation of continuity for nonsteady currents.

1. The Equation of Continuity for Charge and Current. Let us first examine the simple example of a condenser discharging through a resistance, as indicated in Fig. 123.

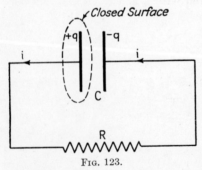

FIG. 123.

Suppose that at a given instant of time the charges on the condenser plates are $+q$ and $-q$, as shown, and that the current at this instant is i. This is a typical example of an open circuit, the flow lines of electric current starting on the positive plate and terminating on the negative plate. Since, by definition, the current is the rate at which charge traverses a cross section of the conducting wire normal to the direction of the flow lines, we see that the law of conservation of charge requires that the rate of increase of charge on a condenser plate be equal to the current into that plate. We have already employed

this relation between charge on a condenser and the current in our
study of a-c circuits.

To formulate this continuity law mathematically, let us imagine
that we construct a *closed* surface which completely encloses the positive plate of the condenser as shown in Fig. 123.   The current *outward* across this surface is i, and this equals the rate of decrease of
charge on the plate, so that we may write

$$i = -\frac{dq}{dt} \tag{10.1}$$

In Eq. (10.1) the left-hand side refers to the current *out* of the volume
enclosed by the surface.   Let us now formulate Eq. (10.1) in more
general terms.   The total current outward across the surface enclosing
a given volume can be written as $\int J_n \, dS$, where J_n is the normal component of the current density at a point where the element of area dS
is located and the integral extends over the whole closed surface [com-
pare Eqs. (5.3) and (5.6)].   Equation (10.1) can then be written in the
form

$$\int_{\substack{\text{closed} \\ \text{surface}}} J_n \, dS = -\frac{dq}{dt} \tag{10.2}$$

This is the general form for the continuity equation for stationary
bodies, in which q represents the charge inside the closed surface.
Equation (10.2) reduces to Eq. (5.6) for steady currents, since in this
case the right-hand side vanishes.   If the charge inside the volume
enclosed by the surface is distributed with a space density ρ, we can
write Eq. (10.2) in the form

$$\int J_n \, dS = -\int \frac{\partial \rho}{\partial t} \, dv \tag{10.3}$$

where the integral on the right-hand side extends throughout the
volume.   We have used the partial derivative $\partial \rho / \partial t$ to indicate the
rate of change of charge density at a fixed point (the point where dv
is located) inside the volume.

2. The Maxwell Displacement Current.   If we now inquire into the
question of the magnetic field produced by transient, or nonsteady,
currents, we find that the Ampère circuital law, which states that the
mmf around a closed path is equal to the current traversing *any* surface
bounded by the closed path, breaks down for open circuits.   We can
carry through the discussion best for the simple case of a parallel-plate

condenser being charged.   In Fig. 124 are shown the condenser and a
closed circular path σ surrounding the wire leading to the positive
plate.   The mmf $\oint H_s\,ds$ around this closed path should equal the

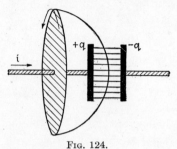

current traversing any area of which
this path is a boundary.   If we consider the shaded plane area, we find
this mmf equal to $-i$.   If, on the other
hand, we construct a hemispherical
surface, as shown, with the same perimeter, we find this mmf equal to *zero*,
since no current crosses this area.
Hence Ampère's circuital law in the
form we have been employing cannot

FIG. 124.

be correct, leading as it does to an ambiguous result, and we are confronted with the problem of generalizing this law so that it will have
general validity.

     A satisfactory solution of this problem was first given by Maxwell,
and it consists of generalizing the concept of electric current to include
not only conduction and convection currents but also a new kind of
current, called *displacement current*, which exists whenever an electric
field (or more precisely, the electric displacement vector D) varies with
time.   We can obtain the correct form for this displacement current
by considering the circuit of Fig. 124.   If we construct an expression
for a displacement current in the space between the condenser plates
(the region where the electric field of the condenser varies with time)
which just equals the current carried by the wires, the Ampère circuital
law will then give a unique answer for the mmf around a closed path,
and the ambiguity which we have found will disappear.   In other
words, we must postulate a displacement current such that the total
current (the sum of conduction or convection current and displacement
current) leaving any *closed* surface is zero.   This will be so in our
example if the displacement current emerging from the curved surface
of Fig. 124 just equals the current entering across the plane shaded
area.   The latter has a magnitude dq/dt according to the equation of
continuity, and this can be written as

$$\frac{dq}{dt} = A\,\frac{d\sigma}{dt}$$

where A is the area of the plate and σ the surface charge density.   Since
for the parallel-plate condenser $D = \sigma$, we arrive at the following
expression for the displacement current between the condenser plates:

$$i_d = A \frac{\partial D}{\partial t} \tag{10.4}$$

and a corresponding current density

$$J_d = \frac{\partial D}{\partial t} \tag{10.5}$$

Equation (10.5) is now postulated to be true in general; consequently, whenever an electric field changes with time, a current as given by this equation and its magnetic field are generated. The magnetic field so produced is identical with that produced by a corresponding conduction or convection current. This remarkable discovery of Maxwell introduces a fundamental symmetry into the basic laws of electromagnetism. The Faraday induction law states that changing magnetic fields generate electric fields, and the Maxwell assumption implies conversely that changing electric fields generate magnetic fields.

We can now reformulate the Ampère circuital law so that it holds in all cases, for both open and closed circuits. The total current, conduction or convection plus displacement, crossing any closed surface is zero; hence we may say that all distinction between open and closed circuits has disappeared. The vector field of electric current density, if one includes displacement current density, is solenoidal, and the lines of flow always form closed curves. If we write the equation of continuity in the form

$$\int_{\substack{\text{closed}\\\text{surface}}} J_n \, dS + \frac{\partial q}{\partial t} = 0 \tag{10.6}$$

we can use Gauss's law for the flux of the electric displacement vector across this closed surface and have

$$\int_{\substack{\text{closed}\\\text{surface}}} D_n \, dS = q$$

where q is the charge inside this surface. Substituting this value of q in Eq. (10.6), there follows

$$\int_{\substack{\text{closed}\\\text{surface}}} \left(J_n + \frac{\partial D_n}{\partial t} \right) dS = 0 \tag{10.7}$$

or

$$\int_{\substack{\text{closed}\\\text{surface}}} (J_n + J_{dn}) \, dS = 0 \tag{10.8}$$

and the form of the Ampère circuital law remains unaltered if we replace the ordinary electric current i by the sum of this current and the displacement current. We thus have

$$\oint H_s \, ds = i + \int \frac{\partial D_n}{\partial t} \, dS \tag{10.9}$$

This is one of the fundamental laws of electromagnetic theory.

Note that the displacement current across any surface is just equal to the time rate of change of the flux of D across that surface. Thus, in Eq. (10.4), the displacement current between the condenser plates is just the rate of change of the flux DA leaving either plate. In ordinary conducting bodies, the contribution of the displacement current to the total current is entirely negligible for low frequencies. To see this, let us suppose there is an alternating current density $J = J_0 \sin \omega t$ at some point in a medium of conductivity σ. From Ohm's law, we have $J = \sigma \mathcal{E}$, or $\mathcal{E} = J/\sigma$. Hence the displacement current density at this point will be

$$J_d = \frac{\partial D}{\partial t} = \epsilon \frac{\partial \mathcal{E}}{\partial t} = \frac{\epsilon}{\sigma} \frac{\partial J}{\partial t} = \frac{\omega \epsilon}{\sigma} J_0 \cos \omega t$$

$$J_d = \frac{2\pi f \epsilon}{\sigma} J_0 \cos \omega t$$

with f the frequency of the alternating current and electric field. Thus the displacement and conduction currents are 90° out of phase with each other, and the ratio of the rms values of these currents is $2\pi f \epsilon/\sigma$.

We have no information concerning the value of ϵ for metals, so let us for the time being assume it is equal to ϵ_0 as in vacuum. Now since $\epsilon_0 \cong (10^{-9}/36\pi)$ farad/m and since σ is of the order of magnitude of 10^7 mhos/m for good conductors, the ratio of displacement current to ordinary current is of the order of $10^{-17}f$. We thus see that, even if ϵ were much larger than ϵ_0, the displacement current can be neglected in conducting bodies for frequencies up to optical frequencies. Even at ultrahigh radio frequencies, there is no sensible error introduced by taking the conduction current to be the total current. In nonconducting bodies, however, this is not the case, and in empty space the displacement current is the total current. This discussion thus justifies the tacit assumption that conduction current is the total current in the conductors forming the a-c circuits of Chap. 9.

We have now arrived at the point where we can collect the fundamental relations constituting the basis of electromagnetic theory, at least for empty space. These relations, known as the Maxwell equations, are

$$\oint \mathcal{E}_s \, ds = -\int \frac{\partial B_n}{\partial t} \, dS; \qquad \oint H_s \, ds = \int \left(J_n + \frac{\partial D_n}{\partial t} \right) dS$$

$$\int_{\substack{\text{closed} \\ \text{surface}}} B_n \, dS = 0; \qquad \int_{\substack{\text{closed} \\ \text{surface}}} D_n \, dS = \int \rho \, dv \tag{10.10}$$

to which we add the supplementary relations

$$B = \mu_0 H; \qquad D = \epsilon_0 \mathcal{E} \qquad \text{for vacuum}$$

and, in the case of conductors, $J = \sigma \mathcal{E}$.

3. Plane Electromagnetic Waves in Vacuum. Now let us examine some of the consequences of the introduction of the concept of displacement current. We treat the case of empty space in which no charges or convection currents are present, and hence the only current is displacement current. For this case of empty space, the fundamental Maxwell equations take the form:

$$\oint \mathcal{E}_s \, ds = -\int \frac{\partial B_n}{\partial t} \, dS \tag{10.11}$$

$$\oint H_s \, ds = +\int \frac{\partial D_n}{\partial t} \, dS \tag{10.12}$$

$$\int_{\substack{\text{closed} \\ \text{surface}}} B_n \, dS = 0 \tag{10.13}$$

$$\int_{\substack{\text{closed} \\ \text{surface}}} D_n \, dS = 0 \tag{10.14}$$

The last two of these equations are not independent of the first and can be derived from them, since they state that the lines of B (or H) and those of D (and $\mathcal{E}$) close on themselves in empty space. The proof is left to the reader.

In general, the solutions of Eqs. (10.11) to (10.14) yield electric and magnetic fields depending on the three space coordinates and on the time. We can, however, obtain a simple but important solution for which the electric and magnetic field vectors depend only on one space coordinate, let us say x, and on the time. For this case, Eqs. (10.13) and (10.14) require that the electric and magnetic field vectors be at right angles to the x-axis, *i.e.*, that the x-components of all the vectors vanish. To see this, let us apply Eq. (10.13) at a given instant of time to the closed surface of an infinitesimal cube of sides dx, dy, and dz (Fig. 125).   Equation (10.13) states that the total flux of B emerging from the faces of this cube is zero.   Since the components of B do not vary with y and z, the flux entering the volume across one of the faces $dx\,dy$ or $dx\,dz$ is just equal to the flux leaving across the corresponding opposite face.   For the faces $dy\,dz$, the flux leaving through the right-hand face is $B_x\,dy\,dz$, where B_x is the value of this component at the point where this right-hand face is located.   Similarly, the flux leaving across the left-hand face is $-B_x\,dy\,dz$, where now B_x is taken

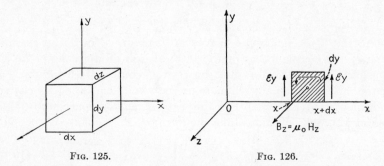

Fig. 125.   Fig. 126.

at the point where this face is located.   (The outward normal at this left-hand face is $-x$.)   Since the sum of these terms must vanish in accordance with Eq. (10.13), it follows that B_x must have the same value at both faces $dy\,dz$ and hence cannot vary with x.   A similar proof holds for the electric displacement D.

Let us start with the simplest assumption, $viz.$, that $\mathcal{E}$ has only one component, $\mathcal{E}_y$, which depends on x and on t.   We now apply Eq. (10.11) to the elementary circuit shown in Fig. 126, proceeding in a counterclockwise direction as shown.   The horizontal portions yield no contribution to the emf since $\mathcal{E}_s$ vanishes for these sides.   For the right-hand vertical side we have

$$\int \mathcal{E}_s \, ds = (\mathcal{E}_y)_{x+dx} \, dy$$

and for the left-hand side the corresponding term is

$$\int \mathcal{E}_s \, ds = -(\mathcal{E}_y)_x \, dy$$

Thus we obtain for Eq. (10.11)

$$\oint \mathcal{E}_s \, ds = [(\mathcal{E}_y)_{x+dx} - (\mathcal{E}_y)_x] \, dy = -\frac{\partial B_z}{\partial t} \, dx \, dy \qquad (10.15)$$

Now $(\mathcal{E}_y)_{x+dx} - (\mathcal{E}_y)_x$ is just the increase in $\mathcal{E}_y$ between the points x and $x + dx$ and can be written as $(\partial \mathcal{E}_y/\partial x)\,dx$. Substituting this value in Eq. (10.15), there follows

$$\frac{\partial \mathcal{E}_y}{\partial x} = -\frac{\partial B_z}{\partial t} = -\mu_0 \frac{\partial H_z}{\partial t} \quad (10.16)$$

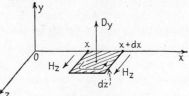

Next we calculate the mmf according to Eq. (10.12) around the elementary circuit shown in Fig. 127, proceeding in the direction shown.

FIG. 127.

We find exactly as in the preceding calculation

$$\oint H_s\,ds = [(H_z)_x - (H_z)_{x+dx}]\,dz = -\frac{\partial H_z}{\partial x}\,dx\,dz$$

and from Eq. (10.12) this must equal

$$\int \frac{\partial D_n}{\partial t}\,dS = \frac{\partial D_y}{\partial t}\,dx\,dz$$

There then follows

$$\frac{\partial H_z}{\partial x} = -\frac{\partial D_y}{\partial t} = -\epsilon_0 \frac{\partial \mathcal{E}_y}{\partial t} \quad (10.17)$$

The simultaneous solution of Eqs. (10.16) and (10.17) will then yield the electric and magnetic fields. We already see that in order to have fields of the type we are investigating, the electric vector generates a magnetic vector perpendicular to it (in our case B_z), and vice versa. If we differentiate Eq. (10.16) with respect to x, we obtain

$$\frac{\partial^2 \mathcal{E}_y}{\partial x^2} = -\mu_0 \frac{\partial^2 H_z}{\partial t\,\partial x}$$

and differentiating Eq. (10.17) with respect to t,

$$\frac{\partial^2 H_z}{\partial x\,\partial t} = -\epsilon_0 \frac{\partial^2 \mathcal{E}_y}{\partial t^2}$$

from which we obtain immediately

$$\frac{\partial^2 \mathcal{E}_y}{\partial x^2} = \epsilon_0 \mu_0 \frac{\partial^2 \mathcal{E}_y}{\partial t^2} \quad (10.18)$$

One can easily show that the other magnetic and electric vectors, H_z, B_z, and D_y satisfy exactly the same equation. The product $\epsilon_0 \mu_0$ is the reciprocal of the square of a velocity. If, as before, we denote this velocity by c, we have [see Eq. (7.10)]

$$c = \frac{1}{\sqrt{\epsilon_0 \mu_0}} = 3.00 \times 10^8 \text{ m/sec} \quad (10.19)$$

Written in terms of c, Eq. (10.18) becomes

$$\frac{\partial^2 \mathcal{E}_y}{\partial x^2} = \frac{1}{c^2} \frac{\partial^2 \mathcal{E}_y}{\partial t^2} \tag{10.18a}$$

Equation (10.18) or (10.18a) is the differential equation for one-dimensional wave motion, the so-called *wave equation*, which has already been encountered in the study of elastic vibrations and acoustics, and the solutions represent waves traveling along the x-axis with a velocity $c = 1/\sqrt{\epsilon_0 \mu_0}$. Here we encounter a direct and important consequence of the assumption of a displacement current: the prediction of the existence of *electromagnetic waves* traveling in empty space with a velocity c which can be predicted from purely electrical measurements. The fact that the numerical value of c is very nearly 3×10^8 m/sec, which is the velocity of light, led Maxwell to propose an electromagnetic theory of light, one of the brilliant contributions to physics of the nineteenth century. Nowadays the existence and observation of electromagnetic waves have become commonplace, but in Maxwell's time this prediction provided a critical test for his theory.

We see from our derivation that only transverse waves are predicted in empty space, both the electric and magnetic vectors being perpendicular to the direction of propagation and to each other. Let us consider a traveling sinusoidal wave satisfying Eq. (10.18a). For such a wave we can write for $\mathcal{E}_y$,

$$\mathcal{E}_y = \mathcal{E}_0 \sin \omega \left(t - \frac{x}{c} \right) \tag{10.20}$$

This represents a wave traveling along the positive x-axis with an amplitude $\mathcal{E}_0$, frequency $f = \omega/2\pi$, and velocity c. The wavelength of this wave is given as usual by

$$\lambda = \frac{c}{f} \tag{10.21}$$

Since the phase of the wave described by Eq. (10.20) is by definition the argument $\omega[t - (x/c)]$ of the sine function, we see that the surfaces of constant phase are planes whose normal is the x-axis, given at any definite instant of time by the equation $x = constant$. These surfaces of constant phase travel in the positive x-direction with the uniform velocity c. Thus the waves described by Eq. (10.20) are called *plane waves*, and the wave velocity c is often referred to as the *phase velocity* of these waves. Consider a fixed plane $x = constant$, transverse to the direction of propagation. At all points of this plane, the electric field intensity $\mathcal{E}_y$ oscillates in simple harmonic motion with angular frequency ω and amplitude $\mathcal{E}_0$, and all these motions are in phase with each other. The lines of $\mathcal{E}$ in such a plane are the lines of a uniform field in the y-direction. Thus at any fixed point in space the electric vector performs simple harmonic motion along a fixed direction, the y-axis, and the magnetic vector performs a similar vibration in a direction normal to this, the z-axis. Such a wave is called a *linearly polarized* wave, since the electric field vector at any point is directed along a fixed line at all instants of time. More generally, for a definite frequency, one has both y- and z-components of $\mathcal{E}$ (and corresponding z- and y-components of H) of arbitrary amplitudes and phases, since

$\mathcal{E}_y$ is independent of $\mathcal{E}_z$ and both satisfy the wave equation. Thus the resultant electric vector at a fixed point of space will vary with time in such a manner that it sweeps out an ellipse in a y-z plane, the superposition of two mutually orthogonal simple harmonic motions of arbitrary amplitudes and phase difference. This is shown diagramatically in Fig. 128. Such a wave is called *elliptically polarized*, and a circularly polarized wave

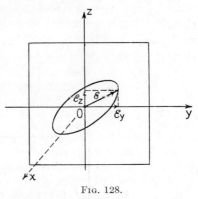

Fig. 128.

is the special case of the ellipse with equal major and minor axes; *i.e.*, the two simple harmonic motions are of equal amplitude and of 90° phase difference.

We now must investigate the relations between the amplitudes and phases of the electric and magnetic vectors in a traveling plane electromagnetic wave. While it is true that the magnetic field vector satisfies the same wave equation [Eq. (10.18)] as the electric field vector, it is not independent of the latter, since one must satisfy Eqs. (10.16) and (10.17). This is a more stringent condition than that of satisfying only the wave equation. Suppose we start with Eq. (10.20) for the electric vector of a linearly polarized wave,

$$\mathcal{E}_y = \mathcal{E}_0 \sin \omega \left(t - \frac{x}{c} \right)$$

and differentiate this with respect to the time t. There follows

$$\frac{\partial \mathcal{E}_y}{\partial t} = \omega \mathcal{E}_0 \cos \omega \left(t - \frac{x}{c} \right)$$

Substituting this in Eq. (10.17), we find

$$\frac{\partial H_z}{\partial x} = -\omega \epsilon_0 \mathcal{E}_0 \cos \omega \left(t - \frac{x}{c} \right)$$

and integrating with respect to x

$$H_z = c \epsilon_0 \mathcal{E}_0 \sin \omega \left(t - \frac{x}{c} \right)$$

Since $c = 1/\sqrt{\epsilon_0 \mu_0}$, this can be written as

$$H_z = \sqrt{\frac{\epsilon_0}{\mu_0}}\, \mathcal{E}_0 \sin \omega \left(t - \frac{x}{c} \right) = \sqrt{\frac{\epsilon_0}{\mu_0}}\, \mathcal{E}_y \qquad (10.22)$$

showing that the magnetic vector oscillates in phase with the electric vector and that the amplitudes of the electric and magnetic field strengths are related by

$$\sqrt{\mu_0}\, H_0 = \sqrt{\epsilon_0}\, \mathcal{E}_0 \qquad (10.23)$$

Now since the dimensions of $\mathcal{E}$ are volts per meter and those of H are amperes per meter, the ratio $\mathcal{E}_0/H_0 = \sqrt{\mu_0/\epsilon_0} \cong 377$ ohms $\cong 120\pi$

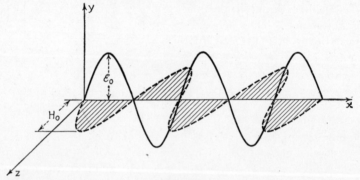

Fig. 129.

ohms is an impedance and is called the *wave impedance* of the traveling plane wave. Since for a traveling plane wave, $\mathcal{E}_y$ and H_z are in phase, the wave impedance for such a wave is a resistance. *In a traveling plane electromagnetic wave in empty space, the ratio of electric to magnetic field strength is equal to $\sqrt{\mu_0/\epsilon_0}$ at any point of space at all times.*

In Fig. 129 are shown the space variations of $\mathcal{E}$ and H in a traveling sinusoidal plane wave which is linearly polarized.

4. Energy Flow and the Poynting Vector. Electromagnetic waves such as we have just encountered carry energy, and this propagated energy is usually observed by absorption, *i.e.*, allowing the waves to impinge on matter and measuring the consequent changes in the absorbing system. Considering, as before, electromagnetic waves in empty space, the law of conservation of energy states that the net flow of energy out of any fixed volume in space must equal the rate of decrease of electromagnetic field energy inside this volume.

In Chaps. 4 and 8 we have seen that one can consider the energy stored in electric and magnetic fields as distributed throughout the region of space where these fields are present with densities $\epsilon_0 \mathcal{E}^2/2$ and $\mu_0 H^2/2$, respectively. We have developed these expressions for static fields but shall now assume that the same interpretation and formulas hold for time-varying fields. Thus the total electromagnetic energy inside a volume v is

$$U = \tfrac{1}{2} \int (\epsilon_0 \mathcal{E}^2 + \mu_0 H^2)\, dv \qquad (10.24)$$

where the integration is to be carried out over the whole region v. Let us rewrite this equation in a form appropriate to the problem of the plane waves of the preceding section. Since in this case the electric and magnetic field vectors ($\mathcal{E}_y$ and H_z) depend only on the x-coordinate at a given instant of time, we take as our volume a cylinder of cross section A and altitude dx in the x-direction. Equation (10.24) then takes the special form

$$U = \frac{\epsilon_0 \mathcal{E}_y^2 + \mu_0 H_z^2}{2} A\, dx \qquad (10.24a)$$

and the time rate of decrease of this field energy is

$$-\frac{\partial U}{\partial t} = -A \left(\mathcal{E}_y \frac{\partial D_y}{\partial t} + H_z \frac{\partial B_z}{\partial t} \right) dx \qquad (10.25)$$

where we have set $\epsilon_0 \dfrac{\partial \mathcal{E}_y}{\partial t} = \dfrac{\partial D_y}{\partial t}$ and $\mu_0 \dfrac{\partial H_z}{\partial t} = \dfrac{\partial B_z}{\partial t}$. Now from Eqs. (10.16) and (10.17), we have $\dfrac{\partial B_z}{\partial t} = -\dfrac{\partial \mathcal{E}_y}{\partial x}$ and $\dfrac{\partial D_y}{\partial t} = -\dfrac{\partial H_z}{\partial x}$, so that Eq. (10.25) becomes

$$-\frac{\partial U}{\partial t} = A\, dx \left(\mathcal{E}_y \frac{\partial H_z}{\partial x} + H_z \frac{\partial \mathcal{E}_y}{\partial x} \right) = A\, dx\, \frac{\partial}{\partial x} (\mathcal{E}_y H_z) \quad (10.25a)$$

As already stated, this rate of decrease of field energy must equal the net rate of flow of energy out of the volume across the bounding surfaces. In our special case, there can be no energy flow in the y- or z-directions (since the fields depend only on x and t) so that one has energy flow across the two faces of area A, as indicated in Fig. 130, outward across the right-hand face and inward across the left-hand face.

Now let S be the rate of energy flow across the face per unit area. The net rate of flow out of the volume is accordingly

$$(SA)_{x+dx} - (SA)_x = A \frac{\partial S}{\partial x} dx \qquad (10.26)$$

Comparing this with Eq. (10.25a), we see that the vector S, which in this special case is evidently S_x, has the value

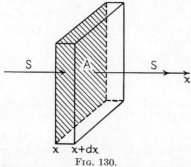

$$S_x = \mathcal{E}_y H_z \qquad (10.27)$$

The vector **S,** known as the *Poynting* vector after its discoverer, is called the *intensity*, or *power density*, of electromagnetic radiation and is the power per unit area transferred across a surface element normal to the direction of flow of energy. It is measured in watts per square

Fig. 130.

meter in the mks system. We note further that the right-hand side of Eq. (10.27) is just the x-component of the vector product of $\mathcal{E}$ and H, so that we may write

$$\mathbf{S} = (\boldsymbol{\mathcal{E}} \times \mathbf{H}) \qquad (10.28)$$

This is the correct general form for the Poynting vector and shows that the energy flow is at right angles to the plane defined by the two vectors $\boldsymbol{\mathcal{E}}$ and $\mathbf{H}$, *i.e.*, along the direction of propagation in our case of a traveling plane wave.

In the special case of linearly polarized traveling plane waves, one can use the fact that, in accordance with Eq. (10.22), $\sqrt{\epsilon_0}\, \mathcal{E}_y = \sqrt{\mu_0}\, H_z$ to obtain the magnitude of the Poynting vector in the form

$$S = \sqrt{\frac{\epsilon_0}{\mu_0}}\, \mathcal{E}_y^2 = c\epsilon_0\mathcal{E}_y^2 \qquad (10.29)$$

using the relation $c = 1/\sqrt{\epsilon_0\mu_0}$. This shows that the power density at a given point of space varies with the time but that the energy flow is always in the same direction, along the positive x-axis in the direction of propagation. The time-average power per unit area is given by

$$\bar{S} = c\epsilon_0\overline{\mathcal{E}_y^2} = c\epsilon_0\mathcal{E}_{rms}^2 = \frac{c}{2}\,\epsilon_0\mathcal{E}_0^2 \qquad (10.30)$$

where $\mathcal{E}_0$ is the amplitude of the electric field strength, since the average value of $\sin^2 \omega[t - (x/c)]$ is $\frac{1}{2}$.

Equation (10.29) has a simple physical interpretation. Since $\epsilon_0 \mathcal{E}^2 = \mu_0 H^2$ for a traveling plane wave, (10.29) can be written as

$$S = \frac{c}{2} (\epsilon_0 \mathcal{E}^2 + \mu_0 H^2) \tag{10.31}$$

which states that the Poynting vector at any point is equal to the propagation velocity c times the total energy density at that point. Consider a unit area normal to the direction of energy flow. The energy traversing this area in time dt is $S \, dt$, and this will fill a cylindrical volume of base unity and altitude $c \, dt$. Thus the energy density at this point should be $S \, dt/c \, dt = S/c$, in agreement with Eq. (10.31).

Problems

1. Starting from the equation of continuity in the form

$$\int J_n \, dS + \int \frac{\partial \rho}{\partial t} \, dv = 0$$

and Gauss's law, show that in a conducting medium obeying Ohm's law ($J = \sigma \mathcal{E}$) the following relation holds in any volume element inside the medium:

$$\left(\frac{\partial \rho}{\partial t} + \frac{\sigma}{\epsilon_0} \rho \right) dv = 0$$

From this, show that if one has an initial charge density ρ_0 at any point inside the conductor, the charge density ρ at any later time t at this point is given by

$$\rho = \rho_0 e^{-(\sigma/\epsilon_0)t}$$

The time constant ϵ_0/σ is known as the *relaxation time* of the conducting material.

2. A parallel-plate condenser with circular plates each of area A is connected to an a-c generator so that the charge on the plates varies as $q = q_0 \sin \omega t$. Neglecting end effects, the lines of H are circles with centers on the axis of symmetry of the system. Show that the magnetic field intensity at any point between the plates is given by

$$H = \frac{\omega r q_0}{2A} \cos \omega t$$

where r is the distance from the axis to the field point.

3. In Prob. 2 derive an expression for the flux of magnetic induction B in the space between the plates.

4. A long, solid cylindrical conductor of radius R has a thin transverse air gap cut in it. If the conduction current density is $J = J_0 \cos \omega t$ at all points

inside the conductor, find the magnetic field in the gap at a point located at a distance $R/2$ from the axis of the cylinder.

5. The region between the plates of a parallel-plate condenser is filled with a material medium of permittivity ϵ_0 and resistivity ρ. The condenser is initially charged and discharges through the material medium.

Show that the total current density (displacement plus conduction) is zero at any point between the plates during the discharge.   Neglect fringing.

6. Compute the frequencies of electromagnetic waves of the following wavelengths: 10^5 m (audio frequencies); 10^2 m (radio frequencies); 10 microns (heat waves); 5,000 A (optical frequencies); 0.1 A (X rays).   (1 micron $= 10^{-6}$ m; 1 A $= 10^{-10}$ m.)

7. Following the method outlined in the text, show that for a plane wave traveling in the x-direction, the electric and magnetic field vectors satisfy the relations

$$\frac{\partial \mathcal{E}_y}{\partial x} = -\frac{\partial B_z}{\partial t} ; \qquad \frac{\partial \mathcal{E}_z}{\partial x} = \frac{\partial B_y}{\partial t}$$

$$\frac{\partial H_z}{\partial x} = -\frac{\partial D_y}{\partial t} ; \qquad \frac{\partial H_y}{\partial x} = \frac{\partial D_z}{\partial t}$$

From these equations show that $\mathcal{E}_y$ and $\mathcal{E}_z$ separately satisfy the wave equation [Eq. (10.18)].

8. Prove that the superposition of two linearly polarized traveling plane waves of the same frequency gives a circularly polarized traveling wave if the two original waves are polarized at right angles to each other, have equal amplitudes of the electric field strengths, and are 90° out of phase with each other.

9. A plane radio wave, traveling in the x-direction with a frequency of 600 kc/sec, is linearly polarized with the electric vector in the y-direction.   It transmits an average power per unit area of 29.8 watts/m².

a. What is the wavelength of this wave?

b. What are the amplitudes of the electric and magnetic field strengths?

10. A long, straight, cylindrical conductor of radius a carries a steady current i uniformly distributed over its cross section.   The conductivity of the conductor is σ.

a. Find the electric field strength $\mathcal{E}$ and the magnetic field intensity H at any point within the conductor (magnitudes and directions).

b. Derive an expression for the Poynting vector at this point, stating its direction.

c. From your answer to part *b*, show that there is a flow of energy *into* the conductor across its surface which is equal to the rate of heating in the conductor.

11. A very long solenoid of n turns per unit length carries a current which increases uniformly with the time, $i = kt$, so that the magnetic field energy increases with time.

a. What is the magnetic field H inside the solenoid at time t?

b. Calculate the induced electric field $\mathcal{E}$ at a point P at a distance r from the solenoid axis. What is its direction? (Note the symmetry about the solenoid axis.)

c. Compute the magnitude of the Poynting vector at the point P. What is its direction?

d. Consider a cylinder of length l and radius equal to that of the solenoid, and coaxial with the solenoid. Using your answer to part *c*, find the rate at which energy flows into the volume enclosed by this cylinder, and show that it is equal to $d(\frac{1}{2}Li^2)/dt$, where L is the self-inductance of a length l of the solenoid.

12. The average rate at which the earth receives radiant energy from the sun at noon is 2.2 cal/min-cm². Find the rms values of the electric field intensity $\mathcal{E}$ and the magnetic induction B in sunlight at the earth's surface.

13. A 100-watt lamp radiates all the energy supplied to it uniformly in all directions. Compute the rms values of the electric and magnetic field strengths at a point 1 m from the lamp. What is the electromagnetic energy density at this point?

14. A plane electromagnetic wave with a maximum value of the electric field intensity of 100 volts/m is normally incident on a surface which is perfectly absorbing. The mass of the surface is 10^{-2} kg/m², and its specific heat is 0.2. Find the rate of increase of temperature of the surface.

15. Two linearly polarized plane waves traveling in the same direction (along the x-axis) have their electric vectors in the same direction (the y-axis) but have different amplitudes and frequencies. Prove that the average power density (the average rate of energy flow per unit area) of the resultant wave is equal to the sum of the average power densities of the individual waves. (Average over a large number of periods.)

From this show that the rms value of $\mathcal{E}$ for the resultant wave is the square root of the sum of the squares of the rms values of $\mathcal{E}$ for the individual waves.

16. A linearly polarized plane electromagnetic wave of wavelength 4.0 m travels along the x-axis with its electric vector $\mathcal{E}$ directed along the y-axis and of amplitude 150 volts/m. A loop antenna in the form of a square loop with its sides 1 m long is set up in the x-y plane with its edges parallel to the x- and y-axes.

Compute the rms induced emf in the loop antenna.

CHAPTER 11

RADIATION OF ELECTROMAGNETIC WAVES

In the preceding chapter we have seen that the introduction of the concept of displacement current by Maxwell led to the prediction of the possibility of free electromagnetic waves in empty space. We now inquire into the sources of electromagnetic waves, *i.e.*, the methods of generating waves of different wavelengths. The electromagnetic spectrum is most conveniently classified according to the sources utilized for the production of the radiation of different wavelengths and in a broad sense falls into two large divisions: one has first—and this is the region which will occupy our attention in this chapter—the *long-wave region*, comprising waves of wavelength longer than about 1 mm in empty space; and, second, the short-wave region from about 1 mm down to the shortest waves known. The fundamental difference between these two regions lies in the so-called *coherence* of the radiation. In the short-wavelength region the electromagnetic radiation field consists of the superposed effects of a large number of elementary wave trains, each of atomic origin; one has no control over the relative phases, polarizations, and lengths of these elementary wave trains. Such radiation, for which the relative phases of the individual elementary waves bear no fixed relations to one another and hence have a completely random distribution, is called *incoherent*. In the long-wave region, on the other hand, the radiation can be generated by large-scale generators or oscillators and is *coherent;* amplitude, phase, and length of the wave trains can be controlled and maintained with fixed relative values. The difference between incoherent and coherent radiation is quite similar to the difference between the motion of a large number of molecules (in kinetic theory), for which the positions and velocities of the individual molecules are entirely random and uncontrollable, and the motion of one or more large-scale particles, for which the individual motions may be controlled.

We defer the discussion of atomic radiation (heat, light, X rays, etc.) to later chapters and consider only the long-wavelength region in this chapter. Here we shall concern ourselves principally with plane electromagnetic waves of the sort studied in Chap. 10 and with *spherical* waves, waves for which the constant-phase surfaces are the surfaces

202

of concentric spheres.   It should be pointed out that the term "spherical wave" does not necessarily imply spherical symmetry of the distribution of wave amplitude over a surface of constant phase—the amplitude may vary in a complicated manner from point to point of such a spherical surface—but simply that these constant-phase surfaces are spherical.

1. Electromagnetic Waves on Wires.   In a traveling electromagnetic wave, the electric and magnetic vectors vary with both position and time, the changing magnetic field inducing an electric field and the changing electric field (the displacement current density) inducing a magnetic field.   Since stationary electric charges produce electrostatic fields, and since charges moving with constant velocity (steady currents) produce steady magnetic fields, it is evident that accelerated charges or time-varying currents are required to generate electromagnetic-wave fields.   The simplest sort of accelerated motion of charges or variation of current with time is simple harmonic motion, and we have already encountered this sort of oscillation for a simple circuit consisting of an inductance and a capacitance (Fig. 131).   Neglecting the resistance in the circuit, the conduction current in this circuit will vary sinusoidally (as will the charges on the condenser plates) with a frequency f given by

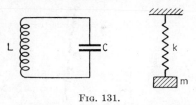

Fig. 131.

$$f = \frac{1}{2\pi} \sqrt{\frac{1}{LC}} \qquad (11.1)$$

This circuit is the analogue of the mechanical system of a mass m moving under the action of a spring of stiffness coefficient k, the motion being simple harmonic with a frequency

$$f = \frac{1}{2\pi} \sqrt{\frac{k}{m}} \qquad (11.1a)$$

For the mechanical motion there is a periodic interchange of the kinetic energy of the mass m (assuming that it is large enough compared to the mass of the spring so that the latter may be neglected) and the potential energy of the spring.   It must be stressed that the mass m (the carrier of kinetic energy) and the spring (the carrier of potential energy) are completely separated.   Similarly in the electric circuit, there is a periodic interchange of the electric energy in the condenser field (the analogue of potential energy) and the magnetic energy (the analogue of kinetic energy) of the field of the inductance.   Here again one has complete separation of the electric and magnetic energies, neglecting the relatively small magnetic field generated by the displacement current between the condenser plates.   This separation of the "seats" of electric and magnetic energies becomes more and more complete, the larger the inductance L and the capacitance C. Since an electromagnetic wave requires the spatial overlapping of the fields of $\mathcal{E}$ and H, it is virtually impossible to produce such waves with the circuit of Fig. 131, just as one cannot obtain mechanical waves from the spring and mass of the same figure.

In mechanics we have seen that wave motion can be set up in extended continuous bodies in which mass and restoring forces are continuously distributed throughout the media.   Such is the case of a stretched string or of an air column in a tube.   In these cases we may no longer consider the potential energy restricted to one region of space and the kinetic energy to another, but there is a periodic variation of both potential and kinetic energy at each point of the medium. Now exactly the same requirements must be satisfied in the electrical problem if wave motion is to be possible.   Our circuit must not possess concentrated capacitance and inductance, but the geometrical configuration must be such that both the electric and magnetic fields overlap and coexist in the same region of space.   Perhaps the simplest circuit which fulfills this requirement is a transmission line consisting of a pair of parallel wires or the more symmetrical coaxial cable. Here we may think of the two conductors forming the plates of an extended condenser, the electric field being largely in the region of space between them, and the currents carried by these conductors give rise to a magnetic field in the same region of space.   Thus we should expect that electromagnetic waves could be set up in this system, and we shall now show that this is true.

Consider a very long parallel pair of wires connected to an a-c generator, as shown in Fig. 132.   We shall consider the case for which the resistance of the conductors is negligible, so that the charges on the wires flow along their surfaces.   At any instant of time there will be a definite distribution of charge on the conductors, and this distribution will change with time, giving rise to a current distribution.   If

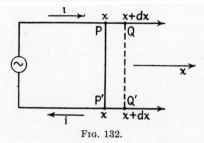

FIG. 132.

τ is the charge per unit length (linear charge density)—this varies with position and time—then, at a given instant of time, the charge residing on the element of length $dx = PQ$ (Fig. 132) is $\tau\,dx$, with an equal and opposite charge on the element $P'Q'$. The charge density is related to the current by the equation of continuity. For the case at hand, we have for the rate of decrease of charge on the element dx (PQ)

$$- \frac{\partial q}{\partial t} = - \frac{\partial}{\partial t}\,(\tau\,dx) = - \frac{\partial \tau}{\partial t}\,dx$$

and this must equal the difference of the currents at Q and at P

$$\left[di = \left(\frac{\partial i}{dx}\right) \partial x \right]$$

Thus we have

$$- \frac{\partial \tau}{\partial t} = \frac{\partial i}{\partial x} \tag{11.2}$$

If now C' denotes the capacitance per unit length of the line, then the voltage E between P and P' (at the point x) is related to the charge density by

$$\tau = C'E \tag{11.3}$$

and, substituting in Eq. (11.2), we obtain

$$\frac{\partial i}{\partial x} = - C' \frac{\partial E}{\partial t} \tag{11.4}$$

Furthermore the voltage drop along the line between the planes PP' at x and QQ' at $x + dx$ is $-dE = -(\partial E/\partial x)\,dx$, and this is in turn

$$- \frac{\partial E}{\partial x}\,dx = L'\,dx\,\frac{\partial i}{\partial t}$$

where L' is the inductance per unit length of the line. This can be rewritten as

$$\frac{\partial E}{\partial x} = -L' \frac{\partial i}{\partial t} \tag{11.5}$$

Equations (11.4) and (11.5), when integrated, determine the current and voltage distribution along the transmission line. Differentiating Eq. (11.4) with respect to t and Eq. (11.5) with respect to x, we can eliminate i from these equations and find

$$\frac{\partial^2 E}{\partial x^2} = L'C' \frac{\partial^2 E}{\partial t^2} \tag{11.6}$$

which is the wave equation, showing that electromagnetic waves may exist for this transmission line. If one eliminates E from Eqs. (11.4) and (11.5) in a similar manner, one obtains for the current i

$$\frac{\partial^2 i}{\partial x^2} = L'C' \frac{\partial^2 i}{\partial t^2} \tag{11.7}$$

showing that the current (and charge) also obeys the wave equation. The velocity of these electromagnetic waves is given by

$$v = \frac{1}{\sqrt{L'C'}} \tag{11.8}$$

Now it is a remarkable fact that for any pair of *parallel* straight conductors of uniform but otherwise arbitrary cross section, the product of inductance per unit length and capacitance per unit length is just equal to $\epsilon_0\mu_0 = 1/c^2$; hence the velocity given by Eq. (11.8) is just the velocity of free electromagnetic waves in empty space. We can check this statement for the coaxial line. For this case, Eq. (4.20) gives $C' = 2\pi\epsilon_0/\ln(b/a)$, and Eq. (8.16) gives $L' = \mu_0 \ln(b/a)/2\pi$. If, for example, the generator at the end of the line ($x = 0$) of Fig. 132 generates a voltage $E_0 \sin \omega t$, then in the steady state one obtains a sinusoidal voltage wave, traveling along the line, given by

$$E = E_0 \sin \omega \left(t - \frac{x}{c} \right) \tag{11.9}$$

A similar expression for the traveling wave of current may be obtained directly from Eq. (11.4) or (11.5) when one uses Eq. (11.9) for E.

Thus far in our discussion of electromagnetic waves on a perfectly conducting transmission line we have employed the language of circuit theory, using the concepts of capacity and inductance. Now let us examine the problem in terms of field theory, *i.e.*, in terms of the electric and magnetic fields in the space around the conductors, so that we may see clearly the connection between circuit ideas and the plane electromagnetic waves of Chap. 10. For this purpose it will be easier to visualize the state of affairs by imagining the wires replaced by flat parallel conducting strips without changing the essentials of the problem. Then the lines of $\mathcal{E}$ will be parallel to each other, and at a given instant of time the magnitude of $\mathcal{E}$ will be constant in a fixed plane perpendicular to the length of the line and equal to E/d, with d the separation of the conductors. This neglects fringing, and we must confine ourselves to points well within the conductor edges. Similarly, near this central region, the lines of B (or H) will be parallel to each other and at right angles to both $\mathcal{E}$ and x, and the magnitude of either will be essentially constant in this region.   Thus we are led to the identical picture for the electromagnetic field between the conductor strips that we had for a linearly polarized plane wave in free space, $\mathcal{E}$ having only a y-component and H a z-component.   It now becomes evident that the equation for the traveling voltage wave [Eq. (11.9)] is identical with that for $\mathcal{E}_y = E/d$, which one derives directly from the Maxwell equations [compare Eq. (10.20)].   Accordingly we have traveling waves of $\mathcal{E}$ and H with the Poynting vector

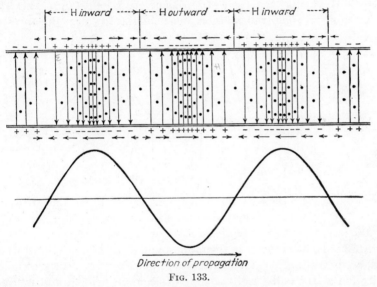

Fig. 133.

directed along the line (along the x-axis) so that the energy flow is in this direction.   The state of affairs is illustrated schematically in Fig. 133 for a traveling sinusoidal wave at a given instant of time. The vertical lines terminating on the conductors represent the electric field, the magnitude of $\mathcal{E}$ indicated by the line spacing.   The dots indicate the magnetic field distribution, the density of dots indicating roughly the manner in which the magnitude of H varies along the line. The arrows just above and below the $+$ and $-$ charges indicate the current distribution on the conductors.   To obtain the picture of a traveling sine wave, we must imagine the whole diagram moving uniformly to the right.   The sine curve of the lower sketch represents the variation with distance along the line of either charge, electric or magnetic field intensity, current, or voltage between conductors, since they are all in phase with each other.   It must be emphasized that these results hold strictly only for infinitely good conductors, for which the charges reside on the surface. When resistance is taken into account, the propagation velocity becomes less than that of electromagnetic waves in empty space, and the fields are distorted, there being a component of the Poynting vector directed perpendicular to and into the conductors. However, at very high frequencies, because of skin effect, the current is concentrated very near the conductor surfaces. The wave velocity then approaches c and is independent of the conductor material.

Up to this point we have restricted our attention to *traveling* waves on an infinitely long transmission line. Just as for mechanical waves,

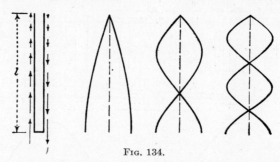

Fig. 134.

one obtains reflections of these waves at the end of a line when the latter is of finite length, and in some cases one may obtain *pure standing waves*. Thus, for example, suppose we have a line such as that of Fig. 132 of length l, open at the far end and short-circuited at the near end, as shown in Fig. 134. In this case one has very nearly complete reflection at the ends, and the superposition of incident and reflected waves gives rise to standing waves of the allowed modes, just as for mechanical waves. In Fig. 134 are sketched the first three modes of oscillation of a line open at one end, short-circuited at the other, representing the current distribution along the line. The arrows indicate the current distribution on both wires at a given instant of time for the fundamental mode. The analogies to vibrating mechanical systems are evident. In contrast to the case for traveling waves, the voltage and current are 90° out of phase at every point; consequently there is no propagation of energy on the average, merely an oscillation back and forth along the line. Thus there is a current node at the open end and a voltage maximum there, whereas at the short-circuited end, there is a voltage node and current maximum. One can show readily that the standing-wave pattern of the electric and magnetic fields is similar to that of voltage and current, the electric field having a node at the short-circuited end and an antinode at the open end, with the opposite behavior of the magnetic field.

In the lowest or fundamental mode of oscillation, the voltage between the wires is given by the equation

$$E = E_m \sin \omega_0 t \sin \frac{\pi x}{2l} = E_m \sin \omega_0 t \sin \frac{2\pi x}{\lambda_0} \qquad (11.10)$$

where $\omega_0 = 2\pi f_0 = 2\pi c/\lambda_0$ and $\lambda_0 = 4l$. From Eq. (11.4) we have

$$\frac{\partial i}{\partial x} = -\omega_0 E_m C' \cos \omega_0 t \sin \frac{\pi x}{2l}$$

Integrating with respect to x, we find for the current distribution

$$i = \frac{2l\omega_0}{\pi} E_m C' \cos \omega_0 t \cos \frac{\pi x}{2l} \qquad (11.11)$$

which shows clearly the 90° phase difference between voltage and current both for the space distribution at a given instant of time and for the sinusoidal time variations at a given point on the line. Further details are left to the problems.

2. The Radiation Field of an Oscillating Dipole. We have just seen how both traveling and standing electromagnetic waves can be produced by currents and charges on a pair of parallel conductors, and we must now inquire into the question as to how these guided waves can be disengaged from the conductors and become free electromagnetic waves. This is the problem of the radiation of waves from accelerated charges and is sufficiently complicated so that we cannot undertake a quantitative analysis. We shall therefore arrive at the radiation formulas with the help of qualitative and semiquantitative considerations.

Since the Maxwell displacement current is primarily responsible for the possibility of existence of free electromagnetic waves, let us consider more carefully the distribution of displacement current for waves on a transmission line. In any case the flow lines of current (conduction and displacement current) must form closed curves. For the transmission line, the lines of displacement current density terminate on the conductors, since they are coincident with the lines of $\mathcal{E}$, and there they join continuously with the lines of conduction current on the conductor surfaces. This is in sharp contrast to the situation for free electromagnetic waves in empty space, where there exists no conduction current and the lines of displacement current density (and hence of $\mathcal{E}$) themselves form closed curves. To understand how free electromagnetic waves can be produced by currents or by waves on conductors, we must see why the lines of $\mathcal{E}$ should break away from the conductors and close on themselves. The key to the solution of this problem lies in the fact that electromagnetic disturbances are propagated with a *finite*, rather than an infinite, velocity. Consider the electric and magnetic fields at a distance r from an oscillating charge distribution on an element of length of a conductor. The fields due to this charge will oscillate essentially in phase with the charge and current variations, provided the distance r is very much shorter than the wavelength of electromagnetic waves for the same frequency. In this case the time required for a change in the charge and current to produce a corresponding change in the fields is very short compared to the period of oscillation; consequently, at any instant of time the fields are essentially the same as would be produced by a static charge and steady current of the same values as the instantaneous charge and current at the given instant of time. On the other hand, if we consider the state of affairs at a distance r large compared to a wavelength, *i.e.*, when the time of propagation of the fields from the source to the field point is much longer than the period of an oscillation, then *retardation effects*, as they are termed, become important; the fields are different from the patterns obtained from fixed charge distributions and steady currents, and this field pattern is that of traveling waves. Suppose we fix our attention on two field points, both lying on a straight line from the source and both at distances from the source much larger than a wavelength. Furthermore, let the separation of these two points be just half a wavelength. At a fixed instant of time, there will be a definite direction of $\mathcal{E}$ at the outer point, and clearly the direction of $\mathcal{E}$ at the nearer field point will be just reversed, since the time required for the field to propagate from one field point to the other is just half a period. In this time interval the charge and current distributions on the source will have just reversed. Clearly the lines of $\mathcal{E}$ (and $\partial\mathcal{E}/\partial t$) passing through both field points cannot conceivably both terminate on the conductor which is the source, and since the lines cannot start or stop in empty space, they must close on each other, forming the closed lines of $\mathcal{E}$ necessary for free electromagnetic waves. In the intermediate region of space, which is of the order of a wavelength distant from the source, the field patterns are very complex. This is the transition region between the two types of fields just discussed.

When electromagnetic waves travel on a transmission line, such as a pair of parallel wires, the fields are confined largely to the region of space near the conductors, making the geometrical arrangement unfavorable for radiation. Let us now consider what happens when we deform the circuit of Fig. 134 by increasing the angle between the wires until they eventually form a straight conductor (Fig. 135).

The electric field produced by a fixed charge distribution on this circuit evidently spreads out over an increasingly large region of space as the angle between the original pair of conductors is increased. In Fig. 135d we have a single straight wire (an antenna), on which we must visualize not a static distribution of charge but a standing wave of charge and current, oscillating sinusoidally with the time, such as the fundamental mode of oscillation of Fig. 134. The actual distribution of charge and current will have to be maintained by some suitable

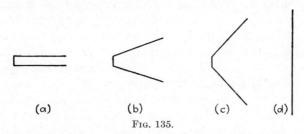

(a)   (b)   (c)   (d)

Fig. 135.

external source of emf. At any point of this antenna, *i.e.*, in any length element *dl*, the current and charge will vary sinusoidally with the time, but there will be a progressive phase shift of these sinusoidal oscillations as the element *dl* moves along the antenna. Hence to calculate the radiation field of such a system, we must superpose the contributions from all the elementary lengths *dl*, taking into account the relative phases of these contributions. Thus the fundamental problem is that of studying the field of an a-c element *i dl*, and as we shall show shortly, this is equivalent to a tiny dipole (a point dipole) oscillating in simple harmonic motion. An antenna of finite length becomes essentially equivalent to such a point dipole if it is driven in *forced* oscillation at frequencies much below its lowest natural frequency. In this case, essentially no phase difference exists between the currents at different points of the conductor, and its length is very small compared to a wavelength and hence to the distances from the antenna to the wave-field regions of space.

We are now ready to discuss the nature of the radiation field of an oscillating dipole in more detail. The lines of *B* or *H* produced by such a dipole or equivalent current element are circles with their centers on the dipole axis, just as for the magnetic field of a straight wire, and this is true at all distances from the source although the variation of magnitude with distance is very different at near and distant points. The distribution of lines of electric field intensity is quite complicated, becoming relatively simple only at large distances.   In this wave-field

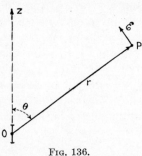

Fig. 136.

region, the lines of $\mathcal{E}$ are perpendicular both to H and to the radius vector drawn from the dipole source to the field point P.   This is illustrated in Fig. 136.   The vector H at the point P is directed outward from the plane of the page.   Furthermore, the magnitudes of $\mathcal{E}$ and H are related by $\sqrt{\epsilon_0}\,\mathcal{E} = \sqrt{\mu_0}\,H$, just as for plane waves. The Poynting vector $\mathbf{S} = \boldsymbol{\mathcal{E}} \times \mathbf{H}$ is directed outward along r, so that energy travels radially outward from the source at O, and we

have spherical electromagnetic waves.   Before we discuss the analytical expressions for $\mathcal{E}$ and H of these spherical waves, let us consider the physical nature of the field.

The oscillating charge and current on the antenna generate electric and magnetic fields which propagate outward from the source with the velocity of light, c.   During a half cycle, the fields build up in one direction, and then they reverse and decrease, building up in the opposite direction.   These alternations of the field strengths lag behind the charge and current alternations in the source, the lag increasing with increasing distance from the source because of the finite velocity of propagation of these fields.   If there were no phase lag (infinite velocity of propagation), the average power flowing into the field would be zero averaged over one cycle, as much energy flowing out as returning in this time interval, just as in the case of the field energy of a condenser or inductance at low frequencies.   Because of the progressive lag with distance, however, there is not exact cancellation of inward and outward power flow from the source, and this yields the small amount radiated in the form of the spherical waves mentioned previously.   It must not be thought that these waves exist only at large distances from the source.   They are present in all space, even close to the source.   The resultant electromagnetic field, however, is to be thought of as a superposition of this wave field and the other oscillating field, which does not represent traveling waves.   The latter field, the energy of which alternately leaves and returns to the source, is very large compared to the wave field near the antenna but decreases much more rapidly with distance from the source than does the wave field, so that only at distances large compared with the wavelength does the resultant field become practically that of traveling spherical electromagnetic waves.

We now turn to the variation of the magnitudes of $\mathcal{E}$ and $\mathbf{H}$ with position and time. Since they are related by $\sqrt{\epsilon_0}\,\mathcal{E} = \sqrt{\mu_0}\,H$, it will be sufficient to consider one of them. First consider the variation with distance r from the source and with the time t. We should expect $\mathcal{E}$ to vary sinusoidally with time with a frequency equal to that of the dipole but retarded in phase by an angle $2\pi r/\lambda = \omega r/c$, with ω the angular frequency and λ the wavelength. Furthermore, the amplitude of this oscillating vector must be proportional to $1/r$, as is evident from the conservation of energy: the total power flow across a spherical surface of radius r must be independent of r, since there are no sources or sinks of energy in empty space. The Poynting vector, which is proportional to $\mathcal{E}^2$, must therefore vary as $1/r^2$, so that when it is integrated over the surface of a sphere (the area of which is $4\pi r^2$), the result does not depend on the radius of this spherical surface. Thus we expect an expression for $\mathcal{E}$ (and for H) of the form

$$\mathcal{E} \sim \frac{1}{r}\sin\omega\left(t - \frac{r}{c}\right) \qquad (11.12)$$

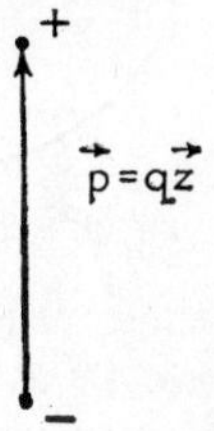

We have been referring to the source either as a current element on an antenna or as an oscillating dipole. Let us examine the equivalence of these sources. Let $p = qz$ be the dipole moment at any instant of time and $P = qz_0$ its maximum value, with z_0 the maximum separation of the charges of the dipole (Fig. 137). Since for simple harmonic motion

$$z = z_0 \sin \omega t$$

we have

$$p = qz = P \sin \omega t$$

Now a charge q moving with a velocity v is equivalent to a current element $i\,dl$, so that

$$\frac{dp}{dt} = q\frac{dz}{dt} = qv = \omega P \cos \omega t = i\,dl = I\,dl \cos \omega t$$

Thus an oscillating dipole is entirely equivalent to a sinusoidal current element $i\,dl$, whose amplitude is equal to the angular frequency times the maximum dipole moment and which is 90° out of phase with the oscillating dipole.

The magnitude of $\mathcal{E}$ depends further on the angle θ (Fig. 138)

Fig. 137.

between r and the axis of the dipole, in just the same manner as the field of a *static* dipole, being maximum for $\theta = \pi/2$, zero for $\theta = 0$, and proportional to $\sin \theta$ for intermediate values of θ. Thus the complete time and space dependence of $\mathcal{E}$ and H in the wave field is, using (11.12),

$$\sqrt{\epsilon_0}\, \mathcal{E} = \sqrt{\mu_0}\, H \sim \frac{\sin \theta}{r} \sin \omega \left(t - \frac{r}{c} \right) \qquad (11.13)$$

and there remains only the question of the proportionality constant.

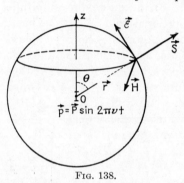

FIG. 138.

As already mentioned, accelerated charges (varying currents) generate electromagnetic waves, whereas stationary charges and steady currents give rise to static electric and magnetic fields, respectively. Thus we should expect the proportionality constant of (11.13) itself to be proportional to the acceleration of the oscillating dipole charge, *i.e.*, to the quantity $\omega^2 P$, and this is precisely the result which one obtains from the exact theory. We now write the complete expression for the magnitudes of the electric and magnetic vectors for the spherical wave radiated by an oscillating dipole:

$$|\mathcal{E}| = \frac{\omega^2 P}{4\pi\epsilon_0 c^2} \frac{\sin \theta}{r} \sin \omega \left(t - \frac{r}{c} \right) \qquad (11.14)$$

and

$$|H| = \sqrt{\frac{\epsilon_0}{\mu_0}} |\mathcal{E}| = \frac{\omega^2 P}{4\pi c} \frac{\sin \theta}{r} \sin \omega \left(t - \frac{r}{c} \right) \qquad (11.15)$$

where we have used the relation $c = 1/\sqrt{\epsilon_0\mu_0}$ to obtain Eq. (11.15). The directions of these vectors (at a given instant of time) are shown in Fig. 138. Since both $\mathcal{E}$ and H vary as $\sin \theta$, the power density S of the wave is not spherically symmetric but varies as $\sin^2 \theta$, with maximum radiation at right angles to the direction of the dipole moment and no radiation along its axis. The surfaces of constant phase, however, are concentric spherical surfaces.

As a final step, we shall calculate the total rate of emission of electromagnetic energy from the dipole. The magnitude of the Poynting vector is, remembering that $\mathcal{E}$ and H are perpendicular to each other,

$$|S| = |\mathcal{E}| \cdot |H| = \frac{\omega^4 P^2}{16\pi^2 \epsilon_0 c^3} \frac{\sin^2 \theta}{r^2} \sin^2 \omega \left(t - \frac{r}{c} \right)$$

using Eqs. (11.14) and (11.15), and this vector is normal to the constant-phase surfaces. Since the time average over a cycle of $\sin^2 \omega[t - (r/c)]$ is $\frac{1}{2}$, the average rate of energy flow per unit area across a sphere of radius r is

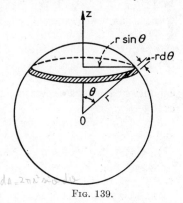

$$\bar{S} = \frac{\omega^4 P^2}{32\pi^2 \epsilon_0 c^3} \frac{\sin^2 \theta}{r^2} \qquad (11.16)$$

and to obtain the total radiated power, we must evaluate the integral $\int \bar{S} \, dA$ over the surface of a sphere of radius r. The appropriate element of area is a ring of width $r \, d\theta$ and circumference $2\pi r \sin \theta$ (Fig. 139), this ring being the locus of all the points of the spherical

Fig. 139.

surface having the same value of θ, so that the average radiated power is

$$\frac{\overline{dE}}{dt} = \int \bar{S} \, dA = \frac{\omega^4 P^2}{16\pi\epsilon_0 c^3} \int_0^\pi \sin^3 \theta \, d\theta \qquad (11.17)$$

To evaluate the integral, we write

$$\int_0^\pi \sin^3 \theta \, d\theta = \int_0^\pi (1 - \cos^2 \theta) \sin \theta \, d\theta$$

$$= \int_{\theta=0}^{\theta=\pi} (\cos^2 \theta - 1) d(\cos \theta) = \left[\frac{\cos^3 \theta}{3} - \cos \theta \right]_0^\pi = \frac{4}{3}$$

Substituting this value in Eq. (11.17), we have finally

$$\frac{\overline{dE}}{dt} = \frac{\omega^4 P^2}{12\pi\epsilon_0 c^3} = \sqrt{\frac{\mu_0}{\epsilon_0}} \frac{\omega^4 P^2}{12\pi c^2} \qquad (11.18)$$

Thus we see that the average rate of emission of energy from an oscillating dipole is proportional to the square of the amplitude of the dipole moment and to the fourth power of the frequency.

The extension of the foregoing results to the case of an antenna of finite length on which the current distribution is prescribed is a straightforward integration of the expressions for $\mathcal{E}$ and H over the elements of length of the antenna, taking into account the variations of the phase of the current with position on the antenna. We shall not carry it through, however, since we shall have occasion later to solve a similar problem in optics which will bring out all the essential points.

Problems

✓ **1.** An a-c voltage $E = E_0 \sin \omega t$ is applied to one end of a very long transmission line which consists of a pair of parallel conductors. Neglecting the resistance of the conductors, show that the generator delivers a current i to the line which is related to the voltage by $E = \sqrt{L'/C'}\, i$, where L' and C' are the inductance and capacitance per unit length of the line, respectively.

✓ **2.** Suppose the transmission line of Prob. 1 is a coaxial cable, the central conductor having a radius a and the sheath a radius b. Assuming ideal conductors:

a. Compute expressions for $\mathcal{E}$ and H at any point between the conductors, and from these obtain the magnitude and direction of the Poynting vector.

b. Find the rate of energy flow perpendicular to a cross section of the cable by integrating the Poynting vector over this area, and show that its average value equals the average power delivered by the generator.

✓ **3.** For the coaxial line of Prob. 2, prove that the magnitudes of the electric and magnetic field vectors are related as in a plane wave, *viz.*,

$$\sqrt{\epsilon_0}\,\mathcal{E} = \sqrt{\mu_0}\,H$$

✓ **4.** Starting from Eq. (11.10) of the text for the voltage distribution in a standing wave on a line of length l (the fundamental mode), derive an expression for the current distribution on the line using Eq. (11.15) of the text, and show that this is identical with the result expressed by Eq. (11.11), using $L'C' = 1/c^2$. Show that the ratio of maximum voltage to maximum current is $\sqrt{L'/C'}$.

5. A pair of parallel wires, each of length 3 m, form a resistanceless line which is short-circuited at *both* ends.

a. Compute the frequencies of the first three modes of oscillation of this system.

b. Write a general expression for the frequencies of the standing waves which may be set up on these wires.

6. Standing waves are set up on a coaxial line 3.0 m long. The radius of the center conductor is 0.20 cm, and the inner radius of the outer conductor is 2.0 cm. Assume ideal conductors. The current on this line is given by

$$i = 2.0 \sin \omega t \cos \frac{2\pi x}{3}$$

with i in amperes, x in meters, x being measured from one end of the line.

a. Is the line open or short-circuited at either end? What are the frequency and wavelength of this wave?

b. Derive an expression for the voltage E between the conductors as a function of x and t. What is the maximum voltage and at what positions does it occur?

c. Compute the rms values of $\mathcal{E}$ and H at a point 1.0 cm from the axis in the central section of the line, *i.e.*, at $x = 1.5$ m.

7. A coaxial cable of length 4.0 m, radius of the inner conductor 2.0 mm and inner radius of the outer cylinder 2.0 cm, is short-circuited at both ends. A standing wave is set up of frequency equal to that of the fundamental mode. The rms value of the current in the short-circuiting element at one end of the cable is 5.0 amp.

a. Write expressions for the energy density of the electric field and of the magnetic field at an arbitrary point inside the cable between the conductors, and find an expression for the total energy density at this point.

b. Integrate your answer to part *a* over the space between the conductors to find the total electromagnetic energy of the wave, showing that it is constant.

c. Find the total electromagnetic energy of this wave in joules.

8. A lossless transmission line 6.0 m long is short-circuited at one end, and a voltage $E = 2.0 \sin \omega t$ is applied to the other end. The frequency ($f = \omega/2\pi$) of the applied voltage is 33.3×10^6 cycles/sec.

a. Find the maximum value of the voltage in the standing wave set up on this line. At what point or points does it occur?

b. How many voltage nodes are present between the ends of the line, and what are their locations?

9. An antenna of length l is driven at a frequency $\omega/2\pi$ small compared to its lowest natural frequency, so that it carries an alternating current of amplitude I. Show that the expressions for the electric and magnetic field strengths in the radiation field of this antenna take the forms

$$|\mathcal{E}| = \sqrt{\frac{\mu_0}{\epsilon_0}} \frac{Il}{2\lambda} \frac{\sin \theta}{r} \sin \omega \left(t - \frac{r}{c} \right)$$

and

$$|H| = \frac{Il}{2\lambda} \frac{\sin \theta}{r} \sin \omega \left(t - \frac{r}{c} \right)$$

where λ is the wavelength of the emitted waves.

Using the above equations, derive the following formula for the average rate of energy radiation from the antenna:

$$\frac{\overline{dE}}{dt} = \frac{\pi}{3} \sqrt{\frac{\mu_0}{\epsilon_0}} I^2 \left(\frac{l}{\lambda} \right)^2$$

10. A radio station employs an antenna of length 30 m and broadcasts on a frequency of 10^6 cycles/sec = 1 megacycle/sec. If the antenna is to radiate 5 kw, compute the rms value of the antenna current, using the results of Prob. 9.

CHAPTER 12

ELECTRONIC CONDUCTION IN VACUUM AND IN METALS

We have now reached the point where we must turn to a discussion of the electrical and magnetic behavior of material bodies. Thus far our principal task has been the development of the fundamental laws of electromagnetism for empty space, and to accomplish this, it has been necessary to introduce certain facts concerning the electrical properties of matter, *e.g.*, the distinction between conductors and insulators, and Ohm's law. These have been kept to a minimum, however, and now we proceed to a more detailed investigation of the laws governing the electromagnetic behavior of matter. The situation is somewhat analagous to that in the study of mechanics. There, after the formulation of Newton's laws of motion and their application to particles and to rigid bodies, one turns to the field of the mechanics of deformable bodies. One is then forced to inquire into the nature of the internal forces which hold material bodies together and finds that there are two distinct modes of approach to this problem. First, there is the large-scale, or macroscopic, viewpoint, treating material bodies as continuous media; and second, there is the more fundamental, but more complicated, atomic viewpoint. In a similar manner, one can approach the problems of the electrical and magnetic behavior of matter in the same dual manner, and we shall do this, but we shall place more emphasis on the atomic interpretation than is done ordinarily in mechanics.

There is overwhelming evidence that atoms are composed of electrically charged particles, a central nucleus carrying practically all the atomic mass and possessing a positive charge equal to an integral multiple of the electronic charge, let us say Ze. Z is known as the *atomic number*, and it is this number that characterizes the chemical elements. Thus the nucleus of ordinary hydrogen, the so-called *proton*, has $Z = 1$, the helium nucleus has an atomic number $Z = 2$, etc., throughout the whole periodic table of the elements. Each atom possesses Z electrons, so that it is normally uncharged as a whole. These electrons are distributed more or less spherically around the central nucleus. They are in rapid motion about the nucleus and are prevented from escaping principally by the strong Coulomb attractive

218

forces between nucleus and electrons. The mass of the proton is approximately 1,840 times that of an electron, or 1.67×10^{-27} kg. Atoms possessing a larger or smaller number of electrons than their normal content are called *ions*, positive ions if they possess fewer than Z electrons and negative ions if they possess more than Z electrons. One essential point must always be kept in mind in thinking of any model of an atom, *viz.*, that it is an open structure, the average distances between electrons and between electrons and nucleus being very large compared to the dimensions of either the nucleus or an electron.

From an atomic viewpoint the conduction of electricity in material bodies is due to the motion of electrons or ions or both. In electrolytes the current is due to the migration of both the positive and negative ions of the solute under the influence of an externally applied electric field. Migration of ions is also possible under the influence of strong fields in certain solid crystals which possess a definite space-lattice arrangement of positive and negative ions, as in the case of silver bromide. In this chapter we shall concern ourselves only with *electronic* currents. The simplest case is that of conduction of electricity by electrons in high vacua, such as in an ordinary radio tube. Somewhat more complicated is the conduction of electricity in metals, where electrons can move throughout the metal. These electrons, the so-called *free*, or *conduction*, electrons, can be thought of as valence electrons of the metallic atoms which have been liberated from their parent atoms by the mutual interaction of the latter when they are packed together as tightly as they are in a metallic lattice. These liberated electrons form a sort of gas and are relatively free, belonging to the metal as a whole rather than to individual atoms. Finally in the case of electrical discharges in gases, both mobile ions and electrons are present; the latter are mainly responsible for the current, but the presence of the former gives rise to quite complicated phenomena.

1. Thermionic Emission; Electronic Currents in High Vacua. Before formulating the laws governing electronic currents in vacuum, we must discuss briefly the methods of liberating electrons from metals. When an electron is removed from a metal, work must be done against the attractive forces which normally prevent its escape. The work per unit charge required to remove an electron from a metal is called the *work function* of the metallic surface and is of the order of magnitude of a few volts. This work must be done no matter what method of liberation is employed, various methods differing in the manner in which the requisite energy is supplied to the escaping electron.

In the *photoelectric effect*, the electrons gain energy from the absorption of light. Electrons liberated by bombarding a metal with electrons (so-called *secondary electrons*) pick up their excess energy from the impinging electrons. Bombardment by positive ions or by neutral atoms carrying more than their normal configuration energies (metastable atoms) can also liberate electrons. Very intense electric fields can pull electrons out of metals (so-called *cold emission*), and finally, heating the metal can impart sufficient thermal energy to some of the electrons to enable their escape in a manner analogous to the thermal evaporation of a liquid. This phenomenon of *thermionic* emission has become commonplace through application to radio tubes, etc.

Consider a piece of metal with a plane surface in vacuum maintained at a definite temperature. We picture the conduction electrons inside a metal as forming a gas and shall treat them as free. These free electrons possess kinetic energy, and it was formerly supposed that they behaved just like the atoms of an ideal gas in that the average kinetic energy of an electron was $\frac{3}{2}kT$ (k is Boltzmann's constant) in accordance with the law of equipartition of energy. However, the experimental fact that the contribution by the conduction electrons to the specific heat of a metal is exceedingly small has always been a serious difficulty for the free-electron picture. We know now, however, that conduction electrons in a metal do not obey the equipartition law and that their energy is practically independent of temperature, increasing but slightly as the metal temperature is raised. This small increase of energy, however, is just what is needed to enable the faster electrons to escape. Returning now to the metallic sample, we picture some of the electrons escaping from the surface and forming a negatively charged cloud just outside this surface. This negative *space charge* inhibits the further release of electrons, and equilibrium is established. The density of electrons outside the metal is so small compared to its value inside that the external electrons do behave like an ideal gas and possess the normal amount of kinetic energy, $\frac{3}{2}kT$ per electron. If these electrons are drawn off to a collecting plate maintained at a higher potential than the emitting surface, more electrons escape, and there is a limiting rate (at each temperature) at which escape can occur. The corresponding maximum electronic current between emitter and collecting plate is called *saturation* current. The saturation current density varies very markedly with temperature in close analogy with the evaporation rate of a liquid. The law governing this saturation current density is known as *Richardson's equation*, and we present it without proof:

$$J = AT^2 e^{-e\phi/kT} \tag{12.1}$$

ϕ is the work function of the metal, and hence $e\phi$ is the potential energy gain of an electron escaping from the metal. A is a constant depending on the metal but having a value of

$$60 \text{ amp/cm}^2\text{-}°\text{C}^2 = 6.0 \times 10^5 \text{ amp/m}^2\text{-}°\text{C}^2$$

for many clean surfaces. Equation (12.1) has been verified over an enormous range of the variables involved; in fact it would be difficult to find any other electrical equation which has been verified over a wider range. The exponential dependence on temperature reminds one strongly of the vapor-pressure law for liquids.

When the collector (anode) potential is not sufficiently high to establish the saturation current of Eq. (12.1), a steady-state current smaller than the saturation current is set up, and one speaks of the current being limited by space charge. We shall investigate the laws governing these space-charge-limited currents for the simple case of plane-parallel electrodes, of separation sufficiently small relative to the surface dimensions of either so that electric field strength and potential vary only with an x-coordinate normal to the planes of the electrodes as in the corresponding condenser problem. Since we are concerned with a steady electric current, the electric field and potential obey electrostatic laws. Our first task is to reformulate Gauss's theorem, relating field intensity to charge density, in the form of a differential equation valid at each point of space. From this we then obtain a relation between potential and charge density in the form of a differential equation known as *Poisson's* equation. This differential form is more convenient for many purposes of application than the integral form of Gauss's theorem.

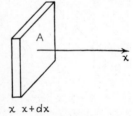

Fig. 140.

Poisson's Equation in One Dimension. We apply Gauss's theorem in the form

$$\int D_n \, dS = \int \rho \, dv$$

to the volume element of Fig. 140, for which the x-axis is normal to the faces A; the volume element has a thickness dx and is located at x. In our application, the vector D has only an x-component, and this may vary with x. The flux of D emerging from the volume element of Fig. 140 is

$$\int D_n \, dS = (DA)_{x+dx} - (DA)_x = \frac{dD}{dx} \, (A \, dx) = \frac{dD}{dx} \, dv$$

so that Gauss's theorem becomes

$$\frac{dD}{dx} = \rho$$

or

$$\frac{d\mathcal{E}}{dx} = \frac{\rho}{\epsilon_0} \tag{12.2}$$

using $D = \epsilon_0 \mathcal{E}$.

Finally, since $\mathcal{E} = - \text{grad } V = -dV/dx$ for the case at hand, Eq. (12.2) becomes

$$\frac{d^2 V}{dx^2} = - \frac{\rho}{\epsilon_0} \tag{12.3}$$

This is Poisson's equation in one dimension. Note that if $\rho = 0$, denoting the absence of space charge, the integration of Eq. (12.3) yields the uniform electric field of the parallel-plate condenser.

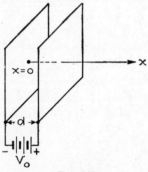

Fig. 141.

Returning now to our original problem of space-charge-limited currents, let the electrode separation be d, the hot cathode grounded (its potential equal to zero), and let the anode potential be maintained at a value V_0 above ground (Fig. 141). The steady current is carried by a stream of electrons from cathode to anode, and the magnitude of the current density J is related to the velocity v of the electron stream and the charge density by

$$J = |\rho|v = nev \tag{12.4}$$

with n the electron density at any point and e the magnitude of the charge on an electron. In Eq. (12.4) both n and v vary from point to point, *i.e.*, with x, but their product is constant and independent of position. If we denote by v_0 the average initial velocity of the electrons in the x-direction (as they leave the cathode), we have from the conservation of energy

$$\tfrac{1}{2}mv_0^2 = \tfrac{1}{2}mv^2 - eV \tag{12.5}$$

or, solving for v,

$$v = \left(v_0^2 + \frac{2e}{m} V \right)^{\tfrac{1}{2}} \tag{12.6}$$

Now since the charge density ρ is related to the electron density n by $\rho = -ne$, Eq. (12.3) may be rewritten with the help of Eqs. (12.6) and (12.4) as

$$\frac{d^2V}{dx^2} = \frac{ne}{\epsilon_0} = \frac{J}{\epsilon_0}\left(v_0^2 + \frac{2e}{m}V\right)^{-\frac{1}{2}} \tag{12.7}$$

The variation of potential with position between the electrodes will thus be obtained if we can integrate this equation. Multiplying each side of Eq. (12.7) by $2(dV/dx)\,dx$, and using the identity

$$\frac{d}{dx}\left[\left(\frac{dV}{dx}\right)^2\right] = 2\frac{dV}{dx}\frac{d^2V}{dx^2}$$

we can integrate once and obtain readily

$$\left(\frac{dV}{dx}\right)^2 - \left(\frac{dV}{dx}\right)_0^2 = \frac{2J}{\epsilon_0}\frac{m}{e}\left[\left(v_0^2 + \frac{2eV}{m}\right)^{\frac{1}{2}} - v_0\right] \tag{12.8}$$

where $(dV/dx)_0$ is the negative of the electric field intensity at the cathode surface and we have set $V = 0$ for $x = 0$.

Thus far our equations are quite general, holding equally well for saturation or space-charge-limited current. What, then, is the physical distinction between these two cases, and how can we insert this information into Eq. (12.8)? Let us start by considering Eq. (12.3). Since the right-hand side of this equation is everywhere positive (ρ is negative because of the negative electronic charge), the plot of potential against distance from the cathode must be a curve which is concave upward everywhere. This is equivalent to stating that the slope of the curve increases with increasing x. If the charge density ρ were negligibly small, V would be a linear function of x. As ρ increases in magnitude, the curve takes the form shown in (A) of Fig. 142, and if $|\rho|$ becomes large enough, a minimum in the curve will occur, as shown in curve (B). The critical curve which divides these two types

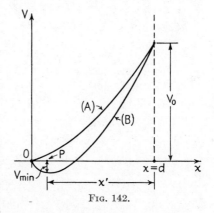

Fig. 142.

is evidently the one for which the field, and hence the slope at $x = 0$, becomes equal to zero. The potential distributions without minima correspond to saturation current, since the electric field is everywhere negative and every electron leaving the cathode will reach the anode. On the other hand, the presence of a potential minimum at P indicates a relatively large electron density at this point (the curvature is greatest at P), and the field between the cathode and P is positive (a decelerating field) because of the repulsive force action of these electrons. In this case, some of the electrons leaving the cathode (the slower ones, of energy less than eV_{min}) will turn around and return to the cathode. Thus only a fraction of the emitted electrons reach the anode, and this is the case of space-charge-limited current. We now see that we must consider not only the average initial velocity of the electrons but that we must take into account the fact that the electrons leave the cathode with a distribution of velocities (in fact a Maxwellian distribution) such that a larger and larger fraction return to the cathode, the more pronounced the potential minimum. However, since the number of electrons leaving the cathode with energies greater than 1 electron-volt is entirely negligible at ordinary cathode temperatures, we need not concern ourselves with potential minima for which V_{min} is greater than 1 volt.

It is then possible to obtain an approximate solution to Eq. (12.8) by shifting the origin of coordinates from O to P (Fig. 142). If the anode potential V_0 is the order of 100 volts, we may consider V in Eq. (12.8) as measured from the potential at P without much error and also may neglect the initial average velocity v_0 (now the velocity at P). Since dV/dx is zero at the new origin P, we set $(dV/dx)_0$ equal to zero in Eq. (12.8), and this equation becomes

$$\left(\frac{dV}{dx}\right)^2 = \frac{2J}{\epsilon_0}\left(\frac{2m}{e}\right)^{\frac{1}{2}}V^{\frac{1}{2}}$$

or

$$\frac{dV}{dx} = \left(\frac{2J}{\epsilon_0}\right)^{\frac{1}{2}}\left(\frac{2m}{e}\right)^{\frac{1}{4}}V^{\frac{1}{4}} \tag{12.9}$$

which yields upon integration

$$V = \left(\frac{9J}{4\epsilon_0}\right)^{\frac{2}{3}}\left(\frac{m}{2e}\right)^{\frac{1}{3}}x^{\frac{4}{3}} \tag{12.10}$$

satisfying the condition $V = 0$ for $x = 0$. Equation (12.10) gives very nearly the potential distribution between the position of the potential minimum and the anode. The current-voltage relation is obtained by noting that $V = V_0$ for $x = x'$. Inserting these values in Eq. (12.10) and solving for J, one obtains readily

$$J = \frac{4\epsilon_0}{9} \sqrt{\frac{2e}{m}} \frac{V_0^{\frac{3}{2}}}{x'^2} \tag{12.11}$$

Thus a current density proportional to the $\frac{3}{2}$ power of the anode potential is predicted, provided the value of x' does not vary appreciably with V_0. Actually the potential minimum lies so close to the cathode that x' may be replaced by d to a good degree of approximation, and Eq. (12.11) becomes

$$J = \frac{4\epsilon_0}{9} \sqrt{\frac{2e}{m}} \frac{V_0^{\frac{3}{2}}}{d^2} \tag{12.12}$$

and this is known as the Langmuir-Child equation. It can be shown that the proportionality between current and the $\frac{3}{2}$ power of the anode potential is independent of the geometrical arrangement of cathode and anode, subject to the limitations imposed by the approximations employed in our derivations.

2. Electrical Conductivity of Metals. The electrical conductivity of a metal is defined with the help of Ohm's law, and this law can be written in differential form as

$$\mathbf{J} = \sigma \mathcal{E} \tag{12.13}$$

We shall now show how our elementary picture of free electrons leads to Ohm's law and to a formula for the conductivity. Our model consists of free electrons wandering about among fixed positive metallic ions with random velocities, very much like the molecules of a gas. Since on the average there is no resultant force acting on any one conduction electron, we imagine these electrons moving in a region of constant potential, the average internal potential of the metal. If a uniform electric field is established and maintained within the metal, each free electron will accelerate under the action of a constant force of magnitude $e\mathcal{E}$. However, any one electron will not move far before colliding with a metallic ion and losing the kinetic energy gained from the electric field. The average effect of these collisions with the ions is the same as if there were a friction force acting on the electrons, and we shall assume that this is like viscous friction, proportional to the electron speed. Thus the average motion of an electron is governed by the equation

$$e\mathcal{E} - kv = m\frac{dv}{dt} \tag{12.14}$$

If now the external uniform field $\mathcal{E}$ is taken in the x-direction, according to Eq. (12.14) the electron will drift with a constant velocity given by

$$v = \frac{e\mathcal{E}}{k}$$

This is the steady-state solution of Eq. (12.14).   With n the number of electrons per unit volume, the ensuing steady current density is

$$J = nev = \frac{ne^2\mathcal{E}}{k} \tag{12.15}$$

Comparison with Eq. (12.13) yields for the conductivity

$$\sigma = \frac{ne^2}{k} \tag{12.16}$$

Thus the conductivity is proportional to the space density of free electrons.   The foregoing analysis is exceedingly crude and neglects completely the random kinetic energy of the electrons in the absence of an external field.   Actually this energy is very large compared to the amount gained by an electron between collisions with ions, and the drift speed of the electrons is very small compared to their random speeds.

We now refine our calculation to include these facts and dispense with the rough picture of a viscous force.   Let us assume that after each collision an electron, having transferred the energy it has gained from the external electric field to the lattice, starts again with its initial random speed.   The time between two successive collisions will be different for different electrons, but we consider the average collision time τ.   This collision time is equal to l/u, where l is the mean free path of the electrons and u the random speed.   During this time an electron accelerates uniformly along the field direction, and the average velocity gained over and above its initial velocity component in this direction is

$$v = \frac{1}{2} a\tau = \frac{1}{2} \frac{e\mathcal{E}}{m} \tau = \frac{1}{2} \frac{e\mathcal{E}}{mu} l$$

It is this average excess velocity which is to be identified with the electron drift velocity, and hence

$$J = nev = \frac{ne^2\mathcal{E}}{2mu} l$$

so that the conductivity σ is given by

$$\sigma = \frac{ne^2 l}{2mu} \tag{12.17}$$

This is a much more satisfactory formula than (12.16), and it is essentially the result of a much more elaborate calculation based on a free-electron model and modern statistical theo y.   Since we know that the mean kinetic energy of the electrons in a metal is practically independent of temperature and that the number of free electrons per unit volume presumably does not vary appreciably with temperature, the observed temperature dependence of metallic conductivity is to be sought in the variation of the mean free path l.

Actually the conductivities of pure metals vary very nearly inversely as their absolute temperature, and there are good reasons for believing that the mean free path varies this way also, at least at sufficiently high temperatures that the thermal vibrations of the metallic ions are mutually independent.

3. Thermoelectric Effects.   The most important thermal effect of electric currents in metallic conductors is Joule heating.   This heating is an irreversible effect, independent of the current direction.   There exist in addition three very closely related *reversible* effects, involving thermal and electrical energies, called thermoelectric effects, and we shall examine these briefly in this section.

a. The Seebeck Effect.   If a closed circuit is constructed of two (or more) different metallic conductors, and the junctions between dissimilar metals are maintained at different temperatures, an electric current is observed in the circuit.   This effect is termed the Seebeck effect after its discoverer.   A simple circuit consisting of two metals A and B with junctions at P and Q is shown in Fig. 143, and let the temperature T_2 of junction Q be higher than T_1, that of junction P. Such a device is known as a *thermocouple* and is used extensively as a temperature-measuring instrument.   The emf around this circuit is called a *thermal* emf, and it depends on both the junction temperatures and the two metals.   We shall denote this thermal emf by E_{AB}, the order of the subscripts indicating the current direction *at the hot junction Q* when this emf is positive. Thus in Fig. 143, E_{AB} is positive, and the current is from metal A to metal B at junction Q.   The interposition of a third metal C in series with the thermocouple circuit leaves the thermal

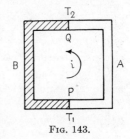

Fig. 143.

emf unaltered provided the junctions with this third metal are maintained at the same temperature.

b. The Peltier Effect.   When an electric current is maintained across the junction of two dissimilar metals, the junction temperature changes unless heat is supplied or removed by external means. The rate at which heat must be supplied to the junction to maintain its temperature constant is proportional to the current and changes sign when the current direction is reversed. This phenomenon of the evolution or absorption of heat at junctions of dissimilar metals is called the Peltier effect. It occurs whether the current is produced by an external agency or is spontaneously developed by the action of the thermocouple itself. Thus, in Fig. 143, the temperature T_2 of junction Q tends to drop (heat must be supplied to maintain it constant), and the temperature T_1 of junction P tends to rise. From the existence of the Peltier heating one infers the existence of an emf at the junction between two different metals. This Peltier emf will be denoted by Π_{AB}, indicating that the junction is between the metals A and B, and *a positive sign will mean that heat must be supplied to the junction to maintain its temperature unaltered when the current direction is from A to B.* This Peltier emf is, in general, a function of temperature. If a charge q is transported across the junction, the heat which must be supplied during this process is Πq.

c. *The Thomson Effect.* The third effect was predicted by Sir William Thomson (Lord Kelvin) on the basis of theoretical thermodynamic arguments. If different parts of the *same* metallic conductor are maintained at different temperatures, a temperature gradient and steady heat current will exist in the metal. If now an electric current is set up, the temperature distribution will be disturbed, and the accompanying evolution or absorption of heat throughout the metal (in addition to Joule heating) comprises the Thomson effect. The Thomson heat which must be supplied or removed to maintain a steady temperature distribution is reversible, changing sign with the direction of the electric current, and it is proportional to the product of the temperature gradient and the electric current. *The existence of a temperature gradient inside a metal then implies the coexistence of an electric potential gradient.*

Consider an element of length of a metallic wire, and let the temperature difference between the ends of this length element be dT. If the *Thomson emf* due to this temperature gradient is denoted by dE', we define the *Thomson coefficient* σ by the relation

$$\sigma = \frac{dE'}{dT} \qquad (12.18)$$

and call the coefficient *positive if the emf tends to drive electric current inside the metal along the temperature gradient, i.e., from low to high temperatures.* For a finite length of conductor with its ends maintained at temperatures T_1 and T_2 ($T_2 > T_1$), the Thomson emf along the conductor is evidently given by

$$E' = \int_{T_1}^{T_2} \sigma \, dT \qquad (12.19)$$

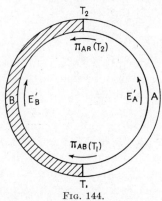

FIG. 144.

The thermal emf of a thermocouple is the sum of the Peltier and Thomson emfs in the circuit, so that the Seebeck effect does not require separate explanation if one can explain the existence of the Peltier and Thomson effects. Consider the thermocouple circuit of Fig. 144. It is shown as a closed circuit for simplicity, but we can imagine it opened and connected to a potentiometer so that the thermal emf may be measured with zero current. Let $T_2 > T_1$, so that the Peltier and Thomson emfs shown in the figure correspond to positive coefficients. From Fig. 144 it is evident that the net thermal emf E_{AB} is given by

$$E_{AB} = \Pi_{AB}(T_2) - \Pi_{AB}(T_1) + E'_A - E'_B \qquad (12.20)$$

or, using Eq. (12.19),

$$E_{AB} = \Pi_{AB}(T_2) - \Pi_{AB}(T_1) + \int_{T_1}^{T_2} \sigma_A \, dT - \int_{T_1}^{T_2} \sigma_B \, dT \quad (12.21)$$

It is often useful to write this equation in differential form. This may be obtained by applying Eq. (12.21) to a thermocouple with its cold junction at temperature T and its hot junction at temperature $T + dT$. The result is obviously

$$e_{AB} = \frac{dE_{AB}}{dT} = \frac{d\Pi_{AB}}{dT} + (\sigma_A - \sigma_B) \qquad (12.22)$$

where $e_{AB} = dE_{AB}/dT$ is called the *thermoelectric power* of the thermocouple. Equation (12.22) is essentially a statement of the first law of thermodynamics applied to a thermocouple. Application of the second law (we omit the derivation) gives

$$\frac{d}{dT}\left(\frac{\Pi_{AB}}{T}\right) + \frac{1}{T}(\sigma_A - \sigma_B) = 0 \qquad (12.23)$$

where T is the absolute temperature. From Eqs. (12.22) and (12.23) there follow the relations

$$\Pi_{AB} = T \frac{dE_{AB}}{dT} \tag{12.24}$$

$$\sigma_A - \sigma_B = -T \frac{d^2E_{AB}}{dT^2} \tag{12.25}$$

Thus from a knowledge of thermocouple emfs as functions of the temperature, one can compute the Peltier emf for the two metals and the difference of the Thomson coefficients.

In tabulating the thermoelectric properties of metals, it is usual to use lead as a reference metal, since its Thomson coefficient is zero. Consider a thermocouple constructed of lead and some other metal with one of the junctions kept at 0°C. Experimentally, one finds that the thermal emf of this thermocouple can be represented very nearly by a quadratic function of the temperature of the hot junction over a considerable range of temperature. Thus we may write

$$E = at + \tfrac{1}{2}bt^2 \tag{12.26}$$

where t is the hot-junction temperature in degrees centigrade. a and b are known as the Seebeck coefficients. Table III gives values for several metals referred to lead. A positive sign corresponds to an electric current from lead to the metal at the hot junction, so that lead corresponds to the metal A of our previous discussion.

TABLE III

Metal	a, μv/°C	b, μv/°C^2
Aluminum...............	−0.47	+0.003
Bismuth.................	−43.7	−0.47
Copper.................	+2.76	+0.012
Gold...................	+2.90	+0.0093
Iron (soft).............	+16.6	−0.030
Nickel.................	+19.1	−0.030
Platinum (Baker)........	−1.79	−0.035
Silver.................	+2.50	+0.012
Steel.................	+10.8	−0.016

In order to use Table III to compute the thermal emf of a thermocouple constructed of two arbitrary metals A and B, one uses the relation

$$e_{AB} = e_B - e_A \tag{12.27}$$

where e_{AB} is the thermoelectric power of the thermocouple, e_A and e_B are the thermoelectric powers of thermocouples made of metal A and lead and of metal B and lead, respectively.   The proof of this equation is left to the problems.

It then follows that

$$e_{AB} = (a_B - a_A) + (b_B - b_A)t \qquad (12.28)$$

where the a's and b's are the values listed in the table.

We must now inquire into an atomic interpretation of the Peltier and Thomson effects.   Qualitatively, the free-electron gas picture provides a simple explanation of these effects.   When a junction is made between two different metals (at the same temperature), one essentially brings together two electron gases of different densities and pressures.   There is a tendency for diffusion, but this cannot proceed far because of the charges on the electrons, and in equilibrium, a difference of potential is established between points on opposite sides of the interface so that diffusion forces are just balanced by electrostatic forces.   This internal potential difference between two metals must then be equal to the Peltier emf at the junction.   In a rough way, one may consider the Peltier emf as a seat of emf at the boundary, the nonelectrical forces acting in this seat of emf being the diffusion forces.   The work done by this seat of emf on the circuit when an electric current is present is equal to the heat inflow from the surroundings.

For the Thomson effect, consider a straight metallic rod with one end in boiling water and the other in melting ice.   There will be a uniform temperature gradient and a consequent steady heat current in the rod. We picture the thermal conductivity of the metal as due to the transport of energy by free electrons, the free electrons near the hot end gaining thermal (kinetic) energy in excess of these near the cold end. Now since there is no electric current in the rod, a condition must be established for which equal numbers of electrons traverse a cross section of the rod in opposite directions per unit time.   Those moving toward the cold end have somewhat higher energies than those moving in the opposite direction; hence there is a net transfer of energy, but not of charge, across this surface.   In general, this balance will not be attained under the influence of a temperature gradient *alone,* so that an electric field will be created inside the rod of such magnitude and direction that the above conditions are satisfied.   This electric field is to be identified with the Thomson potential gradient.

Problems

1. For clean tungsten the work function is 4.5 volts, and the constant A in Richardson's equation is 60 amp/cm²-°C².   Compute the saturation current densities for tungsten at $T = 1000°$ abs and $T = 2500°$abs. What is the ratio of these two currents?

2. A high-vacuum diode formed of two plane-parallel plates each of area 1.0 cm² carries a current of 1 ma when the anode potential is 180 volts above the cathode potential.

Find the speed with which the electrons strike the anode and the electron density (number per unit volume) in the immediate neighborhood of the anode.

3. For plane-parallel electrodes of separation d, plot to scale the variation of potential and electric field as functions of the distance from the cathode for space-charge-limited currents.

4. A high-vacuum diode formed of two parallel plates, each of area 4.0 cm² and of separation 2.0 mm, carries space-charge-limited current. Find the total current when the anode-cathode potential difference is 240 volts.

5. Assuming that the total space-charge-limited current between a hot cathode and an anode can depend only on e/m (ratio of electronic charge to mass), on V_0 (potential difference between anode and cathode), and on d (the electrode separation), show by dimensional analysis that this current must be given by

$$i = B\epsilon_0 \sqrt{\frac{e}{m}}\, V_0^{\frac{3}{2}}$$

where B is a dimensionless constant.

6. A copper wire of cross section 0.040 cm² carries a steady current of 50 amp. Assuming one free electron per metal atom, compute:

a. The number of free electrons per unit volume.

b. The average drift speed of these electrons.

c. The mean collision time of these electrons with the metallic ions.

The density of copper is 8.9 g/cm³; its atomic weight is 64; and its resistivity is 1.77×10^{-8} ohm-m.

7. Derive Eqs. (12.24) and (12.25) of the text from Eqs. (12.22) and (12.23).

8. Prove that the thermoelectric power of a pair of metals is equal to the difference between the thermoelectric powers of these metals each taken in conjunction with the same reference metal [Eq. (12.27) of the text].

9. Show that the thermal emf of a thermocouple constructed of two metals A and B is given by

$$E_{AB} = (a_B - a_A)(t_2 - t_1) + \tfrac{1}{2}(b_B - b_A)(t_2^2 - t_1^2)$$

where t_1 and t_2 are the cold- and hot-junction temperatures, respectively, in degrees centigrade.

10. The "neutral" temperature of a thermocouple is the temperature at which the thermoelectric powers of the two metals (each with respect to lead) are equal, so that the thermal emf is a maximum with respect to varying temperature of the hot junction. Show that the thermal emf of the couple may be written in the form

$$E = e_0(t_2 - t_1) \left(1 - \frac{t_1 + t_2}{2t_n}\right)$$

where e_0 is the thermoelectric power of the thermocouple at 0°C and t_n is the neutral temperature.

11. The thermoelectric power of a metal A is 17.5 μv/°C at 0°C, and is zero at 360°C; that of a metal B is 5μv/°C at 450°C and zero at -50°C.

What is the emf of a thermocouple constructed of these two metals with the cold junction at 0°C and the hot junction at the neutral temperature?

12. Compute the Peltier emf for a copper-nickel junction at 0°C and the Thomson coefficients for each of these metals.

13. A thermocouple is constructed of gold and iron of thermoelectric powers $(2.8 + 0.01t)$ and $(17.5 - 0.048t)$ μv/°C, respectively. Calculate and plot the emf of this thermocouple as a function of the hot-junction temperature from 0 to 700°C, if the cold junction is maintained at 0°C. What is the neutral temperature and the maximum emf obtainable from this couple?

14. A copper-iron thermocouple has a cold-junction temperature of 20°C What is the maximum emf obtainable with this couple?

15. Three metals A, B, and C are available for making a thermocouple and have the following thermoelectric powers in microvolts per degree centigrade: metal A, $17.5 - 0.048t$; metal B, $2.8 + 0.010t$; metal C, $8.0 - 0.030t$. If the junction temperatures are 0 and 400°C, which pair of metals will give the largest emf? What is this emf?

16. A copper-iron thermocouple is used to measure the temperature of a furnace. With the cold junction at 25°C, the emf of the couple as measured with a potentiometer is 1.95 mv. What is the furnace temperature?

17. Prove that the thermal emf of a thermocouple may be written as a quadratic function of the temperature difference between its junctions, *i.e.*, in the form

$$E_{AB} = \alpha(t_2 - t_1) + \tfrac{1}{2}\beta(t_2 - t_1)^2$$

provided that

$$\alpha = (a_B - a_A) + (b_B - b_A)t_1$$
$$\beta = b_B - b_A$$

CHAPTER 13

DIELECTRICS

In this chapter we shall investigate the electrical behavior of insulating nonconducting material bodies, the so-called dielectrics. As previously mentioned, no sharp line of distinction can be drawn between insulators and conductors, but many substances, such as glass, waxes, and some crystals, are very nearly ideal insulators in that they can retain localized charges almost indefinitely. We shall assume in the following that we are dealing with ideal dielectrics and that these dielectrics are *isotropic* (the properties of the substance being the same in all directions at any point) and homogeneous. From an electronic viewpoint, dielectrics are characterized by the fact that the electrons are tightly bound to their parent atoms and cannot be dislodged by ordinary fields. As a result there can be no conduction of electricity by virtue of moving charges as in a conductor, and the conductivity of an ideal dielectric is zero. If an uncharged dielectric is located in a field-free region of space, the positive and negative charges in any small volume element produce no potential or electric field, and we say that the "center of gravity" of these positive and negative charges coincide. If, however, such a dielectric is placed in an external electric field, *e.g.*, between the plates of a charged condenser, then the positive charge is pushed in the direction of the field and the negative charge in the opposite direction. The forces holding the charges together may be taken as elastic (for small displacements) so that when such a separation of positive and negative charge takes place, there is a restoring force proportional to the distance of separation, and equilibrium is attained. There is thus formed in each volume element a dipole (equal and opposite charges separated from each other), and this dipole is said to be *induced* by the external field, disappearing when the latter is removed. The process of inducing dipoles in dielectrics is called *polarization*. A polarized dielectric produces a field of its own, modifying the external field which gives rise to the polarization.

From an atomic standpoint, the dipole moment induced in a volume element of the dielectric is the average of the dipole moments of all the atoms or molecules in that volume element. There are two cases to be considered: (1) when the atoms or molecules possess no dipole moment in the absence of an external field and (2) the case of molecules (such as HCl) which possess *permanent dipole moments* (the so-called *polar* molecules).   For *nonpolar* molecules (case 1), the induced dipole moment is simply the sum of the induced moments of the individual atoms or molecules.   The induced dipole moment of an atom or molecule is proportional to the magnitude of the external field producing it, and the ratio of this induced moment to the external field strength is called the *polarizability* of the atom or molecule.   When molecules possess permanent dipole moments, the essential point is that of the space orientation of these dipole moments.   In the absence of an external field the orientation is random; hence the average moment in a small volume element is zero, as indicated in Fig. 145a, where the arrows in-

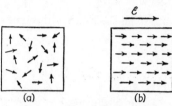

FIG. 145.

dicate the molecular dipole moments.   When an external field ε is applied, the dipoles line up in the direction of this field as shown in Fig. 145b, since this is the position of stable equilibrium, and the sum of the dipole moments is no longer zero.   Actually the thermal motion of the molecules prevents them from lining up completely and tends to maintain the random orientation.   The stronger the external field at a given temperature, the larger is the induced dipole moment of the volume element, and the net result is similar to that for nonpolar molecules, the induced dipole moment increasing with increasing external field.   For ordinary field strengths there is proportionality between the induced dipole moment and the inducing field.   One distinguishes between the two types of polarization discussed above by virtue of the strong temperature dependence of the orientation effect, the polarization decreasing with increasing temperature, whereas the nonpolar case is virtually independent of temperature.

1. The Polarization Vector; Polarization Charge.   To proceed to a quantitative formulation of the laws governing dielectric behavior, consider a material medium in which there are equal and opposite charges e whose "centers of gravity" coincide, so that they produce no external effect.   If an external electric field is applied, these charges become separated by a distance r and an induced dipole of moment

$$\mathbf{p} = e\mathbf{r} \tag{13.1}$$

is created, the vectors $\mathbf{p}$ and $\mathbf{r}$ having the same direction as the external field.   We now introduce a vector called the *polarization vector* $\mathbf{P}$, defined as the *dipole moment per unit volume* in the medium, to describe

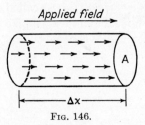

Applied field

A

Δx

FIG. 146.

the polarization state of a dielectric. It is clear that **P** is the vector sum of the atomic or molecular dipoles in a volume element divided by the volume of that element. Thus, if $\mathbf{p}_0$ is the induced dipole moment per atom produced by an externally applied field, the dipole moment $\mathbf{\Delta p}$ induced in a volume element $\Delta v = A\,\Delta x$ (Fig. 146) is the vector sum of all the $\mathbf{p}_0$'s in this element, and the polarization vector **P** becomes

$$\mathbf{P} = \frac{\mathbf{\Delta p}}{\Delta v} \tag{13.2}$$

or, more strictly, as $\Delta v \rightarrow 0$,

$$\mathbf{P} = \lim \frac{\mathbf{\Delta p}}{\Delta v} \qquad \text{as } \Delta v \rightarrow 0 \tag{13.3}$$

If the vector field of P is uniform, we say that the substance is uniformly polarized.

Let us now consider an elementary area ΔA inside a dielectric as shown in Fig. 147. If the medium is polarized by an external field acting in the direction indicated, charges will be pushed across ΔA, and, in fact, the charge

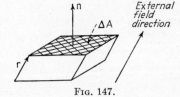

n

ΔA

External field direction

r

FIG. 147.

crossing ΔA will be equal to that originally contained in a slant prism of base ΔA and slant height r [the same r as in Eq. (13.1)]. If r_n is the component of r in the direction of the normal n to the surface element, then this charge is equal to

$$N(er_n)\,\Delta A = P_n\,\Delta A \tag{13.4}$$

where N is the number of dipoles per unit volume created in the dielectric. If ΔA should be an element of the outer surface of a body, then (13.4) represents the surface charge induced on this surface element. We thus have the important result that the surface density of charge σ' induced on the surface of a polarized dielectric is equal to the normal component of the polarization vector at that point. In symbols,

$$\sigma' = P_n \tag{13.5}$$

σ' is positive if P_n is directed along the *outer* normal to the surface, as usual.

If we consider a closed volume element entirely inside the dielectric, the net charge crossing its surface will be zero if the polarization is uniform (P = constant), but if the polarization varies from point to point, there may be more charge leaving than entering the volume element. In this case one can have a charge density created inside this volume element, the so-called *polarization charge density*. If this polarization charge density is denoted by ρ', then ρ' is related to the polarization vector P by

$$\int_{\substack{\text{closed} \\ \text{surface}}} P_n \, dS = -\int \rho' \, dv \qquad (13.6)$$

where the closed surface lies entirely within the dielectric. To prove this equation, we note that according to Eq. (13.4), the surface integral is equal to the charge which leaves the volume across its bounding surface, and hence, according to the conservation of charge, an equal and *opposite* polarization charge is left behind inside the volume; hence the minus sign in Eq. (13.6).

The induced surface and volume polarization charges create an electric field which acts in addition to the external field. In general, this induced dipole field tends to oppose the inducing field with a consequent reduction in the resultant electric field intensity relative to its value in the absence of the dielectric. This can be seen with the help of a simple example. Suppose we have a slab of dielectric, as shown in Fig. 148, placed in a uniform external field $\mathcal{E}$. There will then appear surface charges as indicated [in accordance with Eq. (13.5)], equal and opposite on the two faces, the interior remaining uncharged since $\mathcal{E}$ and P are uniform. This surface charge, although bound to the dielectric, contributes to the resultant field just as do the so-called "real"

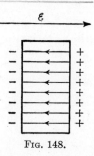

FIG. 148.

charges, such as those which we can place on conductors or move around as we wish. From the figure we see that the field of these induced surface charges opposes the external field inside the dielectric.

2. Relations of $\mathcal{E}$, P, and D. In our discussion of electric fields in empty space, we found it convenient to introduce an electric displacement vector D in addition to the fundamental field vector $\mathcal{E}$. This was defined by $D = \epsilon_0 \mathcal{E}$ for vacuum [see Eq. (3.7)], and this simple and restricted definition must now be generalized for the case of dielectric media, since it is just in this latter case that this auxiliary vector is extremely useful. We shall approach the problem of extending the definition of D with the help of a simple but important example.

Consider a plane-parallel condenser with a slab of dielectric material inserted between the plates, as shown in Fig. 149. Let the area of each plate and slab surface be A, the separation of the metal plates be d, and the slab thickness be d_0. In the figure are shown the field lines

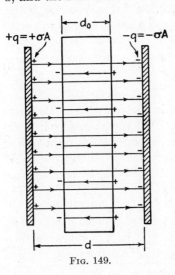

FIG. 149.

starting on the positive charges on the left-hand metal plate and terminating on the right-hand metal plate. The resultant field inside the dielectric slab is to be obtained as the resultant of the field due to the surface charges $\pm \sigma' A$ on the slab surfaces and the field produced by the charges on the metal plates. This exemplifies the general procedure: We replace the dielectric by the induced surface and volume polarization charges (in our example the induced volume charge density is zero because of the uniform polarization) and solve the *vacuum* problem of finding the field due to all the charges, polarization and "real" charges. This then yields the electric field both inside and outside the actual dielectric. Since in Fig. 149 the polarization vector is everywhere constant in magnitude and normal to the slab surfaces, we can write, in accordance with Eq. (13.5),

$$\sigma' = P$$

and hence, for the equivalent vacuum problem, the electric field intensity in the region of space occupied by the dielectric is given by

$$\mathcal{E} = \frac{\sigma - \sigma'}{\epsilon_0} = \frac{1}{\epsilon_0}(\sigma - P) \qquad (13.7)$$

using Gauss's theorem. σ is the "real" surface charge density on the metal plates. If we rewrite Eq. (13.7) as

$$\epsilon_0 \mathcal{E} + P = \sigma$$

we see that σ, which is a measure of D in a parallel-plate condenser in vacuum, is no longer equal to $\epsilon_0 \mathcal{E}$ when matter is present. Hence, *we define D by the more general relation*

$$D = \epsilon_0 \mathcal{E} + P \qquad (13.8)$$

This reduces to our previous definition $D = \epsilon_0 \mathcal{E}$ if P is zero, as in empty space.

In our example, then, we see that Gauss's theorem is still valid with the new definition of D, and because the slab faces are parallel to the condenser plates, the symmetry is not affected by the presence of the dielectric, with the result that the field of D is uniform and has a magnitude σ just as if the dielectric were not there.   This independence of the field of D on the presence of the dielectic is, however, a consequence of the special symmetry of our example and is *not* true in general.   If we rewrite Eq. (13.8) in the form

$$\mathcal{E} = \frac{D}{\epsilon_0} - \frac{P}{\epsilon_0} \qquad (13.9)$$

we see clearly how the field intensity $\mathcal{E}$ is reduced from its vacuum value D/ϵ_0 by the induced polarization field P/ϵ_0.

We now shall prove that Gauss's theorem is valid in general if we use the general definition [Eq. (13.8)] for D.   Consider a closed surface inside a polarized dielectric body.   We replace the dielectric by the induced polarization charge and have a problem in empty space. Gauss's theorem then states that

$$\int_{\substack{\text{closed} \\ \text{surface}}} \epsilon_0 \mathcal{E}_n \, dS = \int (\rho + \rho') \, dv \qquad (13.10)$$

since $\int(\rho + \rho') \, dv$ is the *total* charge inside the surface.   Now since according to Eq. (13.6) we have $\int \rho' \, dv = -\int P_n \, dS$, there follows

$$\int_{\substack{\text{closed} \\ \text{surface}}} (\epsilon_0 \mathcal{E}_n + P_n) \, dS = \int \rho \, dv$$

or

$$\int_{\substack{\text{closed} \\ \text{surface}}} D_n \, dS = \int \rho \, dv = q \qquad (13.11)$$

which is Gauss's theorem, with q the "real" controllable charge inside the surface.

We now have the following general picture: The sources of the field of D are the "real" charges distributed throughout space or placed on conductors; the sources of the field of $\mathcal{E}$ are all the charges, real plus polarization; and the sources of the polarization field are the induced polarization charges; Eq. (13.8) giving the connection among the vectors $\mathcal{E}$, D, and P.

3. Dielectric Constant; Electric Susceptibility.   It was discovered by Cavendish, and later by Faraday, that the capacity of a condenser increased if a dielectric was inserted between the condenser plates. If C is the capacity with the dielectric present and C_0 the capacity without the dielectric, the dimensionless ratio C/C_0 is defined as the *dielectric constant* of the dielectric. It is always greater than unity, only about 0.1 per cent larger for gases, but is of the order of 2 to 10 for solid insulators such as glass, and about 80 for pure water.

Returning to our example of Fig. 149, let us suppose that the whole space between the condenser plates is filled with dielectric so that $d_0 = d$. For this case the capacity of the condenser is

$$C = \frac{\sigma A}{\mathcal{E} d} = \frac{D A}{\mathcal{E} d} \tag{13.12}$$

If we now define the *permittivity*, or *specific inductive capacity*, of the dielectric ϵ by

$$D = \epsilon \mathcal{E} \tag{13.13}$$

Eq. (13.12) becomes

$$C = \frac{\epsilon A}{d} \tag{13.14}$$

Since in vacuum this condenser would have a capacity $C_0 = \epsilon_0 A/d$, the ratio of capacities is $\epsilon/\epsilon_0 = \kappa$, so that

$$\epsilon = \kappa \epsilon_0 \tag{13.15}$$

Note that the total induced charge on the slab faces is $\pm PA$, and since these faces are separated by a distance d, the dipole moment of these charges is PAd. Now Ad is the volume of the slab, and we see that in this case of uniform polarization P is truly the induced dipole moment per unit volume.

If in Eq. (13.8) we write $\epsilon \mathcal{E}$ for D in accordance with Eq. (13.13), we have

$$D = \epsilon \mathcal{E} = \epsilon_0 \mathcal{E} + P$$

or

$$\epsilon = \epsilon_0 \left(1 + \frac{P}{\epsilon_0 \mathcal{E}} \right) \tag{13.16}$$

or again

$$\kappa = 1 + \frac{P}{\epsilon_0 \mathcal{E}} \tag{13.17}$$

Thus the dielectric constant κ and the permittivity ϵ will be truly constant if the polarization P is proportional to the field intensity $\mathcal{E}$. The ratio $P/\epsilon_0 \mathcal{E}$ is known as the *electric* susceptibility χ of the medium,

$$P = \epsilon_0 \chi \mathcal{E} \tag{13.18}$$

so that the relation between dielectric constant and susceptibility is

$$\kappa = 1 + \chi \tag{13.19}$$

Since the electric field strength in a dielectric-filled condenser is reduced by a factor κ over its value for the same vacuum condenser carrying the same charge, and since this result is independent of the particular geometrical shape of the condenser employed, we infer that Coulomb's law for the force between two point charges embedded in an infinite dielectric (infinite so that the field is totally within the dielectric as in the condenser case) has the form

$$F = \frac{qq'}{4\pi\kappa\epsilon_0 r^2} = \frac{qq'}{4\pi\epsilon r^2} \tag{13.20}$$

This law is of *restricted validity*, and we shall give the precise conditions under which it is true in Sec. 6 of this chapter.

4. Cavity Definitions of D and $\mathcal{E}$. We now inquire somewhat more critically just what is meant by electric field intensity inside a dielectric medium. We recall that the field strength $\mathcal{E}$ for empty space is defined as the vector force per unit charge on an infinitesimal positive test charge. In order properly to define $\mathcal{E}$ inside a dielectric, one must provide the possibility of introducing a test charge. This is done, following Lord Kelvin, by imagining a cavity created inside the dielectric, and then one can introduce a tiny charge into this cavity and determine the force on it, at least in principle. In Fig. 150 is

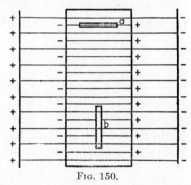

Fig. 150.

shown the parallel-plate condenser with a dielectric slab. Consider a long needle-shaped cavity such as (a) with its long sides parallel to the field. A test charge placed therein would be acted on by the fields of both the real and polarization charges, and thus the force would be $q\mathcal{E}$, if q is the magnitude of the test charge. It is necessary to choose the cavity of the shape and orientation specified in arriving at a definition of $\mathcal{E}$ to avoid the appearance of polarization bound charge on the cavity surface. Thus in a cavity of shape (b), a pillbox with the flat faces perpendicular to the field, there will appear induced surface charges on these faces of density $\pm P$, so that the lines starting on the dielectric slab surfaces will terminate on the cavity faces and none will traverse it.   As a result, only the real charge on the metal plates is effective in producing the force on a test charge in a cavity such as (*b*), and this force will be $qD/\epsilon_0 = q(\mathcal{E} + P/\epsilon_0) = q\kappa\mathcal{E}$, using Eq. (13.17). Thus the field inside cavity (*b*) is D/ϵ_0.   In general, the field inside a cavity depends on the cavity shape and is neither $\mathcal{E}$ nor D/ϵ_0; *e.g.*, the field at the center of a spherical cavity may be shown to be

$$\left[\mathcal{E} + \frac{P}{3\epsilon_0} \right]$$

5. The Dielectric Constant of Gases.   There is one case where it is relatively simple to compute the dielectric constant from an atomic model.   This is the case of a gas, let us say a monatomic gas, at moderate or low pressure, so that the atoms are far enough apart on the average to allow us to neglect the interactions between them.   Each atom has a positive nuclear charge $+Ze$ and a negative charge $-Ze$ on its electrons.   These charges can be displaced relative to each other in an external field and behave as if held together by linear restoring forces.   In a uniform external field $\mathcal{E}$, a charge q in the gas is acted on by the force $q\mathcal{E}$ due to this field and a restoring force $-kx$, if x is the field direction.   In equilibrium we have

$$-kx + q\mathcal{E} = 0$$

or $x = q\mathcal{E}/k$, and the dipole moment created is

$$p = qx = \frac{q^2\mathcal{E}}{k} \tag{13.21}$$

The *polarizability* α of an atom is defined, as stated previously, as the ratio of the induced atomic dipole moment to the field intensity, so that

$$\alpha = \frac{p}{\mathcal{E}} = \frac{q^2}{k} \tag{13.22}$$

If there are n atoms per unit volume, the polarization vector is

$$P = np = n\alpha\mathcal{E}$$

and we have from Eq. (13.17)

$$\kappa = 1 + \frac{n\alpha}{\epsilon_0} \tag{13.23}$$

Now let us try to estimate the atomic polarizability α.   We adopt a simple atomic model, a central point charge $+Ze$, corresponding to the nucleus, surrounded by a uniform spherical distribution of radius

R of negative charge $-Ze$, corresponding to the electrons.   Under the
influence of an external field the positive
charge will move a distance x in the direction
of the field relative to the negative charge, from
O to P in Fig. 151.   When in this position, it
will be attracted back toward O by the negative charge.   From our previous work in electrostatics we can calculate this force by considering all the negative charge inside the
dotted sphere of radius x to be concentrated
at O, the negative charge outside this sphere
yielding no contribution to the force.   The

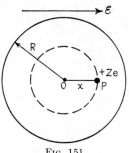

FIG. 151.

negative charge at O is then $q' = -Ze(x/R)^3$ and from Coulomb's law
the attractive force is

$$F = -\frac{Z^2e^2}{4\pi\epsilon_0 x^2}\left(\frac{x^3}{R^3}\right) = -\frac{Z^2e^2}{4\pi\epsilon_0 R^3}x = -kx$$

and this is a linear restoring force.   From Eq. (13.22) we have for the
polarizability, since $q = Ze$,

$$\alpha = \frac{(Ze)^2}{k} = 4\pi\epsilon_0 R^3 \tag{13.24}$$

proportional to the volume of the atom.   Using this value of α in
Eq. (13.23), we find for the dielectric constant of a gas, on the basis
of our rough model,

$$\kappa = 1 + 4\pi nR^3 \tag{13.25}$$

The number of atoms per cubic meter of a gas under standard conditions is about 3×10^{25}, and for the atomic radius R we may use a
rough value of $1 \text{ A} = 10^{-10}$ m.   Thus the term $4\pi nR^3$ becomes approximately 0.4×10^{-3}, or about 0.04 per cent.   This is the actual order
of magnitude of the susceptibility $\kappa - 1 = \chi$ for gases.

  6. Boundary Conditions on D and $\mathcal{E}$.   Our examination of the
manner in which electric intensity and displacement change as one
crosses a boundary separating two dielectric media has thus far been
confined to the special case where the interfacial surface is normal
to the direction of the field vectors.   We must now examine the case
where these vectors are not perpendicular to the interface, and in so
doing we shall be able to see why Coulomb's law is not universally
applicable.   However, the law of Gauss remains one of the fundamental and universally valid laws of electricity.   Consider the case
of two dielectric media of different permittivities ϵ_1 and ϵ_2, and let us

apply Gauss's theorem to the infinitesimal volume enclosed by the pill-

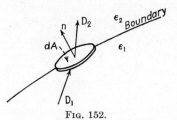

FIG. 152.

box shown in Fig. 152. The pillbox is so located that a portion of the boundary surface lies inside the volume, and we can, by making the pillbox infinitely shallow, neglect the flux of D across its curved surface, which is normal to the boundary between the dielectrics. For the two flat faces, the net flux of D emerging from the volume is $(D_{2n} - D_{1n})\, dA$, so that Gauss's theorem requires that

$$(D_{2n} - D_{1n})\, dA = \sigma\, dA$$

where σ is the surface density of real (not polarization) charge on the interface. D_{1n} and D_{2n} are the normal components of D in the two dielectrics at the point in question. Thus we have

$$D_{2n} - D_{1n} = \sigma \qquad (13.26)$$

or, if the interface is uncharged,

$$D_{1n} = D_{2n} \qquad (13.27)$$

In words, the electric displacement vector must have a continuous normal component when crossing an uncharged boundary surface between two dielectrics. Applied to our previous example of the dielectric slab between condenser plates (Fig. 149), this condition states that the value of D does not change as one crosses the surface of the slab, since the lines of D are normal to this surface. Evidently this will be true in all cases for which the boundary surfaces are normal to the field direction.

For the components of the field tangent to the boundary, we must in general apply the Faraday induction law to a closed path such as that shown in Fig. 153, in which the sides perpendicular to the boundary are made infinitely short compared to the parallel sides dl. As the lengths of the short sides are made smaller and smaller, the area enclosed by the path approaches zero, and consequently the magnetic flux through this area also approaches zero. Hence the Faraday law requires in general that the emf around this path approach zero, just as in the electrostatic case. We then have

$$\oint \mathcal{E}_s\, ds = (\mathcal{E}_{1t} - \mathcal{E}_{2t})\, dl = 0$$

$$\mathcal{E}_{1t} = \mathcal{E}_{2t} \qquad (13.28)$$

where $\mathcal{E}_{1t}$ and $\mathcal{E}_{2t}$ are the tangential components of electric field intensity in media 1 and 2 at the point in question. Note that this condition is automatically satisfied when the boundary is everywhere normal to the field, such as the example of Fig. 149.

The two boundary conditions (13.27) and (13.28) suffice to determine uniquely the relative directions of the lines of $\mathcal{E}$ and D as one crosses an uncharged boundary between two dielectrics in any case.

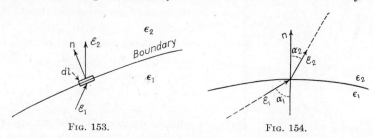

FIG. 153.   FIG. 154.

Let α_1 and α_2 be the angles between the normal to the boundary and the directions of $\mathcal{E}_1$ and $\mathcal{E}_2$ at the point where the normal is drawn, as shown in Fig. 154. We have from Eq. (13.28)

$$\mathcal{E}_1 \sin \alpha_1 = \mathcal{E}_2 \sin \alpha_2$$

and, using Eq. (13.27) with $D = \epsilon \mathcal{E}$,

$$\epsilon_1 \mathcal{E}_1 \cos \alpha_1 = \epsilon_2 \mathcal{E}_2 \cos \alpha_2$$

Dividing one by the other of these equations, there follows

$$\frac{\tan \alpha_1}{\tan \alpha_2} = \frac{\epsilon_1}{\epsilon_2} = \frac{\kappa_1}{\kappa_2} \tag{13.29}$$

and this is the law of refraction for the electric field lines at the boundary of two dielectrics of dielectric constants κ_1 and κ_2, respectively. It is clear that the same law gives the relative direction of the lines of D. Note that the field lines are bent more toward the normal in the medium of smaller dielectric constant. Thus Fig. 154 is drawn for $\kappa_1 > \kappa_2$.

We are now in a position to state precisely the limitations which must be imposed on Coulomb's law [Eq. (13.20)] and on the consequent statement that the field of D is determined *solely* by the positions and magnitudes of the "real" charges. The above statements are valid *only* if

1. The field produced by the real charges is appreciably different from zero in a single homogeneous, isotropic dielectric or in empty space.

2. The boundaries of the dielectrics present are everywhere perpendicular to the field which would exist in the absence of these dielectrics. In the presence of arbitrarily shaped dielectrics of finite size, the only property of the field of D which is unaltered by these dielectrics is the total flux of D, due to the real charges (Gauss's law). At the boundaries the direction of D undergoes a change in general, but the number of lines of D is unaffected by the presence of the boundary. We thus see why Gauss's law is so important. The above statements may be clarified by a simple example of the field produced by a single point charge q in the presence of an infinite slab of dielectric, as shown in Fig. 155. In the absence of the dielectric, the lines of D are radial and are shown dotted in the figure. The solid lines show

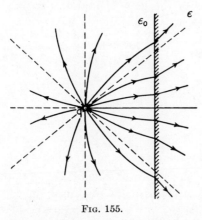

FIG. 155.

the actual field of D in the presence of the dielectric. One sees that the direction (and magnitude) of D is altered even in empty space by the presence of the dielectric. However, the total flux of D is q in any case.

The solution of the general problem, *e.g.*, one such as that of Fig. 155, involves the simultaneous solution of the equations

$$\int_{\substack{\text{closed}\\\text{surface}}} D_n \, dS = q$$

$$\oint \mathcal{E}_s \, ds = 0$$

$$D = \epsilon \mathcal{E}$$

for the case of electrostatic fields, subject to the boundary conditions derived in this section. This involves methods of potential theory which lie beyond the scope of this book.

7. Polarization and Displacement Current in Dielectrics. We now turn to a brief discussion of transient, or nonsteady, fields in dielectrics. For simplicity consider the case of a parallel-plate condenser with a dielectric of permittivity ϵ filling the space between the plates, as shown in Fig. 156. Suppose the switch S is closed and a charging current starts to build up. As the field between the condenser plates increases, the dielectric becomes polarized; positive charge moves as shown across the surface aa, and negative charge moves in the opposite direction.   This motion corresponds to a transient current while the dipoles are being formed, and this current is called polarization current. The polarization current can be expressed in terms of the polarization vector P.   From Eq. (13.4) it follows that the charge crossing the area $aa = A$ in time dt is $A\,dP$, where dP is the increase in the polarization vector in this time interval.   Consequently the polarization current is

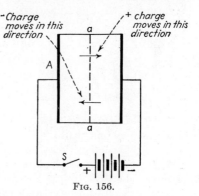

$$i_p = A\,\frac{\partial P}{\partial t} \qquad (13.30)$$

and the corresponding c u r r e n t density is

$$J_p = \frac{\partial P}{\partial t} \qquad (13.31)$$

Fig. 156.

This polarization current contributes to the total displacement current between the condenser plates. This displacement current is given by $A(\partial D/\partial t)$, and, using Eq. (13.8), it can be written as

$$i_d = A\epsilon_0\frac{\partial \mathcal{E}}{\partial t} + A\,\frac{\partial P}{\partial t} \qquad (13.32)$$

Thus the displacement current can be considered as the sum of two terms, one a displacement current $A\epsilon_0(\partial\mathcal{E}/\partial t)$ which would exist in vacuum and the other the polarization current in the dielectric.   The ratio of the polarization to the vacuum displacement current is then, using Eqs. (13.18) and (13.19),

$$\frac{A(\partial P/\partial t)}{\epsilon_0 A(\partial\mathcal{E}/\partial t)} = \frac{\epsilon_0 A\chi(\partial\mathcal{E}/\partial t)}{\epsilon_0 A(\partial\mathcal{E}/\partial t)} = \chi = \kappa - 1 \qquad (13.33)$$

i.e., it is equal to the susceptibility of the dielectric.

More generally, if we consider the case of nonuniform polarization of a dielectric, the total polarization current across a fixed closed surface is given by

$$i_p = \frac{\partial}{\partial t}\int_{\substack{\text{closed}\\ \text{surface}}} P_n\,dS \qquad (13.34)$$

and from Eq. (13.6) we have

$$\int P_n\,dS = -q'$$

where q' is the polarization charge inside the closed surface. Consequently we may write

$$i_p = \frac{\partial}{\partial t} \int P_n \, dS = -\frac{\partial q'}{\partial t} = -\frac{\partial}{\partial t} \int \rho' \, dv \qquad (13.35)$$

where ρ' is the density of polarization charge. Equation (13.35) is just the equation of continuity for polarization charge and current, stating that the polarization current out of the volume equals the rate of decrease of polarization charge inside this volume.

Problems

1. The dielectric constant of helium at 0°C and 1 atm pressure is 1.000074. Find the dipole moment induced in each helium atom when the gas is in an electric field of intensity 10^5 volts/m.

2. Consider a parallel-plate condenser with a material medium of permittivity ϵ between its plates. Following the arguments of Sec. 5, Chap. 4, show that the electrostatic energy density in the material medium is given by

$$u = \frac{\epsilon \mathcal{E}^2}{2} = \frac{D^2}{2\epsilon}$$

and that the plates attract each other with a force

$$F = \frac{A\sigma^2}{2\epsilon} = \frac{\epsilon \mathcal{E}^2}{2} A$$

3. A parallel-plate condenser is connected to a battery which maintains a potential difference V_0 between its plates. A slab of dielectric of dielectric constant κ is inserted between the plates, completely filling the space between them.

 a. Show that the battery does an amount of work $q_0 V_0(\kappa - 1)$ during the insertion process, if q_0 is the charge on the condenser plates before the slab is inserted.

 b. How much work is done by mechanical forces on the slab when it is inserted between the plates?   Is this work done on, or by, the agent inserting the slab?

4. A parallel-plate condenser with plates of area 200 cm² and separation 2.0 mm is immersed in oil of dielectric constant 3.0 and permanently connected to a 300-volt battery.

 a. Compute the charge on the condenser plates.

 b. Find the induced dipole moment per unit volume and the electric field intensity in the oil between the plates.

 c. What is the force of attraction of the plates for each other?

 d. If the plates are separated to a distance of 4.0 mm, maintaining the potential difference constant at 300 volts, calculate the mechanical work done in effecting this separation.

e. How much energy is supplied to the condenser by the battery during the process described in part *d*?

5. A vertical cylindrical condenser of altitude 1.0 m and of capacity 5.0×10^{-11} farad in air is connected through a galvanometer to a 1,000-volt battery. Water of dielectric constant 81 rises between the condenser plates at a uniform rate of 10 cm/sec.

a. Find the charge on the condenser plates (not including polarization charge) when the condenser is half full of water.

b. What is the galvanometer reading in microamperes while the water is rising?

6. A parallel-plate condenser of separation d has a capacity C_0 in air. An insulating slab of dielectric constant κ, thickness $t < d$, and area equal to that of the plates is inserted into the condenser, the slab faces being parallel to those of the condenser. Neglecting end effects, prove that the capacity of the condenser is now

$$C = \frac{C_0}{1 - [(\kappa - 1)/\kappa](t/d)}$$

7. A parallel-plate condenser with circular plates of radius 3.0 cm, separation 3.0 mm, is connected to a 600-volt battery. The plates are separated by two dielectric slabs; one of thickness 2.0 mm and dielectric constant $\kappa_1 = 6$, and the other of thickness 1.0 mm and dielectric constant $\kappa_2 = 3.0$. Neglecting edge effects,

a. Compute the capacity of the condenser thus formed in microfarads.

b. Find the magnitude of the polarization vector in each dielectric.

c. Find the induced surface polarization charge on the interface between the two dielectrics.

8. A glass slab of dielectric constant $\kappa = 10$ and a paraffin slab of dielectric constant $\kappa = 2$, each 1.0 cm thick, are inserted into a parallel-plate condenser of plate separation 3.0 cm, the slab faces being parallel to the surfaces of the condenser plates. The dielectric slabs have surfaces equal in area to those of the condenser plates, and the latter are large enough so that end effects may be neglected.

a. If the surface charge density on the condenser plates is 1.0×10^{-6} coulomb/m², what are the electric field intensities in the empty space between the condenser plates before and after the dielectrics are inserted?

b. If the condenser plates are connected to a 432-volt battery, what are the changes of the charge density on the plates and of the field $\mathcal{E}$ in the empty space occurring when the dielectrics are inserted?

9. A condenser is formed of two concentric, spherical metal shells of radii 2.0 and 6.0 cm. The inner sphere is covered by a wax coating 3.0 cm thick, and the remainder of the space between the spheres is filled with a liquid of dielectric constant 4.2. The dielectric constant of the wax is 2.0.

Find the capacity of the condenser formed in microfarads.

10. If the plates of the condenser in Prob. 9 are maintained at a potential difference of 3,000 volts, compute the total energy stored in the condenser.

What is the surface density of polarization charge on the wax-liquid interface? What is the volume density of polarization charge at any point?

11. The inner sphere of a spherical condenser of inner and outer radii a and b, respectively, is coated with a thin coat of varnish of thickness t and dielectric constant κ. Show that the increase of capacity of the condenser due to the varnish is given approximately by

$$\Delta C = 4\pi\epsilon_0 \left[\frac{b^2(\kappa - 1)}{\kappa(b - a)^2} \right] t$$

12. The dielectric constant of the material between the plates of a parallel-plate condenser varies uniformly from one plate to the other. If κ_1 and κ_2 are its values at the two plates, prove that the condenser has a capacity

$$C = \frac{\epsilon_0 A}{d} \left(\frac{\kappa_2 - \kappa_1}{\ln (\kappa_2/\kappa_1)} \right)$$

What is the volume density of polarization charge as a function of position between the plates?

13. The dielectric constant of hydrogen gas at 0°C and atmospheric pressure is 1.000264.

a. Compute the polarizability of the hydrogen molecule.

b. Assuming that the ideal-gas laws are obeyed, compute the dielectric constant of hydrogen at a pressure of 20 atm and a temperature of -200°C.

14. A spherical condenser with the inner electrode of radius a and outer electrode of inner radius b is filled with a dielectric of varying dielectric constant. At a distance r from the center of the spheres, the dielectric constant is given by $\kappa = r/a$ $(a < r < b)$.

a. Find the capacity of this condenser.

b. Find the surface polarization charge on the inner and outer surfaces of the dielectric, and the distribution of volume polarization charge inside the dielectric.

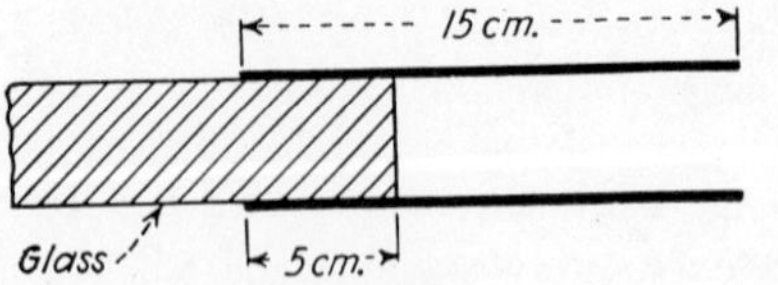

Fig. 157.

15. A parallel-plate condenser is made of two square plates 15 cm on a side separated by a distance of 3.0 mm. A glass slab of dielectric constant 6.0, thickness 3.0 mm, and 15 cm on a side is inserted, as shown in Fig. 157, between the condenser plates. The condenser is connected to a 600-volt battery. Neglect edge effects.

a. Compute the capacity of the condenser so formed.

b. What is the total "real" charge on the condenser plates, and how is it distributed?

c. How much energy is stored in the condenser?

d. Suppose the battery is disconnected, leaving the condenser charged, and the glass slab moves a distance dx to the right. Find an expression for the increase or decrease of energy in the condenser.

e. From your answer to part *d,* compute the force tending to pull the glass slab between the plates. How does it depend on the length of the slab already inserted?

16. Suppose that the thickness of the glass slab in Prob. 15 is 2.0 mm and that the battery is left connected to the condenser plates.

a. Compute the force tending to draw the slab in between the plates.

b. How much work is done on the slab if it starts as shown in Fig. 157 and ends with 10 cm of its length between the plates?

c. How much energy does the battery supply to the system during this process?

d. Compute the change of field energy in the condenser for the process of part *b,* and show that it is equal to the energy supplied by the battery minus the mechanical work done on the glass slab.

17. A cylindrical condenser of length 1 m has a central conductor of radius 2.0 cm and an outer conductor of inner radius 4.0 cm. A length of 50 cm of a long hollow dielectric cylinder of dielectric constant 8.0 (inner radius 2.0 cm, outer radius 4.0 cm) is inserted into the condenser so that it completely fills the space between the condenser plates in the length 50 cm. A potential difference of 30,000 volts is maintained between the plates. Compute the mechanical force exerted on the dielectric cylinder.

18. The central conductor of a cylindrical condenser of length L has a radius r_1 and the inside radius of the outer conductor is r_2. The central conductor is held in place by n equally spaced dielectric disks, each of thickness a, of inner and outer radii r_1 and r_2, respectively. If the dielectric constant of the disk material is κ,

a. Find an expression for the length of a similar air-filled condenser of the same capacity.

b. Find an expression for the fraction of the total charge on the condenser plates which resides on the conductor surfaces not in contact with the disks.

19. A parallel-plate condenser of plate separation d in air is charged by a battery, and the battery is then disconnected. A slab of dielectric of thickness $t < d$ and face area equal to that of either condenser plate is introduced between the plates, the slab faces being parallel to the condenser plates.

Prove that the electrostatic field energy in the condenser is *decreased* by an amount equal to $(v/2)P\mathcal{E}_0$, where v is the volume of the dielectric, P the polarization vector, and $\mathcal{E}_0$ the electric field intensity before the dielectric slab is inserted.

20. Consider the electrostatic field set up in air by a number of fixed charged conductors. If a small rigid dielectric body is introduced into this field at a point far enough from the conductors so that the charge distribution on the latter is not sensibly altered by the introduction of this dielectric body, the field-energy change may be shown in general to be given by

$$U - U_0 = -\tfrac{1}{2} \int P\mathcal{E}_0 \, dv$$

(the result of Prob. 19 is a special case of this general relation). Given the fact that the field intensity $\mathcal{E}$ inside a dielectric sphere is uniform when the sphere is placed in an originally uniform field $\mathcal{E}_0$, and that $\mathcal{E}$ and $\mathcal{E}_0$ are related by

$$\mathcal{E} = \frac{3}{\kappa + 2}\,\mathcal{E}_0$$

derive an expression for the change in field energy produced when a dielectric sphere of radius a is placed in a region where the field originally was $\mathcal{E}_0$. Take the volume of the sphere small enough so that $\mathcal{E}_0$ does not vary appreciably over the region of space occupied by this sphere.

21. Let the dielectric sphere of Prob. 20 be displaced slightly to a point where the original field had a value slightly different from $\mathcal{E}_0$. Compute the change in electrostatic energy, and using the fact that this must equal the mechanical work done on the sphere, show that the mechanical force on the sphere is given by

$$\mathbf{F} = 2\pi\epsilon_0 a^3 \left(\frac{\kappa - 1}{\kappa + 2} \right) \text{grad } \mathcal{E}_0^2$$

22. A small dielectric sphere of susceptibility χ and radius b is placed at a large distance r from a metal sphere of radius a which is maintained at a potential V. Assume that $b \ll r$ and $a \ll r$. Using the result of Prob. 21, derive an expression for the force exerted by the metal sphere on the dielectric sphere.

23. The vertical plates of a parallel-plate condenser are dipped into an insulating liquid of susceptibility χ. Neglecting surface tension, show that if a potential difference V is established between the plates, the liquid will rise between the plates a height h above its initial level, where h is given by

$$h = \frac{\chi \epsilon_0 V^2}{2\rho g d^2}$$

d is the plate separation and ρg the weight per unit volume of the liquid. The susceptibility of air is neglected.

24. Prove that, at an uncharged interface between two dielectrics of dielectric constants κ_1 and κ_2, there is a surface polarization charge density σ' given by

$$\sigma' = \epsilon_0 \mathcal{E}_{1n} \left(1 - \frac{\kappa_1}{\kappa_2} \right)$$

where $\mathcal{E}_{1n}$ is the component of $\mathcal{E}$ in the medium of dielectric constant κ_1 normal to the interface at the point in question.

CHAPTER 14

MAGNETIC PROPERTIES OF MATTER

The subject of magnetism was pursued as a branch of physics entirely distinct from electricity prior to the discoveries of Oersted and Faraday and is probably the older of the two subjects. The early studies of magnetism were concerned with the interactions of permanent magnets and particularly with terrestrial magnetism. The laws governing the magnetic fields of permanent magnets were formulated in a manner analogous to the laws of electrostatics, at least as far as was possible, and even nowadays many treatments of the subject are based on these analogies. In our study, however, we have introduced the magnetic field vectors, at least in empty space, in terms of the electric currents which give rise to them, and we shall continue to use this mode of interpretation for the study of magnetized material bodies. The formulas which we shall obtain will be essentially equivalent to these obtained by the more traditional treatment, but their interpretation will be based on our present-day atomic ideas concerning the origin of the magnetic behavior of matter. This mode of interpretation is not really new, since Ampère pointed out its equivalence to the older scheme. In Ampère's time, however, and until comparatively recently, there was no compelling reason to use one rather than the other mode of interpretation, but today there exists a large amount of evidence that electrons in material bodies are mainly responsible for their magnetic behavior.

Returning to the question of the analogy between electric and magnetic fields, the starting point of electrostatics is Coulomb's law with the consequent possibility of defining and obtaining units of electric charge and electric field intensity. Right at the start, the analogy between electrostatics and magnetostatics breaks down, since it is impossible to produce a "magnetically charged" body. (This has not kept writers from assuming its existence, however.) It is true that a material body can be magnetically polarized so that the external magnetizing field is modified by its presence, but no "magnetic charge" can be imparted to such a body. On the other hand, there are substances, called "magnetically hard," which can be magnetized and retain some of the induced magnetization when the external field is

253

removed.   These substances, permanent magnets, now produce magnetic fields of their own, and their permanent magnetization is almost independent of external fields, at least for weak fields.   We can imagine ideal magnetically hard permanent magnets which are not affected by external fields, and then it becomes possible in principle to employ a tiny permanent bar magnet to investigate and define magnetic field strength and magnetic moments.   In this procedure, the test bar is treated both as a "source" (a dipole source) and as an indicator of magnetic fields.

In Chaps. 6 and 7 we have introduced the concept of the magnetic moment of a tiny current loop, and we can carry this discussion over as it stands to examine the behavior of a very small permanent magnet test bar, thus indicating at the outset a possible interpretation of the magnetization of material bodies.   If such a test bar is suspended by a thread fastened to its center, it will align itself in the direction of the earth's magnetic field at the point where it is located, and, if displaced from equilibrium, will perform angular oscillations with a frequency

$$f = \frac{1}{2\pi} \sqrt{\frac{mB_0}{I}} \qquad (14.1)$$

[see Eq. (6.18)], where m is the magnetic moment of the bar, I its moment of inertia about the axis of suspension, and B_0 the magnetic induction vector of the earth's field. In this experiment the bar is used as an indicator (a magnetometer). Now let us use the bar magnet as a "source" of a field and hold it fixed with its long axis perpendicular to the earth's field (Fig. 158).   The magnetic induction B at point P produced by this magnetic moment at O is (x is large compared to the length of the bar magnet)

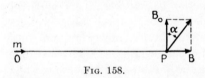

Fig. 158.

$$B = \frac{\mu_0 m}{2\pi x^3} \qquad (14.2)$$

[see Eq. (7.23b)], so that the angle of the resultant magnetic field of the bar magnet and the earth with the direction of the earth's field is given by

$$\tan \alpha = \frac{B}{B_0} = \frac{\mu_0 m}{2\pi B_0 x^3} \qquad (14.3)$$

This angle is readily determined with the help of a compass needle. Equations (14.1) and (14.3) now allow a simultaneous determination of B_0 and m (choosing μ_0 arbitrarily).   We now have a calibrated test body which can be used to measure an arbitrary magnetic field.   This is the method devised by Gauss to measure magnetic moments and the earth's magnetic field in an absolute system of units.   (Gauss used H in place of B and set $\mu_0/4\pi = 1$, leading to the so-called absolute electromagnetic system of units.)

The use of a scalar magnetic potential V_m has already been discussed in Chap. 7, and its convenience in describing the field of permanent magnets has been indicated.   We shall not continue the traditional development further but turn now to a discussion of the magnetic properties of matter on the basis of modern atomic theory.

1. The Electronic Origin of Magnetic Properties.   The fundamental facts concerning the magnetic behavior of material bodies can be presented most clearly by considering a simple experiment.   Consider the magnetic field produced by a closely wound toroidal coil.   In empty space this coil will have a definite inductance L_0.   If now this same coil is wound on a material core, it will be found that the inductance of the toroid is different from L_0; let us say equal to L. Since the inductance (for a given current in the winding) is proportional to the flux of B in the region of space inside the toroid, it follows that, for isotropic homogeneous bodies, the value of B at every point of space in this volume has been changed from its value in vacuum by a factor L/L_0 when the material core is present.   As we shall see shortly, this ratio is equal to the relative magnetic permeability of the material filling the core.   In contradistinction to the corresponding electro-static experiment, in which a dielectric medium inserted between con-denser plates always causes an *increase* of the capacity, the inductance L may be either smaller or larger than the inductance L_0 in the absence of the medium.   If $L < L_0$, we call the material *diamagnetic*, and if $L > L_0$, *paramagnetic*.   For the diamagnetic case, the effect of the material core is to weaken the field of B relative to its value for empty space (keeping the coil current constant), and this is analogous to the dielectric case in electrostatics, in which the field strength is weakened by the presence of the dielectric (keeping the charges on the condenser plates constant).   In this sense there is no electrostatic analogue to paramagnetism, for which the field of B is augmented by the presence of the material medium.

To understand the phenomena of diamagnetism and paramagnet-ism, we must consider the magnetic properties of atoms (and mole-cules).   As has already been pointed out, an atom consists of a massive positively charged nucleus surrounded by a sufficient number of elec-trons to make the atom electrically neutral as a whole.   These electrons perform rapid motion around the nucleus, and when an atom is placed in a magnetic field B, these moving electrons will be acted on by the Lorentz force $-e(\mathbf{v} \times \mathbf{B})$, and their motions will be modified because of this magnetic force.   The change in the electronic motions caused by the Lorentz force is always such that the altered motion tends to weaken the external field B which gives rise to the change. This is the origin of the *diamagnetic* behavior of atoms and hence of matter.   We can see how this comes about with the help of a very simple example.   Consider an electron of charge $-e$ moving with a

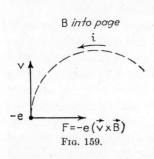

FIG. 159.

velocity v, as shown in Fig. 159.   If a magnetic field B is established into the page, there will be a deflecting force acting on the electron as shown, which would result in the circular dotted path of the figure were the electron free.   This is equivalent to a current i in the direction indicated, and this current produces a magnetic field directed out of the page and hence tends to diminish the externally applied field.   A c t u a l l y, atomic electrons are not free but perform orbital motions, so that such an electron possesses angular momentum about the nucleus and generates a magnetic moment, the latter by virtue of the fact that the orbital motion of a charged particle is equivalent to a small loop.   The torque of the Lorentz force on this electron must act at right angles to its angular momentum (since it is a deflecting force) and cannot change the magnitude of the angular momentum. Hence the angular-momentum vector precesses about the direction of the applied field in a manner similar to the precession of a gyroscope. This precession of the electron orbits induced by a magnetic field is called the *Larmor* precession and gives rise to atomic diamagnetism.

In addition to the magnetic moment produced by the orbital motion of an electron, an electron possesses an inherent magnetic moment very much as if it were a spinning sphere of electric charge, and this is called *electron spin*.   The magnetic moment of an atom will then be the resultant of the orbital and spin magnetic moments of all the electrons of which it is composed.   (There is also a small nuclear magnetic moment, which can be neglected for the present argument.) There are some atoms, *e.g.*, helium in its normal state with two electrons, in which there is no resultant magnetic moment, the magnetic effects of the electrons just neutralizing each other.   Many atoms and molecules, however, do possess resultant magnetic moments in their normal, or ground, states.   The diamagnetic effect discussed in the preceding paragraph will be present whether the atoms have a resultant permanent moment or not; if they have a nonvanishing resultant moment, there exists the possibiliy of a new effect due to the tendency of this moment to orient itself so that its potential energy in the magnetic field is a minimum corresponding to stable equilibrium.   We have already seen in Chap. 6, Sec. 4, that a current loop assumes a stable equilibrium orientation in an external magnetic field such that the plane of the loop is at right angles to the external field, its magnetic moment in the direction of the external field.   In this orientation, the field of the current loop aids the external field at the point where the loop is located.   This orientation effect of atomic magnetic moments gives rise to the *paramagnetic* behavior of matter, the magnitude of the natural atomic magnetic moments being sufficiently large to more than compensate for the diamagnetic effect, which is always present. The paramagnetic effect, being an orientation effect, is similar to the orientation effect of polar molecules in that it is temperature-dependent, increasing with decreasing temperature, since thermal agitation of the atoms and molecules tends to prevent orientation.   The diamagnetic effect is essentially temperature-independent.   It must always be kept in mind that inside paramagnetic bodies the field produced by the permanent atomic magnetic moments tends to aid the external field, whereas for dielectrics the field of the dipoles always tends to *oppose* the external field, whether one has induced or oriented dipoles.

2. Intensity of Magnetization; Amperian Currents.   To describe quantitatively the magnetic behavior of matter, we introduce the concept of a vector M, the so-called *intensity of magnetization*, which is analogous to the polarization vector P in electricity.   This vector is defined as the *induced magnetic moment per unit volume of the magnetized body*.   For isotropic media—and we shall confine our attention to this case—the atomic magnetic moments induced (diamagnetic case) or resulting from the orientation of permanent atomic moments (paramagnetic case) are opposite to or in the direction of the applied field.   Hence the intensity-of-magnetization vector is in the same direction as the applied field at every point of the body.   Consider a volume element Δv inside a magnetic medium, and let $\mathbf{m}_0$ be the magnetic moment per atom produced by the external field.   The total magnetic moment $\Delta \mathbf{m}$ of this volume element is the vector sum of all the atomic $\mathbf{m}_0$'s in this element, and one has

$$\mathbf{M} = \frac{\Delta \mathbf{m}}{\Delta v} \tag{14.4}$$

or, more precisely,

$$\mathbf{M} = \lim \frac{\Delta \mathbf{m}}{\Delta v} \qquad \text{as } \Delta v \to 0 \qquad (14.5)$$

where $\Delta \mathbf{m} = \Sigma \mathbf{m}_0$, the summation extending over all the atoms in Δv. If the vector field of M is uniform, we say that the substance is uniformly magnetized.

Since each magnetic moment m_0 is the equivalent of an elementary current loop, we can equally well attribute the state of magnetization of a body to elementary *circulating currents,* called *Amperian currents* after Ampère, who first suggested them, and these Amperian currents resemble currents in superconductors rather than ordinary currents, since their existence involves no dissipation of energy. In describing the magnetic effects of these Amperian currents, we make use of the construction of Ampère, as presented in Sec. 4, Chap. 7. For simplicity,

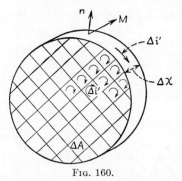

FIG. 160.

consider a uniformly magnetized cross section A of a rod, as shown in Fig. 160, of thickness Δx, and let the direction of the magnetization vector M be into the page. The induced magnetic moments are equivalent to current loops of area ΔA, each carrying the same current $\Delta i'$, as shown, the intensity of magnetization being uniform. By Ampère's construction the totality of these current loop is equivalent to a surface current $\Delta i'$ around the outer surface of the rod in the direction shown. To obtain the relation between this induced surface current (the magnetic analogue of induced surface charges on polarized dielectrics) and the magnetization vector M, we proceed as follows: From the definition of M we have

$$M = \frac{\Delta m}{\Delta v} = \frac{\sum m_0}{A \, \Delta x} = \frac{\sum (\Delta i' \, \Delta A)}{A \, \Delta x} = \frac{\Delta i' \sum \Delta A}{A \, \Delta x} = \frac{\Delta i'}{\Delta x} \qquad (14.6)$$

since $\Sigma \, \Delta A$ is the total cross section A of the rod. The expression $\Delta i'/\Delta x$ is just the *surface density of current,* current per unit length measured along the surface normal to the direction of the current, which we denote by $J^{(s)'}$, the superscript (s) to remind us that it is a surface rather than volume current density. We thus have the fundamental relation

$$J^{(s)'} = M \qquad (14.7)$$

giving the relation between the magnitudes of the induced Amperian surface current density and the magnetization vector M. The speci-fication of the directions of these vectors may be included with the help of a *unit vector* **n** drawn normal to the surface and outward from the volume. From Fig. 160 it is evident that the vector relation

$$\mathbf{J}^{(s)\prime} = \mathbf{M} \times \mathbf{n} \tag{14.8}$$

gives the correct direction of the surface current. Equation (14.8) can be shown to be valid in general. More generally, if the Amperian surface current is on the interface between two magnetic media 1 and 2, the same reasoning as that which led to Eq. (14.8) yields easily

$$\mathbf{J}^{(s)\prime} = (\mathbf{M}_1 - \mathbf{M}_2) \times \mathbf{n} \tag{14.9}$$

where **n** is a unit vector drawn from medium 1 to medium 2 and $\mathbf{M}_1$ and $\mathbf{M}_2$ are the intensities of magnetization in medium 1 and medium 2 at the point where **n** is located, respectively.

Besides the surface Amperian current given by Eq. (14.8) or (14.9), there will appear, in general, a volume distribution of such cur-rents in the case of *nonuniform* magnetization, just as a volume

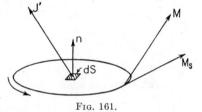

FIG. 161.

density of polarization charge occurs, in general, when there is nonuni-form polarization of a dielectric. It can be readily shown that the Amperian volume currents are re-lated to the magnetization by the relation

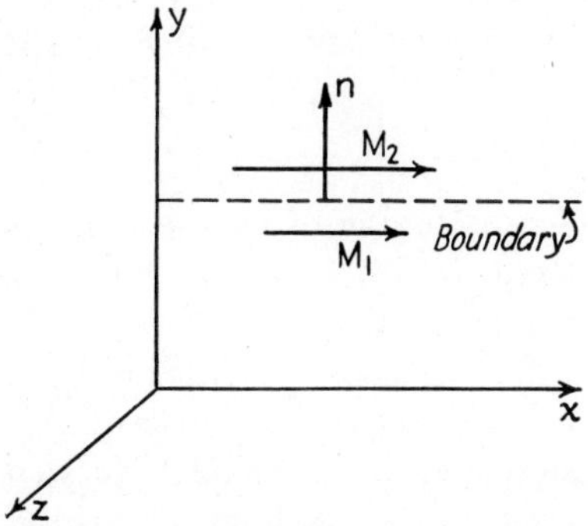

$$\oint M_s \, ds = \int J'_n \, dS = i' \tag{14.10}$$

i.e., the Amperian current i' across any area inside the medium is equal to the line integral of the magnet-ization vector around the boundary of the area, the directions as shown in Fig. 161. Equations (14.9) and (14.10) are not independent of each

FIG. 162.

other, and in fact one can be derived from the other. We shall now show that these equations are but two different ways of expressing the same physical law. Consider first two slabs of uniformly magnetized matter in contact, the plane interface being parallel to the x-z plane and the uniform magnetization in both bodies being in the x-direction (Fig.

162).   Equation (14.9) then gives for the magnitude of the surface current density on the boundary

$$J^{(s)\prime} = M_1 - M_2$$

since M_1 and M_2 are both at right angles to n.   The direction of $J^{(s)\prime}$ is out of or into the page depending on the relative magnitudes of M_1 and M_2.   For a length l of the interface (in the x-direction), the total Amperian surface current is then

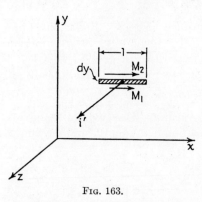

FIG. 163.

$$i' = J^{(s)\prime}l = (M_1 - M_2)l \quad (14.11)$$

Next let us consider a single magnetized body in which the magnetization vector is everywhere parallel to the x-axis but is of magnitude which varies with y.   We apply Eq. (14.10) to the closed loop of long sides l and short sides dy, as shown in Fig. 163; proceeding in a counterclockwise direction, we have

$$\oint M_s \, ds = (M_1 - M_2)l = \int J' \, dS = J'l \, dy = i' \quad (14.12)$$

where M_1 and M_2 are the values of M at y and $y + dy$, respectively. If we now remember that dy is infinitesimal, we see that Eqs. (14.11) and (14.12) are identical in content, since the shaded area in Fig. 163 is equivalent to a length l of the boundary in Fig. 162 and

$$J^{(s)\prime} = J' \, dy$$

3. Relations of B, H, and M.   In our discussion of magnetic fields in empty space, we found it convenient to introduce a magnetic intensity vector H in addition to the fundamental induction vector B. This was defined as B/μ_0 [Eq. (7.4)], and this restricted definition must now be extended for the case of material bodies, since just in this latter case is this auxiliary vector extremely useful.   We shall approach this problem with the help of a simple example, *viz.*, a long solenoid of circular cross section, the length long enough compared to its diameter so that end effects may be neglected, and let us suppose that we insert a cylindrical rod of homogeneous, isotropic material coaxially into the interior of the solenoid (Fig. 164).   Let the number of turns per unit length of the solenoid winding be n and the current i.   If the cylindrical rod were not present, this would produce a uniform magnetic field inside the solenoid.   Thus we see that the rod becomes uniformly magnetized, and we have shown in Sec. 2 that the effect of this magnetization is equivalent to that of Amperian currents which are directed solenoidally (circumferentially) around the surface of the cylindrical rod.   These currents are indicated as dotted in Fig. 164, whereas the "true" current i in the winding is indicated by solid lines.   We now consider the fundamental induction vector B as produced by all the currents, external plus Amperian (just as ε in electrostatics is the field due to *all* the charge, including polarization charge), and replace the

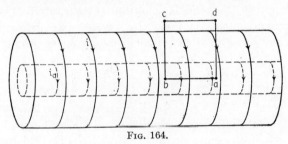

FIG. 164.

material rod by the equivalent Amperian currents, thus leaving a problem in empty space.   The solution of this equivalent vacuum problem then yields the magnetic field in the actual problem both inside and outside the material body.

We now apply Ampère's circuital law to the path *abcd* in the usual manner, and remembering that in our vacuum problem $H = B/\mu_0$, we have (the length *ab* is l) as before

$$\frac{B}{\mu_0}\, l = i_{\text{total}} \qquad (14.13)$$

where i_{total} is the total current, including the Amperian currents, traversing the area *abcd*.   We have for the total current

$$i_{\text{total}} = nli + J^{(s)'}l = (ni + M)l \qquad (14.14)$$

using Eq. (14.7).   Thus Eq. (14.13) gives

$$\frac{B}{\mu_0} = ni + M$$

or

$$\frac{B}{\mu_0} - M = ni \qquad (14.15)$$

Thus we see that ni, which is a measure of H inside such a solenoid in empty space, is no longer equal to B/μ_0 when matter is present, and *we define H by the more general relation*

$$H = \frac{B}{\mu_0} - M \tag{14.16}$$

This reduces to B/μ_0 if M is zero, as in empty space.   We see, *in this special example*, that the field of H is determined by the external currents, and the field of B is that of the total current, external and hidden (Amperian).

We shall now prove that the Ampère circuital law is of unrestricted validity if one uses the general definition (14.16) for H.   To do this, we replace magnetic material bodies by a system of equivalent Amperian currents and have for the equivalent empty-space problem

$$\oint \frac{B_s}{\mu_0} ds = i_{\text{total}} = i + i' \tag{14.17}$$

where, in general, i will include the displacement as well as the conduction current across any area bounded by the closed path. i' is the Amperian current crossing this area.   Now from Eq. (14.10) we have $i' = \oint M_s \, ds$, so that Eq. (14.17) becomes

$$\oint \left(\frac{B}{\mu_0} - M \right)_s ds = i = \int \left(J_n + \frac{\partial D_n}{\partial t} \right) dS$$

or, using Eq. (14.16),

$$\oint H_s \, ds = i = \int \left(J_n + \frac{\partial D_n}{\partial t} \right) dS \tag{14.18}$$

which completes the proof.   In general, then, the mmf (of H) around a closed path equals the "true" current (conduction plus displacement) across a surface bounded by the path, the line integral of M around this path is the Amperian current across the area, and the line integral of B/μ_0 is the total current across the area.

4. Magnetic Permeability; Magnetic Susceptibility.   The general problem of determining the magnetic induction B involves a knowledge of both H and M.   The magnetization vector M, however, is generally a function of H (or B), and consequently we must distinguish among various cases which actually exist in material bodies.   First, let us restrict our attention to those materials for which B, H, and M are all proportional to each other, the magnetization being proportional to the field.   *We define the magnetic permeability μ of the medium by*

$$B = \mu H \tag{14.19}$$

Inserting this expression into Eq. (14.16), we have for the *relative permeability* μ/μ_0

$$\frac{\mu}{\mu_0} = 1 + \frac{M}{H} \qquad (14.20)$$

and the ratio M/H is called the *magnetic susceptibility* χ_m of the material. For most substances (the notable exceptions being iron, nickel, cobalt, and other so-called ferromagnetic materials), the magnetization intensity is proportional to H, and χ_m is a constant. Materials with a negative value of χ_m ($\mu < \mu_0$) are *diamagnetic*, and those for which χ_m is positive ($\mu > \mu_0$) are termed *paramagnetic*. In paramagnetic bodies the Amperian currents aid the external currents, and in diamagnetic media they oppose them. Equation (14.20), written in terms of the susceptibility, becomes

$$\frac{\mu}{\mu_0} = 1 + \chi_m \qquad (14.21)$$

The susceptibilities of ordinary paramagnetic and diamagnetic material are very small compared to unity, being of the order of 10^{-5} for diamagnetic bodies (bismuth is a notable exception with about ten times this susceptibility) and somewhat larger, let us say of the order of 10^{-4}, for paramagnetic bodies. Thus it is possible to treat most substances as nonmagnetic for the purposes of many practical problems.

5. Ferromagnetism. From a practical standpoint, by far the most important magnetic media are the so-called *ferromagnetic* materials, which are characterized by abnormally large values of the magnetization M and by the fact that M is *not* proportional to H; indeed in some substances it is not a single-valued function of H. The elements iron, nickel, and cobalt and a number of alloys display this abnormally large paramagnetic behavior. Equation (14.16) is, of course, valid, since it is a definition, but the permeability defined as B/H is at best a function of H. Not only is the magnetization intensity much larger for these substances than for ordinary paramagnetic bodies (sometimes a million times larger), but also it is possible to attain a limiting saturation value of M at relatively low field strengths. The saturation value of M is relatively independent of the mechanical state and small amounts of impurities, but the *B-H* or *M-H* relation (the so-called magnetization curve) is very strongly dependent on these factors. It is convenient to classify ferromagnetic materials into two groups:

a. Magnetically Soft Substances. These are substances for which M is at least approximately a single-valued function of H. This function is sketched in Fig. 165 and has the following general properties: an initial sharp rise in M and a subsequent flattening out and saturation. Actually there are no strictly reversible ferromagnetics, but one can only speak of "softer" or "harder" magnetic substances depending on the size of the hysteresis loop (see below).

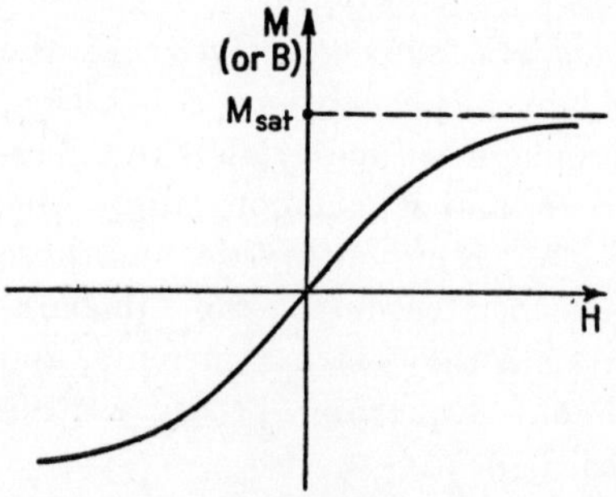

b. Magnetically Hard Substances. In these the magnetization intensity not only is not a single-valued function of H but depends on the previous history of the sample under consideration. If one subjects an initially unmagnetized sample of magnetically hard steel to an increasing magnetic field H, *e.g.*, by using a toroidal coil filled with the material and increasing the coil current, the initial magnetization curve (shown dotted in Fig. 166) is not unlike that of Fig. 165. If now the applied field is reduced and reversed, the magnetization follows the solid curve PAQ. The value of M for $H = 0$, the ordinate OA in Fig. 166 (a measure of the so-called "remanence"), and the reversing field OB required to reduce M to zero (the so-called "coercive force") can be used as measures of the magnetic hardness of the material. If

FIG. 165.

one now carries the magnetization back to the point P by increasing H, the lower curve is followed, and this cyclic operation is just what occurs in a-c transformers. The loop $PAQCP$ is called a "hysteresis" loop, and there is an energy loss whenever such a loop is traversed. This energy loss is due to internal friction effects when the permanently magnetized domains characterizing ferromagnetics are re-oriented by the field.

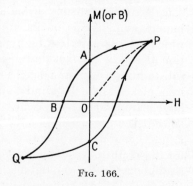

FIG. 166.

Consider a toroidal coil closely wound around a steel core of cross section A and mean length l. When a current is set up in the magnetizing coil, energy is supplied at the rate Ei, with E the voltage across the coil and i the current it carries. Neglecting the resistance of the winding (including this would simply add the ordinary i^2R heating), this voltage is given by Faraday's law as $E = NA(dB/dt)$, where N is the number of turns of the coil. The value of H is related to the current by $H = Ni/l$, so that $i = Hl/N$, and the power input is

$$Ei = (Al)H\frac{dB}{dt} = vH\frac{dB}{dt}$$

where v is the volume of the specimen.   The total work done in carrying the substance around the hysteresis loop is hence

$$W = \int Ei\,dt = v\int H\frac{dB}{dt}\,dt = v\oint H\,dB \qquad (14.22)$$

so that the hysteresis loss per cycle per unit volume is equal to the area of the loop on a B-H diagram.

In the interior of a permanent magnet, the direction of the magnetic intensity H is generally opposite to that of the magnetization and induction.   Such a magnetic state corresponds to a position on the portion of the curve of Fig. 166 lying between A and B.   Furthermore, the internal field of such a magnet depends, for a given magnetization, on the geometrical shape of the magnet.

6. Boundary Conditions on B and H.   Thus far in our discussion of the magnetic behavior of material bodies, we have confined our attention principally to the case of a single material medium completely occupying the spatial region where the magnetic field existed, or to the case where the boundary surface between two media (the case of Fig. 164) was everywhere parallel to the magnetic field direction prior to the introduction of the material body.   In both these cases the direction of the lines of B or H is unaltered by the presence of the material body, and we are not concerned with the possibility of refraction of these lines at the interface.   We now investigate the relations which hold at a boundary which is not parallel to the lines of force, *e.g.*, at a boundary surface between two media of permeabilities μ_1 and μ_2. Since the field of B is solenoidal (the lines of B closing on themselves), the net flux of B emerging from any closed volume is zero.   We apply this condition to the shallow pillbox shown in Fig. 167, and we may neglect the flux of B emerging from the curved sides, since it vanishes as the altitude of the pillbox approaches zero (the interface always lying between the flat faces).

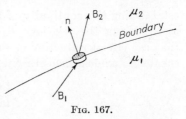

Fig. 167.

The flux of B out of the top face is $B_{2n}\,dA$, where B_{2n} is the normal component of B_2 at the point where dA is located.   Similarly the magnetic flux out of the bottom face is $-B_{1n}\,dA$.   Hence we have

$$B_{2n}\, dA - B_{1n}\, dA = 0$$

or

$$B_{1n} = B_{2n} \tag{14.23}$$

The normal component of B must be continuous across the boundary surface between two media.   Note that this condition is automatically fulfilled if the boundary is parallel to the lines of B.

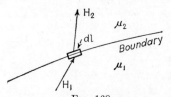

FIG. 168.

For the tangential field components, we apply the Ampère circuital law to the closed path of Fig. 168, in which the sides perpendicular to the boundary are made vanishingly small compared to the other sides, each of length dl.   As this occurs, the displacement current through the area enclosed by the path becomes vanishingly small and does not contribute to the mmf around the path.   This mmf is

$$\oint H_s\, ds = H_{1t}\, dl - H_{2t}\, dl$$

and this must equal the "true" current across the area enclosed by the elementary path.   If the surface density of this current on the interface is $J^{(s)}$, we have

$$H_{1t}\, dl - H_{2t}\, dl = J^{(s)}\, dl$$

or

$$H_{1t} - H_{2t} = J^{(s)} \tag{14.24}$$

as the relation which holds between the tangential components of H. If no true surface current is present (there may be Amperian currents, however), $J^{(s)} = 0$, and Eq. (14.24) becomes

$$H_{1t} = H_{2t} \tag{14.25}$$

establishing the continuity of the tangential component of H for this case.   Using the relations $B_1 = \mu_1 H_1$, $B_2 = \mu_2 H_2$, one finds readily that the law of refraction of the lines of B or H at an interface which carries no true surface current is

$$\frac{\tan \alpha_1}{\tan \alpha_2} = \frac{\mu_1}{\mu_2} \tag{14.26}$$

where α_1 and α_2 are the angle between the field lines and the normal to the interface in media 1 and 2, respectively [compare Eq. (13.29)].

We now can state precisely the conditions under which the Ampère rule [Eq. (7.5)] may be used to calculate the field of H, and thereby bring out clearly the generality of the Ampère circuital law, which is universally valid, compared to the Ampère rule. From our analysis of the boundary conditions it becomes clear that the Ampère rule will give the correct field of H in two cases:

1. When the magnetic field produced by the "real" currents is appreciably different from zero in a single homogeneous, isotropic material medium or in empty space.

2. When the boundary surface between bodies is everywhere parallel to the magnetic lines, so that the field pattern is unaffected by the presence of the boundary surface.

Condition (2) follows from the fact that Eq. (14.23) is automatically satisfied, and Eq. (14.25) ensures a continuous change in H across the boundary. Only in the above two cases is it true that the field of H is completely and uniquely determined by the true currents and their relative positions, whereas the mmf (of H) around *any* closed path is always given uniquely by the true current (including displacement current) which traverses any surface bounded by this path. A simple example may help to clarify the implications of these statements. Consider the magnetic field of a very long solenoid in air carrying a steady current. In the central portion of this solenoid the field is confined to the region of space enclosed by the winding and is uniform in this region (see Sec. 3, Chap. 7). If a long cylindrical rod of magnetic material is inserted coaxially into this solenoid, as in Fig. 164, the field of H is exactly as it was before (still confining our attention to the central portion of the solenoid), and the pattern of magnetic lines is unchanged. The only change is that of the magnitude of B inside the magnetic cylinder. Now, however, let us imagine that a short cylinder of this magnetic material is inserted coaxially into this central region of the solenoid. The whole field pattern is changed violently, and the field is neither uniform in the central region of the solenoid nor is it confined to the space enclosed by the solenoid winding. A good qualitative picture of the field may be obtained in this case with the help of the concept of Amperian currents, replacing the material cylinder by a solenoid of equal length. The number of ampere turns of this short equivalent solenoid may be enormous if the cylinder is ferromagnetic. The field pattern is now the superposition of the uniform field of the original long solenoid and the nonuniform field produced by this finite Amperian solenoid in vacuum. It thus becomes evident that the presence of the flat surfaces of the rod (or the ends of the equivalent Amperian solenoid) play an important part in modifying the original uniform field pattern.

Let us look into the effect of these boundaries more closely in a very simple case. Consider the situation where the magnetic field lines are perpendicular to the plane interface between two media, as in Fig. 169. Here the lines of H are indicated near the surface for the case $\mu_2 > \mu_1$. Since the field is normal to the boundary, the tangential components of H are zero, satisfying Eq. (14.25). Equation (14.23) requires that $\mu_1 H_1 = \mu_2 H_2$, or

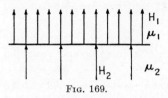

FIG. 169.

$$H_1 = \frac{\mu_2}{\mu_1} H_2$$

so that the number of lines of H emerging per unit area of the interface into medium 1 is larger than the number incident per unit area on the boundary in medium 2. This discontinuity is not present for the lines of magnetic induction, since $B_1 = B_2$. Whenever new lines of force start (or stop) at definite points of space, it is natural to think of these new lines as originating in "sources" of the field at these points. Thus we may say that it is possible to have sources of the field of H but not of B. These sources of H are called *magnetic poles*. Because B is the fundamental magnetic vector and H is merely a useful auxiliary aid to calculation, no deeper physical significance can be attributed to these poles. They constitute a convenient mode of description for magnetic fields, and they are extremely useful when one deals with many engineering problems, especially those in which one is interested in the field in an air gap in an otherwise closed "magnetic circuit" (see below) composed of a ferromagnetic material of high relative permeability.

One can set up a measure of magnetic pole "strength" in terms of the number of lines of H produced by it, just as the number of lines of D produced by an electric charge is, by Gauss's theorem, a measure of the magnitude of the charge. For example, consider an interface area A in Fig. 169, and let us take medium 1 to be vacuum, so that $\mu_1 = \mu_0$, and medium 2 to be a ferromagnetic body. The net number of lines of H starting at the pole on this area A is

$$(H_1 - H_2)A$$

and since we have the relations

$$H_1 = \frac{B}{\mu_0}; \qquad H_2 = \frac{B}{\mu_0} - M$$

where M is the magnetization intensity at the surface, the pole strength of the magnetic pole on this area is

$$\text{Pole strength} = (H_1 - H_2)A = MA \qquad (14.27)$$

or, alternatively,

$$\frac{\text{Pole strength}}{\text{Unit area}} = M \qquad (14.28)$$

More precisely, the M of Eqs. (14.27) and (14.28) is the normal component of M at the surface, as is evident from our derivation. One fact becomes very clear from these considerations, *viz.*, that the constancy of magnetic pole strength implies constancy of the magnetization intensity, and only for substances which are so hard magnetically that the remanent or "permanent" magnetization is practically independent of external fields is it possible to assign even an approximate meaning to the term pole strength as a property of a body independent of its external surroundings. In electrostatics, however, the electric charge on an insulated body is strictly constant and thus can be used uniquely to detect and measure electric fields. With magnetic fields one can never be quite sure of the basic assumption, for, even in weak fields, immersion of a "permanent" magnet in a medium of high relative permeability will certainly modify the pole strength by virtue of the "induced" magnetization and consequent induced poles. For reasons such as these, we have chosen to introduce the concept of magnetic fields on the basis of electric currents rather than with the help of permanent magnets, as is commonly done.

7. Magnetic Circuits; Reluctance. The determination of the field of magnetic induction in the presence of arbitrary magnetic bodies is, in general, a relatively difficult task and requires methods far beyond the scope of this book. The general problem, for steady fields, requires the simultaneous solution of the equations

$$\oint H_s\, ds = i; \qquad \int_{\substack{\text{closed} \\ \text{surface}}} B_n\, dS = 0; \qquad B = \mu H$$

subject to the boundary conditions expressed by Eqs. (14.23) and (14.25). There are, however, certain problems of practical importance involving so-called *magnetic circuits*, for which one can readily obtain approximate solutions. The name magnetic circuit has its origin in analogies between this sort of problem and that of steady currents in linear conductors. The fundamental reason for the analogy lies in the fact that both the field of electric current density and that of magnetic induction are solenoidal, there being no sources or sinks, and the field lines close on themselves in both cases.   Comparing the equations

$$J = \sigma \mathcal{E} \quad \text{and} \quad B = \mu H$$

(the first is Ohm's law), one looks upon μ as analogous to the conductivity σ.   Now, the electric current can be confined easily to conducting bodies, and, for linear conductors such as wires, the flow lines of current are parallel to the wire surfaces and are uniformly distributed over the conductor cross sections, if the latter are uniform.   For this case, Ohm's law applied to a simple series circuit takes the form

$$E = \oint \mathcal{E}_s \, ds = iR$$

where the resistance R is related to the conductivity by $R = l/\sigma A$, with l and A the conductor length and cross section, respectively.

In the corresponding magnetic circuit one has a closed path of

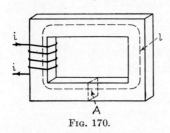

highly permeable material such as soft iron, as shown in Fig 170, with an exciting winding of N turns carrying a steady current i. We make the following assumptions:

FIG. 170.

1. The lines of B are confined to the circuit and are parallel to the boundaries of the magnetic medium.   The higher the relative permeability μ/μ_0 and the smaller the cross section A relative to the mean length l of the circuit, the more nearly is this fulfilled.

2. The magnetic permeability μ is constant.   This is not nearly so true as the fact that σ is constant (at a fixed temperature) for a conductor.   We shall use μ to denote an average value.

3. The magnitudes of H and B in any cross section of the circuit may be replaced by mean values over such a cross section.   This involves a choice of mean length l of the circuit which, at least in practical cases, has not a very small ratio of cross-section dimension to length.

With the above assumptions one can set up equations analogous to those of the corresponding electrical circuit.   The mmf around the path l is, using Ampère's circuital law,

$$\oint H_s \, ds = Hl = Ni$$

where now H is the mean value of H in the material and l the mean length.   From this we obtain the magnetic flux

$$\Phi = BA = \mu HA = \frac{Ni\mu A}{l}$$

or, rewritten,

$$\Phi = \frac{Ni}{l/\mu A} = \frac{\text{mmf}}{\Re} \tag{14.29}$$

where Ni is the mmf around the circuit and the script $\Re$ is called the *reluctance* of the magnetic circuit.   Writing Ohm's law for the corresponding simple series circuit as

$$i = \frac{\text{emf}}{R}$$

we see that $\Re$ is the analogue of electrical resistance.   From the similarity of the equations, we see that, subject to the same assumptions, the analysis of two or more reluctances in series or in parallel can be

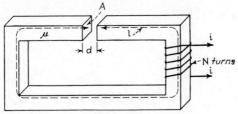

FIG. 171.

handled by the same method.   We shall illustrate this for the case of a simple electromagnet, as shown in Fig. 171, in which there is an air gap of length d.   Denoting by H the value of H inside the iron and by H_0 its value in the air gap, we have for the closed path $(l + d)$,

$$\text{mmf} = \oint H_s\, ds = Hl + H_0 d = Ni$$

If we take the effective air-gap area to be the same as the iron cross section A (this neglects fringing and is a good approximation only if $d^2 \ll A$), we can set $\Phi = BA$.   From the above equation we have

$$B\left(\frac{l}{\mu} + \frac{d}{\mu_0}\right) = Ni$$

using the fact that $B = \mu H$ and is continuous at the air-gap boundaries, so that

$$\Phi = BA = \frac{Ni}{(l/\mu A) + (d/\mu_0 A)} = \frac{\text{mmf}}{\Re + \Re_0}$$

with $\mathcal{R}$ and $\mathcal{R}_0$ the reluctances of the iron circuit and air gap, respectively. Thus we see that reluctances in series add just as do resistances. The mmf across the gap is given by

$$\mathcal{R}_0\Phi = \frac{Ni}{1 + (l\mu_0/d\mu)}$$

and if the ratio l/d is 100, let us say, and the relative permeability of the iron is 2,000, then this mmf is $\frac{20}{21}$ of the total mmf around the circuit, i.e., about 95 per cent of the "drop" is across the air gap.

Problems

1. An atomic electron moves in a circle of radius r with a velocity v. Show that the angular-momentum and magnetic-moment vectors produced by this motion have the same direction, and find the ratio of magnetic moment to angular momentum. If this circulating electron is in a uniform magnetic field B, whose direction makes an angle θ with the magnetic moment, show that the circular orbit precesses about the direction of the magnetic field with a precessional angular velocity $\omega = eB/2m$, independent of θ and v. This is the Larmor precession.

2. A very long solenoid having 2,000 turns per meter is wound on an iron core 3.0 cm in radius and carries a steady current of 10 amp. The relative permeability of the iron (assumed constant) is 1,000. Neglecting end effects, calculate:

   a. The self-inductance per meter length of the solenoid.

   b. The intensity of magnetization inside the iron.

   c. The induced surface Amperian current per meter length of the surface of the core.

   d. The number of turns per meter length of an air solenoid of similar dimensions to produce the same inductance.

   e. The magnetic field energy stored per meter length of the solenoid.

3. A toroidal coil of mean radius 10.0 cm and of cross section 5.0 cm^2 is wound on a core of relative permeability 800. If the winding of 1,500 turns has a resistance of 2.0 ohms, compute the time constant of the coil.

4. A large uniformly magnetized specimen of iron contains a cavity in the form of a needle-shaped hole, and a cavity in the form of a thin pillbox. The axes of these cavities are parallel to the magnetic induction. Given B and H in the iron, find B' and H' in the cavities.

5. A needle-shaped piece of iron and a thin disk of iron of permeability μ are placed in a region of space where there is a uniform magnetic field B. The axes of the specimens are parallel to B. Find B' and H' in the iron. Compute the intensity of magnetization in each specimen in an applied field $B = 10^{-4}$ weber/m^2, assuming $\mu = 1,000\mu_0$.

6. A long straight copper wire 1.0 cm in diameter is surrounded coaxially by a long hollow iron cylinder of relative permeability 1,000, inner radius 2.0 cm, and outer radius 3.0 cm. The wire carries a steady current of 20 amp.

a. Compute the total magnetic flux inside a 1-m length of the iron cylinder.

b. The induced Amperian currents on the iron cylinder surfaces are parallel or antiparallel to the current in the copper wire and uniformly distributed over these surfaces. Find the magnitudes of these currents on the inner and outer surfaces of the hollow iron cylinder and their directions relative to the current in the copper.

c. Compute the intensity of magnetization at a point 2.5 cm from the axis of the system.

d. Prove that the Amperian current density inside the iron is zero.

e. Show that the magnetic field outside the iron is the same as if the iron were absent.

7. A very long solenoid of radius R is wound with n turns per unit length, and a long cylindrical rod of radius $r < R$ is placed coaxially inside the solenoid.

a. If the permeability of the rod material is μ, derive an expression for the self-inductance per unit length of the solenoid.

b. A coil of N turns is wound around the cylindrical rod, and the outer winding carries an alternating current $i = I \sin \omega t$. Derive an expression for the emf induced in the secondary coil of N turns when this coil is on open circuit.

8. A 1,200-turn toroid is wound on an iron ring of mean diameter 18 cm and cross section 6.0 cm^2 and carries a steady current of 2.0 amp. The relative permeability of the iron is 1,500.

a. Compute the flux of B in the ring.

b. If an air gap of length 0.50 mm is cut in the ring, compute the flux in the air gap, taking its effective area equal to that of the ring.

c. Find the coil inductance with and without the air gap.

d. Calculate the total field energy when there is no air gap.

e. With the air gap, find the total field energy and the field energy in the iron and in the air gap.

9. An iron rod of square cross section (2.0 × 2.0 cm) of relative permeability 800 is bent into the form of a ring of inner radius 5.0 cm, and the ends are welded together. Wire is wound toroidally around the ring to form a coil of 500 turns and carries a steady current of 2.0 amp.

a. Compute the total flux of B in the ring, taking into account the variation of B with position inside the iron. What is the inductance of this coil?

b. What is the magnitude of the Amperian current on the ring surface?

c. Find the average value of B over a cross section of the ring, and the mean radius of the ring (such that product of B at this radius and the area gives the total flux computed in part *a*).

d. Prove that the Amperian current density is zero everywhere inside the iron.

10. A 3.0-mm air gap is cut in the ring of the toroid of Prob. 9.

a. Compute the flux of B in the ring and the self-inductance of the coil.

b. A square slab of iron (2.0 by 2.0 cm) of thickness 2.0 mm and of relative permeability 1,200 is inserted into the air gap so that the edges of one of its faces coincide with those of the air gap of the toroidal core. How much work must be done by the sources which maintain the current constant during the insertion process?

c. What is the increase of magnetic field energy during the process described

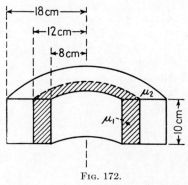

FIG. 172.

in part *b*, and how much mechanical work is done by the force which pulls the slab into the gap?

11. Suppose the iron rod used in the construction of Prob. 9 is hollow, the hollow region being of square cross section 1.5 cm on a side. Compute the inductance of the toroid, taking into account the variation of B with position.

12. A 1,000-turn toroidal coil is wound around a core of square cross section composed of two kinds of iron, as shown in Fig. 172, which depicts one-half the core. The permeabilities of the inner and outer iron rings are $500\mu_0$ and $1,000\mu_0$, respectively. Compute the self-inductance of the toroid.

13. Prove that the magnetic field energy stored in a magnetic circuit can be written as

$$U = \frac{1}{2}\,\Phi^2\Re = \frac{1}{2}\,(\text{mmf})\,\Phi = \frac{(\text{mmf})^2}{2\Re}$$

where Φ is the flux of B in the circuit, $\Re$ the reluctance, and (mmf) is the magnetomotive force around the circuit.

14. Consider the magnetic circuit of uniform cross section A of Fig. 173. The air-gap lengths x are very small compared to the cross-section dimension.

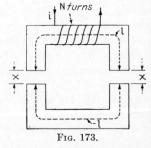

FIG. 173.

a. Using the results of Prob. 13, show that, if the air gaps are closed, the field energy increases by $[(\text{mmf})^2/2]\,[(1/\Re_2) - (1/\Re_1)]$, where $\Re_1$ and $\Re_2$ are the reluctances with and without air gaps, respectively. The current i in the winding is kept constant.

b. Using Faraday's induction law, show that the sources of emf which maintain the current constant do an amount of work on the system equal to twice the increase of field energy when the gaps are closed. What happens to the difference of these energies?

15. Starting with the magnetic circuit of Fig. 173, suppose the top half is held fixed and the bottom half is allowed to move up an infinitesimal distance dx. Derive an expression for the increase of magnetic field energy during this displacement, keeping the current in the magnetizing coil constant. Using the results of Prob. 14, show that the force with which the two sections attract each other is given by

$$F = 2\left(\frac{B^2 A}{2\mu_0}\right)$$

16. Two long iron plungers of relative permeability 1,200 are inserted into a very long solenoid. Each plunger is of 6.0 cm² cross section and fits tightly into the solenoid. If the magnetic induction in the iron is 0.50 weber/m², find the force (in pounds) with which one must pull to separate the plungers.

17. A long solenoid of 1,000 turns per meter contains an iron rod 2.0 cm in diameter cut in two, and carries a current of 3.0 amp in its winding (the primary). Compute the force necessary to separate the two halves if the following experimental data are known: on reversing the current in the primary a charge of 60 microcoulombs flows through a secondary circuit consisting of a 10-turn coil of 100 ohms resistance, wound on the same core.

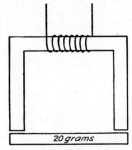

18. A relay is constructed of a rectangular piece of iron, as shown in Fig. 174. The movable portion, of mass 20 g, is connected to the remainder of the relay by guides which permit a vertical motion of 0.50 mm. The total mean length of the magnetic circuit is 10 cm, and its cross section is 1.0 cm². The magnetizing coil has 500 turns.

Fig. 174.

Find the minimum coil current to keep the relay closed (no air gaps) and the minimum coil current to close the relay when it is open (the movable piece 0.50 mm from the core).

19. A magnetic circuit has a core of mean length 30 cm, cross section 6.0 by 6.0 cm, and an air gap 2.0 mm long. The magnetizing coil has 100 turns and carries a steady current of 1.0 amp. A slab of iron 6.0 by 6.0 by 0.20 cm is inserted into the air gap, completely filling it. Assuming the relative permeability of the core material and slab to be constant and equal to 1,200, compute the mechanical work necessary to remove the slab from the air gap.

20. Consider a region of space where there is a magnetic field which is not quite uniform. A rigid magnetic body of permeability μ, volume v, is brought into the field at a point where the magnetic induction was B. Suppose the volume v of the body is small enough so that B does not vary appreciably throughout this volume and that the magnetic susceptibility of the body is extremely small compared to unity (the case of ordinary paramagnetic or diamagnetic materials), so that we may consider the induction B unaltered by the presence of the body. Show that the decrease of magnetic energy caused by this insertion is given very nearly by

$$\frac{v}{2}(\mu - \mu_0)\frac{B^2}{\mu_0^2} = \frac{v}{2}(\mu - \mu_0)H^2$$

with H the original magnetic intensity at the point where the body is located.

Now consider a small displacement of the body to a point where the magnetic field has a slightly different value. Compute the decrease of field energy due to this displacement, and, equating this to the work done by the mechanical force F acting on the body, show that this force F is given by

$$F = \frac{v}{2}\chi_m\mu_0H^2$$

where χ_m the magnetic susceptibility of the body.

21. An electromagnet, shown in Fig. 175, is designed to support a weight

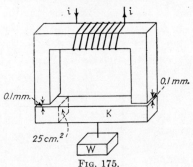

FIG. 175.

of 100 lb (including the weight of the keeper K). The cross section of all parts of the magnetic circuit is 25 cm²; the mean length of the magnetic path in the iron (including K) is 50 cm, and the air gaps are each 0.10 mm long. The permeability of the iron is $1,800\mu_0$. If the wire of the magnetizing coil can carry 1.0 amp, compute the least number of turns in the coil needed to support this weight.

22. Suppose that the iron of Prob. 21 has not a constant permeability but that μ varies with B as follows:

B, webers/m²...............	0.35	0.40	0.44	0.49	0.53	0.58
μ/μ_0......................	1,650	1,600	1,560	1,500	1,450	1,380

Compute the least number of turns needed in the coil, assuming a maximum current of 1.0 amp.

23. A variable inductance consists of a coil wound on a magnetic core of length 50 cm with an adjustable air gap. When the air gap is closed, the inductor has a reactance of 16 ohms at 60 cycles/sec. What length of air gap is required to decrease the reactance to 5 ohms? The relative permeability of the iron is 1,100.

24. A magnetic core of constant length and uniform cross section has an adjustable air gap, and a coil is wound on this core. When the air gap is reduced to zero, the self-inductance of the coil is 3.0 henrys. When the length of the air gap is 0.05 in., the inductance is 1.0 henry. To what length must the air gap be increased to reduce the inductance to 0.20 henry, assuming a constant permeability of the magnetic core?

25. Two coils are wound side by side on the same magnetic circuit. The first has 500 turns, a resistance of 2.5 ohms, a self-inductance of 0.50 henry; and the second has 1,000 turns and a resistance of 50 ohms. If a d-c emf of 4.3 volts is impressed on the first coil, what voltage must be impressed on the second coil so that the magnetic flux in the core will be reduced to zero? What will be the flux in the core when a voltage of 15 volts is impressed on the second coil alone?

26. Consider the volume enclosed by a hemispherical surface in a region where a magnetic field changes with the time. Compare the expressions for the emf induced around the equator of the hemisphere by considering *a.* The magnetic flux crossing the plane surface of the hemisphere.

b. The magnetic flux crossing the curved surface.

Equating these expressions (they both represent the same emf), show that

$$\int_{\substack{\text{closed}\\\text{surface}}} B_n \, dS = 0$$

i.e., that the field of B, not of H, is solenoidal.

CHAPTER 15

ELECTROMAGNETIC WAVES IN MATERIAL BODIES

In Chaps. 10 and 11 we have seen how the concept of displacement current led to the prediction of the possibility of electromagnetic waves, traveling in empty space with a velocity $c = 1/\sqrt{\epsilon_0\mu_0} = 3 \times 10^8$ m/sec (the velocity of light). We have shown that, at least for plane waves, the waves are transverse, both $\mathcal{E}$ and $\mathbf{H}$ having no components in the direction of propagation, and that these vectors are mutually perpendicular. The energy flow in these waves can be described by the Poynting vector $\mathbf{S} = (\mathcal{E} \times \mathbf{H})$, this vector giving the propagation direction as well as the power density or intensity of the wave. In this chapter we shall investigate the behavior of such waves when they are propagated in material media, especially in dielectrics, and in particular we shall examine the phenomena occurring when they impinge on the interface between two dielectrics. According to the electromagnetic theory of light, we should expect that the laws so found will describe optical phenomena, and we shall concern ourselves largely with applications to the field of optics.

1. Plane Waves in Dielectrics. We start with a discussion of electromagnetic waves in uncharged nonconducting stationary bodies, for which the fundamental laws relating the electric and magnetic field vectors may be written in exactly the same form as for empty space, since the density of true charge ρ and the real current density J vanish in both cases. These laws are

$$\int_{\substack{\text{closed} \\ \text{surface}}} D_n\, dS = 0; \qquad \int_{\substack{\text{closed} \\ \text{surface}}} B_n\, dS = 0 \tag{15.1}$$

$$\oint \mathcal{E}_s\, ds = -\int \frac{\partial B_n}{\partial t}\, dS; \qquad \oint H_s\, ds = \int \frac{\partial D_n}{\partial t}\, dS \tag{15.2}$$

In addition, we have the relations $D = \epsilon\mathcal{E}$ and $B = \mu H$. For all but ferromagnetic bodies—and these are conductors—the magnetic susceptibility is so extremely small compared to unity that we may set $\mu = \mu_0$ without appreciable error. Most of the equations, however, will be written in a general form, retaining an arbitrary value of μ.

Let us first review briefly the arguments leading to the equation for

278

linearly polarized waves traveling along the x-axis.   We have seen that Eqs. (15.1) require that the x-components of all the vectors vanish (or at most be constant and hence of no interest for the study of waves) and hence that $\mathcal{E}$ and H (also B and D) must lie in planes normal to the direction of propagation.   Equations (15.2) were then applied to the elementary circuits shown as I and II in Fig. 176.

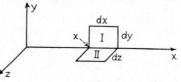

Fig. 176.

The first of Eqs. (15.2) applied to circuit I led to

$$\frac{\partial \mathcal{E}_y}{\partial x} = -\frac{\partial B_z}{\partial t} \tag{15.3}$$

and the second of Eqs. (15.2) applied to circuit II gave

$$\frac{\partial H_z}{\partial x} = -\frac{\partial D_y}{\partial t} \tag{15.4}$$

These equations are to be supplemented by two more in the general case of plane waves traveling along the x-axis with arbitrary polarization, and these are

$$\frac{\partial \mathcal{E}_z}{\partial x} = +\frac{\partial B_y}{\partial t}; \qquad \frac{\partial H_y}{\partial x} = +\frac{\partial D_z}{\partial t} \tag{15.5}$$

although we shall not need to make explicit use of these last two relations.   The only difference in the argument from that of Chap. 11 is now to replace B by μH (instead of $\mu_0 H$) and D by $\epsilon \mathcal{E}$ (instead of $\epsilon_0 \mathcal{E}$).   There then follows the wave equation for $\mathcal{E}_y$

$$\frac{\partial^2 \mathcal{E}_y}{\partial x^2} = \epsilon \mu \frac{\partial^2 \mathcal{E}_y}{\partial t^2} \tag{15.6}$$

and an identical equation for H_z.   For linearly polarized waves, only $\mathcal{E}_y$ and H_z are different from zero, all other components of these vectors being zero.   Equation (15.6) may be written in the form

$$\frac{\partial^2 \mathcal{E}_y}{\partial x^2} = \frac{1}{v^2} \frac{\partial^2 \mathcal{E}_y}{\partial t^2} \tag{15.6a}$$

where $v = \dfrac{c}{\sqrt{\epsilon \mu / \epsilon_0 \mu_0}}$ is the velocity of the wave, which is now different from its velocity c in empty space.   For nonmagnetic bodies we set $\mu/\mu_0 = 1$, and, using $\kappa = \epsilon/\epsilon_0$, we find

$$v = \frac{c}{\sqrt{\kappa}} = \frac{c}{n} \tag{15.7}$$

where κ is the dielectric constant of the medium.   In optics it is customary to denote the ratio of the velocity of light in vacuum to its value in a material medium as the *index of refraction, n,* of the substance.   Hence we predict the relation

$$n = \sqrt{\kappa} \tag{15.8}$$

between the index of refraction and the dielectric constant of a dielectric.   It turns out experimentally that this equality is *not* true in

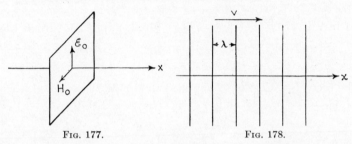

FIG. 177.   FIG. 178.

general, and there are violent exceptions.   For example, water has a refractive index of about 1.3, whereas $\sqrt{\kappa} = 9$.   The reason for this discrepancy lies, not in the inadequacy of the laws of electromagnetism, but rather in the tacit assumption that the dielectric constant is strictly a constant, independent of the frequency of the waves.   This assumption is not justified when dealing with waves of optical frequencies, and we shall investigate the theory of the variation of κ with frequency (or wavelength) in a later chapter on the dispersion of light, *i.e.,* the variation of refractive index with frequency.   Equation (15.6*a*) is satisfied by traveling sinusoidal waves of the form

$$\mathcal{E}_y = \mathcal{E}_0 \sin \omega \left(t - \frac{x}{v} \right) \tag{15.9}$$

with $\omega = 2\pi\nu$, ν the frequency of the wave, and similarly for H_z:

$$H_z = H_0 \sin \omega \left(t - \frac{x}{v} \right) \tag{15.10}$$

These represent plane waves traveling along the positive x-axis and having a wavelength $\lambda = 2\pi v/\omega = v/\nu$, the surfaces of constant phase at a definite instant of time being given by the equations $x = constant$. For example, consider one of these y-z planes, as shown in Fig. 177, in which at a given instant of time, $\mathcal{E}$ and H have their maximum values $\mathcal{E}_0$ and H_0.   One has the same values of $\mathcal{E}$ and H at every point in this plane, and this represents a "crest" of the wave.   The plane containing these maximum values of $\mathcal{E}$ and H moves to the right with the phase velocity v, as is evident from Eqs. (15.9) and (15.10). Thus we can represent a traveling plane wave schematically by a figure such as Fig. 178, in which the vertical lines represent the intersections of the crests with the plane of the page. Halfway between these crests lie the "troughs" of the wave, and the distance between two successive crests (or between two successive troughs) is the wavelength λ.

In Chap. 11 we derived the relation between the amplitudes $\mathcal{E}_0$ and H_0 for plane waves, and since this relation is fundamental for our later considerations, we repeat the derivation here for dielectric media. Equations (15.9) and (15.10) represent the electric and magnetic vectors of the *same* wave only if Eqs. (15.3) and (15.4) are satisfied. This determines the relative values of $\mathcal{E}$ and H. From Eq. (15.9) we find

$$\frac{\partial \mathcal{E}_y}{\partial x} = -\frac{\omega}{v}\,\mathcal{E}_0 \cos \omega \left(t - \frac{x}{v} \right)$$

and from Eq. (15.10)

$$\frac{\partial H_z}{\partial t} = +\omega H_0 \cos \omega \left(t - \frac{x}{v} \right)$$

Substituting in Eq. (15.3), there follows

$$\frac{\mathcal{E}_0}{v} = \mu H_0$$

and, using the relation $v = 1/\sqrt{\epsilon \mu}$, this can be written as

$$\sqrt{\epsilon}\,\mathcal{E}_0 = \sqrt{\mu}\,H_0$$

Since for *traveling* waves $\mathcal{E}$ and H are in phase, we can equally well write

$$\sqrt{\epsilon}\,\mathcal{E} = \sqrt{\mu}\,H \tag{15.11}$$

For nonmagnetic media, Eq. (15.11) takes the more convenient form

$$n\mathcal{E} = \sqrt{\frac{\mu_0}{\epsilon_0}}\,H \tag{15.12}$$

since $\mu = \mu_0$ and $n = \sqrt{\kappa} = \sqrt{\epsilon/\epsilon_0}$. It is left as an exercise for the reader to show that this relation can be obtained equally well by using Eq. (15.4) instead of (15.5).

We shall need expressions for plane waves traveling in an arbitrary direction, not only along the x-axis, and we must obtain the form taken by Eq. (15.9), for example, for this case. First, we note that in

Eq. (15.9) the planes of constant phase are given by $x = constant$. Hence, in the expression for a plane wave traveling in an arbitrary direction, we must replace x by an expression which, when placed equal to a constant, yields the equations of parallel planes whose normals make arbitrary angles with the x-, y-, and z-axes, *i.e.*, the equations of the surfaces of constant phase. Thus we need the general expression for the equation of a plane. Let AA be the intersection of such a plane with the plane of the page, k a vector of *unit length* in a

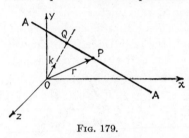

direction perpendicular to the plane, and r the radius vector from the origin O to any point P of the plane (Fig. 179). It is clear from the figure that the projection of the radius vector r along the direction of k (normal to the plane) has the same value (OQ) no matter where the point P lies in the plane. Thus the plane is

Fig. 179.

the locus of all points P, the radius vectors to which have the same projection OQ along the normal. Hence the equation of the plane can be written in the convenient vector form

$$\mathbf{r} \cdot \mathbf{k} = OQ = \text{constant} \tag{15.13}$$

Now let the components of the unit vector $\mathbf{k}$ along the x-, y-, and z-axes be f, g, and h, respectively. The components of $\mathbf{r}$ are x, y, and z (the coordinates of the point P). From the rules for forming the scalar product of two vectors, there follows

$$\mathbf{r} \cdot \mathbf{k} = fx + gy + hz$$

f, g, and h are the cosines of the angles which the normal to the plane (k) makes with the positive x-, y-, and z-axes, respectively. It then follows that the equation of a plane in Cartesian coordinates is

$$fx + gy + hz = \text{constant} \tag{15.14}$$

The equation of a plane wave (of $\mathcal{E}$) traveling in the direction $\mathbf{k}$ normal to the planes of constant phase can now be written. It is

$$\mathcal{E} = \mathcal{E}_0 \sin \omega \left(t - \frac{fx + gy + hz}{v} \right) \tag{15.15}$$

where the vectors $\mathcal{E}$ and $\mathcal{E}_0$ are perpendicular to the direction of propagation (to $\mathbf{k}$), as they must be for a transverse wave. An exactly similar expression holds for $\mathbf{H} = \sqrt{\epsilon_0/\mu_0}\ \mathcal{E}$.   Utilizing Eq. (15.13), we can write Eq. (15.15) in the more concise form

$$\mathcal{E} = \mathcal{E}_0 \sin \omega \left(t - \frac{\mathbf{k} \cdot \mathbf{r}}{v} \right) \tag{15.16}$$

Note that if $\mathbf{k}$ is parallel to the positive x-axis, $f = 1$, $g = h = 0$, and Eq. (15.15) reduces to Eq. (15.9), as it must.

2. Reflection and Refraction of Plane Waves.   Consider a plane electromagnetic wave which travels with a velocity v_1 in a dielectric medium and is incident on an uncharged boundary surface separating this medium from a second dielectric, in which the velocity of electromagnetic waves is v_2.   In accordance with the general boundary conditions developed in Chaps. 13 and 14, waves will be set up in both bodies.   The tangential components of $\mathcal{E}$ and H and the normal components of B and D must be continuous at any point of the interface for all values of time.   In general, it will not be possible to satisfy these conditions by postulating only a wave traveling in the second medium, but one must also require that a reflected wave be generated at the interface and travel back into the first medium.   Application of the boundary conditions then yields the relations which must hold among amplitudes, frequency, and directions of propagation of these various waves.

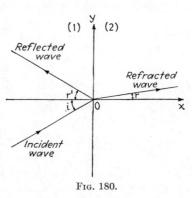

Fig. 180.

For the sake of simplicity, let us consider a plane boundary, which we take as the plane $x = 0$; the x-axis is then normal to this plane, and let the plane determined by the x-axis and the Poynting vector of the incident wave be the x-y plane,[1] as shown in Fig. 180.   In this figure are shown the directions of propagation of the incident, reflected, and refracted (transmitted) waves, denoting the angles between these directions and the x-axis (normal to the interface) by i, r', and r, respectively.   Since, for the incident wave, we have

$$f = \cos i; \qquad g = \sin i; \qquad h = 0$$

the electric vector of this wave may be written in accordance with Eq. (15.15) as

[1] This plane is known as the plane of incidence.

$$\mathcal{E}_1 = \mathcal{E}_{01} \sin \omega_1 \left(t - \frac{x \cos i + y \sin i}{v_1} \right) \tag{15.17}$$

where $\omega_1 = 2\pi\nu_1$ is the angular frequency and v_1 is the phase velocity of the wave in medium 1. The wave normal $\mathbf{k}$ of the transmitted or refracted wave has direction cosines $f = \cos r$, $g = \sin r$, $h = 0$, as is evident from Fig. 180. Hence the electric vector of this wave may be written as

$$\mathcal{E}_2 = \mathcal{E}_{02} \sin \omega_2 \left(t - \frac{x \cos r + y \sin r}{v_2} \right) \tag{15.18}$$

with $\omega_2 = 2\pi\nu_2$ and v_2 the angular frequency and phase velocity in medium 2. Now the boundary conditions, *e.g.*, the continuity of the tangential component of $\mathcal{E}$, must hold at all points of the boundary surface, *i.e.*, for all values of y and z when $x = 0$, and also at all instants of time t. Comparing Eqs. (15.17) and (15.18), in which we set $x = 0$, we see that this can be true only if

$$\omega_1 = \omega_2 \quad \text{or} \quad \nu_1 = \nu_2 \quad \text{and if} \quad \frac{\sin i}{v_1} = \frac{\sin r}{v_2}$$

no matter how we choose the amplitudes $\mathcal{E}_{01}$ and $\mathcal{E}_{02}$. From the first of these conditions, we see that the waves in the two media must be of the same frequency; hence the wavelengths are different. The second relation fixes the direction of propagation of the refracted wave if that of the incident wave is known. Using the relations $v_1 = c/n_1$ and $v_2 = c/n_2$, n_1 and n_2 being the refractive indices of the two media, this relation takes the form

$$\frac{\sin i}{\sin r} = \frac{n_2}{n_1} \tag{15.19}$$

The ratio of the sine of the angle of incidence (i) to the sine of the angle of refraction (r) equals the ratio of the refractive indices. This is the well-known law of refraction in optics and is called *Snell's law*.

Finally, consider the reflected wave. Its wave normal has direction cosines $f = \cos (\pi - r') = -\cos r'$; $g = \sin (\pi - r') = \sin r'$; $h = 0$, remembering that the angles are measured with respect to the *positive* x-axis. Hence Eq. (15.15) for the electric vector of this reflected wave has the form

$$\mathcal{E}_1' = \mathcal{E}_{01}' \sin \omega_1 \left(t + \frac{x \cos r' - y \sin r'}{v_1} \right) \tag{15.20}$$

and we can repeat the arguments of the previous paragraph. Since the boundary conditions must hold at all points of the surface $x = 0$, there follows, from Eqs. (15.17) and (15.20),

$$\sin i = \sin r'$$

or

$$i = r' \tag{15.21}$$

The angle of incidence equals the angle of reflection, another familiar law of elementary optics.

Let us now examine some of the consequences of Snell's law [Eq. (15.19)]. There are two cases: (1) the case for which $n_2 > n_1$ and (2) the case for which $n_1 > n_2$. In the first case, speaking of optical waves, we say that the wave travels from an optically "rarer" to an optically "denser" medium, and conversely for the second case. Since $\sin i$ can take on all values from zero to unity, $\sin r$ [which equals $(n_1/n_2) \sin i$] takes on corresponding values lying between zero and n_1/n_2. Now in the case for which $n_1/n_2 < 1$, this corresponds to a real angle of refraction for every angle of incidence. On the other hand, for waves traveling from an optically denser medium into a rarer one, $n_1/n_2 > 1$, refraction cannot take place for all angles of incidence. If the angle of incidence is less than $\sin^{-1}(n_2/n_1)$, then $\sin r$ has a value between zero and unity, and a real refracted wave exists. For angles of incidence larger than this value, *i.e.*, if $\sin i > n_2/n_1$, the angle of refraction becomes imaginary, and there is no real refracted wave, only a reflected wave. For such a case one speaks of *total reflection*.

When one applies the boundary conditions to the waves described by Eqs. (15.17), (15,18), and (15.20), and to the corresponding expressions for H, the resulting equations fix the vector amplitudes and hence the polarizations and intensities of the reflected and refracted waves relative to the incident wave. The laws of reflection and refraction, embodied in Eqs. (15.19) and (15.21), must hold in any case, provided these waves are present. These laws (which follow from any wave theory of light, not only from electromagnetic theory, as is evident from our derivation) yield information as to the relative directions of the waves but leave the question of relative intensities and polarizations untouched. One can, however, answer the last question with the help of the method indicated above and thus see that the fundamental laws of electromagnetic theory embody not only the laws of so-called geometrical optics, but also those of physical optics.

3. Intensity Relations for Normal Incidence. In this section we shall carry through the calculations for the intensities for the special case of normal incidence, *i.e.*, when the wave normal of the incident wave coincides with that of the boundary. We note first that if the incident wave is linearly polarized, the reflected and refracted waves are also linearly polarized, and the polarization direction (the direction of $\mathcal{E}$) is the same for all three waves. Let $\mathcal{E}_1$ be the electric vector of the linearly polarized incident wave and $\mathcal{E}_1'$ and $\mathcal{E}_2$ those of the reflected and refracted (transmitted) waves, respectively (Fig. 181). At a given instant of time the magnetic vectors H_1, H_1', and H_2 all point into the plane of the paper, and the corresponding directions of the electric

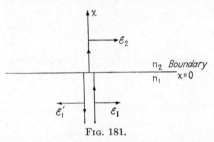

FIG. 181.

vectors are shown. For the reflected wave, $\mathcal{E}_1'$ must be opposite to $\mathcal{E}_1$, so that the Poynting vector S represents a wave traveling along the negative x-axis. One must have either $\mathcal{E}$ or H reversed in phase for the reflected wave (relative to the field vectors of the incident wave), and we

choose $\mathcal{E}$ arbitrarily as the one which is changed. Our final equations will answer uniquely the question as to which vector undergoes a 180° phase change on reflection.

The following conditions must be satisfied at the boundary $x = 0$:

1. The normal component of D must be continuous at the boundary.
2. The normal component of B must be continuous at the boundary.
3. The tangential component of $\mathcal{E}$ must be continuous at the boundary.
4. The tangential component of H must be continuous at the boundary.

In our special case of normal incidence the first two conditions are obviously satisfied, since all the vectors are parallel to the boundary surface. In fact, the first two conditions will be satisfied in general if conditions 3 and 4 are satisfied, using solutions of Eqs. (15.2). The proof of this is left to the problems. Condition 3 yields

$$\mathcal{E}_1 - \mathcal{E}_1' = \mathcal{E}_2 \tag{15.22}$$

and condition 4 gives

$$H_1 + H_1' = H_2 \tag{15.23}$$

In these equations the $\mathcal{E}$'s and H's denote the magnitudes of the vectors for $x = 0$ at any instant of time. Since the vectors $\mathcal{E}_1$, $\mathcal{E}_1'$, and $\mathcal{E}_2$ are given by

$$\mathcal{E}_1 = \mathcal{E}_{01} \sin \omega \left(t - \frac{n_1 x}{c} \right)$$

$$\mathcal{E}_1' = \mathcal{E}_{01}' \sin \omega \left(t + \frac{n_1 x}{c} \right)$$

$$\mathcal{E}_2 = \mathcal{E}_{02} \sin \omega \left(t - \frac{n_2 x}{c} \right)$$

in accordance with the general Eqs. (15.17), (15.18), and (15.20), we see that only at the boundary $x = 0$ can Eq. (15.22) be satisfied for all values of t. Now we make use of the relation between the magnitudes of $\mathcal{E}$ and H for a plane wave and have from Eq. (15.12)

$$H_1 = n_1 \sqrt{\frac{\epsilon_0}{\mu_0}} \, \mathcal{E}_1; \qquad H_1' = n_1 \sqrt{\frac{\epsilon_0}{\mu_0}} \, \mathcal{E}_1'; \qquad H_2 = n_2 \sqrt{\frac{\epsilon_0}{\mu_0}} \, \mathcal{E}_2$$

Equation (15.23) can then be written in the form

$$\mathcal{E}_1 + \mathcal{E}_1' = \frac{n_2}{n_1} \mathcal{E}_2 \tag{15.24}$$

Equations (15.22) and (15.24) show the necessity of assuming the existence of *both* reflected and refracted waves. Were either assumed missing, we could not simultaneously satisfy both these equations. From these equations there follows

$$\mathcal{E}_1' = \left(\frac{n_2 - n_1}{n_2 + n_1} \right) \mathcal{E}_1 \tag{15.25}$$

giving the electric vector of the reflected wave in terms of that of the incident wave. For the transmitted wave one finds

$$\mathcal{E}_2 = \left(\frac{2 n_1}{n_2 + n_1} \right) \mathcal{E}_1 \tag{15.26}$$

Equation (15.25) now shows us that if $n_2 > n_1$, *i.e.*, if the wave is incident on an optically denser medium, the electric vector at the surface undergoes a phase change of 180° upon reflection, and the magnetic vector undergoes no change, as we assumed. On the other hand, if $n_2 < n_1$, as in the case of a beam of light traveling from glass to air, the electric vectors of the incident and reflected waves are in phase at the interface, whereas the magnetic vectors are 180° out of phase with each other.

One is generally more interested in the intensity relations than in amplitude relations. The energy incident per unit area on the boundary surface per unit time is given by the magnitude of the

Poynting vector of the incident wave as

$$|\mathbf{S}_1| = |\boldsymbol{\mathcal{E}}_1 \times \mathbf{H}_1| = n_1 \sqrt{\frac{\epsilon_0}{\mu_0}}\, \mathcal{E}_1^2$$

since $H_1 = n_1 \sqrt{\epsilon_0/\mu_0}\, \mathcal{E}_1$.

The reflected intensity is

$$|\mathbf{S}_1'| = |\boldsymbol{\mathcal{E}}_1' \times \mathbf{H}_1'| = n_1 \sqrt{\frac{\epsilon_0}{\mu_0}}\, \mathcal{E}_1'^2$$

so that the ratio of the reflected to incident intensities is given by

$$R = \frac{|S_1'|}{|S_1|} = \frac{\mathcal{E}_1'^2}{\mathcal{E}_1^2}$$

R is known as the reflecting power of the boundary surface. Using Eq. (15.25), we then have for R

$$R = \left(\frac{n_2 - n_1}{n_2 + n_1}\right)^2 \tag{15.27}$$

as the reflecting power at normal incidence. The reflecting power is always less than unity and approaches this value as n_2 becomes large compared with n_1, or vice versa. For a glass-air boundary, the glass having a refractive index of about 1.5 and the index of refraction of air being set equal to 1, we obtain as the reflecting power of the glass surface

$$R = \left(\frac{0.5}{2.5}\right)^2 = \frac{1}{25} = 0.04$$

Thus about 4 per cent of the intensity of a light beam incident normally on a glass surface is reflected. We note further that the results obtained for normal incidence are independent of the polarization of the incident wave.

The calculation of the intensity relations at dielectric boundaries for an arbitrary angle of incidence follows the same scheme as for normal incidence. It is more involved, however, since the reflecting power depends on the polarization of the incident wave. The formulas for reflecting power are different for linearly polarized waves with the electric vector oscillating in the plane of incidence and for waves with the electric vector oscillating at right angles to the plane of incidence. We shall not carry through these calculations.

The propagation of electromagnetic disturbances in conducting bodies, such as metals, is a much more complicated phenomenon than in dielectrics, so that we must content ourselves with a few qualitative remarks. If we consider metals and assume the validity of Ohm's

law, the Ampère circuital law must be used in a more general form
than that employed in this chapter to take into account conduction
currents. Thus the second of Eqs. (15.2) should be written as

$$\oint H_s\, ds = \int \frac{\partial D_n}{\partial t}\, dS + \sigma \int \mathcal{E}_n\, dS$$

The effect of the last term on the right would be to modify our equations so that, even in the simple case of an electric field with but one
component, say $\mathcal{E}_y$, which depends only on x and t, $\mathcal{E}_y$ is determined
by an equation more complicated than the wave equation. It is still
true that the disturbances will be transverse, and they will to some
extent resemble ordinary transverse waves. The essential differences

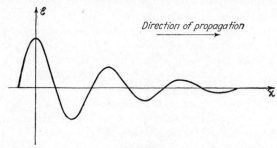

Fig. 182.

for traveling plane electromagnetic waves in metals as compared to
those in dielectrics may be summarized as follows:

1. The amplitude of the vector ($\mathcal{E}$ or H) decreases exponentially as
x increases. Thus the Poynting vector decreases as the wave progresses, and the rate of decrease of this vector is a measure of the Joule
heating produced in the metal. We say that we have a space-damped
wave.

2. The velocity of propagation depends on the frequency, even if ϵ
and σ are assumed independent of frequency.

3. The magnetic and electric vectors are not in phase with each
other, as they are in the case of traveling plane waves in dielectrics.
In Fig. 182 is shown the variation of the amplitude of the electric
vector with distance in the direction of propagation of an electromagnetic wave in a conducting medium.

Problems

1. Consider a linearly polarized plane wave, of the form of Eqs. (15.9) and
(15.10), traveling in a nonconducting medium. Show, by using Eq. (15.4)
of the text, that the electric and magnetic vectors are related by $\sqrt{\epsilon}\, \mathcal{E} = \sqrt{\mu} H$

2. Consider a closed volume in an uncharged dielectric medium. By
applying Eqs. (15.2) to a closed path on the surface of this volume, prove that

Eqs. (15.1) are satisfied. From these results, show that solutions of Eqs. (15.2) which satisfy the boundary conditions that tangential $\mathcal{E}$ and H are continuous across a boundary surface between two dielectrics will automatically satisfy the boundary conditions that the normal components of B and D are continuous at the boundary.

3. The electric field intensity of a linearly polarized plane wave traveling in a nonmagnetic dielectric of dielectric constant $\kappa = 2$ is given by Eq. (15.16). The magnitude of $\mathcal{E}_0$ is 50 volts/m, the frequency is 10^3 megacycles/sec, and the vector $\mathbf{k}$ is in the x-y plane at an angle of 30° with the positive x-axis. The vector $\mathcal{E}_0$ is also in the x-y plane.

a. What is the direction of propagation of the wave? What is its wavelength and what is the direction of $\mathcal{E}$?

b. What are the magnitudes and directions of H, B, and D?

c. What is the direction and average value of the Poynting vector?

d. What is the average energy density at any point of space? How is this related to your answer to part c?

4. Find the equation for the electric vector $\mathcal{E}$ of a plane electromagnetic wave which satisfies the following:

a. Its frequency is 9×10^8 cycles/sec.

b. It travels in a medium of refractive index $\frac{4}{3}$.

c. Its direction of propagation (the unit vector $\mathbf{k}$) makes an angle of 30° with the z-axis and lies in the plane bisecting the angle between the x- and y-axes, all components of $\mathbf{k}$ being positive.

d. It is linearly polarized in the plane bisecting the angle between the $+x$- and $+y$-axes.

e. The average value of its Poynting vector is $1/2\pi$ watts/m².

5. Given a cube of edge a, the edges lying along the x-, y-, and z-axes, and the origin O at one corner of the cube.

a. What is the angle between an edge of the cube and the body diagonal from the origin O to the opposite corner P?

b. Find the equation of the plane which is perpendicular to this body diagonal and contains the point P.

c. At what points does this plane intersect the x-, y-, and z-axes?

6. A plane wave of light is incident on one side of a glass plate which has a thickness d.

a. Show that the plane wave emerging from the other side of the plate has the same direction of propagation as the incident wave.

b. Consider a given normal of the incident wave. Prove that as the wave passes through the glass, this normal undergoes a lateral displacement given by

$$\frac{d \sin (i - r)}{\cos r}$$

where i and r are the angles of incidence and refraction at the first glass surface.

7. A plane wave of light is incident on a glass prism of refractive index 1.60 in air, as shown in Fig. 183. The prism angles are all 60°, and the direction of propagation of the incident wave makes an angle of 60° with the face on which it is incident. What is the deviation angle *D* between the directions of the incident and emerging waves?

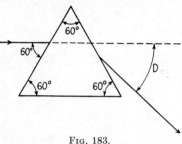

FIG. 183.

8. A plane light wave is incident normally on the face *AB* of a glass prism, as shown in Fig. 184. The index of refraction of the glass is 1.50. Find the smallest or largest value of the angle α such that the wave will be totally reflected at the surface *AC*:

a. If the prism is surrounded by air.

b. If the prism is surrounded by a liquid of refractive index 1.40.

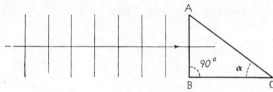

FIG. 184.

9. Liquid of refractive index 1.63 stands at a height of 2.0 cm in a flat-bottomed glass vessel. The index of refraction of the glass is 1.50. Show whether or not a plane wave of light incident on the top surface of the liquid can be totally reflected at the bottom surface.

10. A vessel full of water of refractive index 1.33 has a flat, tightly fitting glass cover of refractive index 1.50. Show whether or not light incident on the top of the glass cover can be totally reflected at the glass-water boundary.

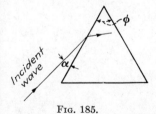

FIG. 185.

11. Find the largest value of the angle ϕ of the glass prism of Fig. 185 such that a light wave incident as shown will pass through the prism

a. When the prism is in air.

b. When the prism is immersed in water of refractive index 1.33.

The index of refraction of the glass is 1.55, and the angle α is small enough so that cos α is practically equal to unity.

12. A plane wave of light in water of refractive index $n_1 = \frac{4}{3}$ is incident at an angle *i* on a rectangular glass block of refractive index n_2, as shown in Fig. 186. As the angle of incidence *i* is varied, it is found that the beam refracted at A is totally reflected at B for all angles i smaller than 45°.   What is the index of refraction of the glass?

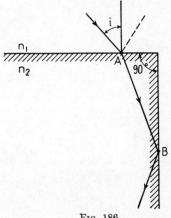

FIG. 186.

13. A plane light wave passes normally through a glass plate with plane-parallel faces. Assuming that the intensities, rather than the amplitudes, of the waves reflected and transmitted by the two faces add (this will be true in practice if the glass plate is thick compared to the wavelengths of the light employed),

a. Compute the ratio of intensity of the transmitted wave to that of the incident wave, taking into account only one reflection at each of the glass faces.

b. Set up a general expression for the above ratio, taking into account all the internal reflections inside the glass.

14. A plane light wave is normally incident on the liquid surface of Prob. 9. If the electric field vector of the incident wave has a peak value of 10 volts/m, compute the intensity of the wave transmitted through the glass vessel. (Consider only one reflection at each interface.)

15. Two dielectrics of refractive indices n_1 and n_2 are in contact along a plane boundary. A plane wave traveling in the medium of index n_1 is normally incident on the boundary. Compute expressions for the Poynting vector for the incident, reflected, and transmitted waves, and show that the energy incident on the boundary per unit time equals the sum of the energies carried away from the boundary per unit time by the reflected and transmitted waves.

16. a. Show, for the case of an electromagnetic disturbance traveling in a metal along the x-axis with the electric vector parallel to the y-axis, that Eqs. (15.3) and (15.4) of the text become

$$\frac{\partial \mathcal{E}_y}{\partial x} = - \frac{\partial B_z}{\partial t}$$

and

$$\frac{\partial H_z}{\partial x} = - \frac{\partial D_y}{\partial t} - \sigma \mathcal{E}_y$$

where σ is the conductivity of the metal.

b. From the above equations show that $\mathcal{E}_y$ and H_z each satisfies an equation of the form

$$\frac{\partial^2 \mathcal{E}_y}{\partial x^2} = \epsilon \mu \frac{\partial^2 \mathcal{E}_y}{\partial t^2} + \mu \sigma \frac{\partial \mathcal{E}_y}{\partial t}$$

17. Using the equations of Prob. 16, part a, show that in a metal the rate of decrease of electromagnetic field energy in a volume element $dx\, dy\, dz$ is equal to the net rate at which energy flows out of this volume element (computed from the Poynting vector) plus the rate of Joule heating in the element.

CHAPTER 16

GEOMETRICAL OPTICS AND SIMPLE OPTICAL INSTRUMENTS

In Chap. 15 we have seen how the fundamental laws of electromagnetism led to the laws of the reflection and refraction of plane waves at a boundary separating two dielectric media. By far the most important practical application of these laws is to the case of the reflection and refraction of light waves, electromagnetic waves of wavelengths ranging from about 4×10^{-5} cm to about 7×10^{-5} cm in air, at the surfaces of mirrors and lenses. In this chapter we shall concern ourselves specifically with this type of problem. The general problem of following the propagation of electromagnetic waves is far too complicated to allow a complete analysis in this book. We may, however, make a few remarks concerning some of the simpler aspects of the general method, which is embodied in a principle known as *Huygens' principle*. Suppose that we know the shape of one of the constant-phase surfaces of a wave, *e.g.*, one of the crests of the wave, at some instant of time. We can find the shape of this wave surface at a later time Δt by considering the various points on the original wave surface as sources of secondary spherical waves which diverge from these points. If one constructs spheres of radii equal to $v \Delta t$, v being the phase velocity of the waves, with centers at the various points on the initial wave surface, the envelope of these spherical wavelets then yields the shape of this wave surface at a time Δt later. Thus in Fig. 187 there is shown the trace of the initial wave surface AA and its trace at a time Δt later. This geometrical construction (Huygens' construction) is only part of the story, however, and offers no advantage over the simpler

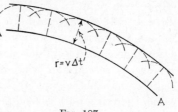

FIG. 187.

method of *rays* which we shall discuss shortly. To complete the analysis, we must know how the amplitudes of these secondary wavelets vary with direction, and it turns out that this variation of amplitude with direction of propagation is rather complicated. It is just the solution of this part of the problem which is prohibitively difficult.

In our study of plane waves we have seen that the constant-phase surfaces could be described by constructing the normals to these surfaces (the wave normals, or *rays*), and one can follow the motion of these surfaces by moving along the directions of these rays. This mode of description is evidently possible for waves other than plane waves. For example, in the case of spherical waves in a homogeneous medium, the rays consist of straight lines radiating in all directions from a common point, and the surfaces of constant phase are concentric spherical surfaces. If the Poynting vector is directed outward from the center, one speaks of a *diverging* wave, if toward the center, of a *converging* wave. One is often interested in following the motion of a limited portion of a wave surface, and one can construct a bundle, or *pencil*, of rays through this portion of the surface. Such a pencil of rays is called a *beam*, and for plane waves the beam consists of a parallel bundle of rays. For a spherical portion of a wave surface the rays diverge from (or converge on) a point *F*, known as the *focal point* of the pencil, as indicated in Fig. 188.

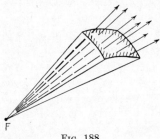

Such a pencil is called *stigmatic*. The pencil of rays from a portion of a wave surface which has different radii of curvature in two mutually orthogonal directions (such as a surface shaped like a blowout patch) forms an *astigmatic* pencil, and the rays do not pass through a common point. In the case of the propagation of waves in a homogeneous medium the rays always are straight lines, and the wave surfaces do

F

Fig. 188.

not change shape as the wave propagates. If, however, the velocity varies from point to point, the rays will be curved lines, and the wave surfaces will not maintain an unaltered shape.

Thus far our remarks are valid for waves of any wavelength, and the advantage gained by describing wave motion in terms of rays becomes evident if we consider what happens when we try to form a narrow beam from a plane wave by allowing the latter to fall on a screen, in which there is a hole, placed perpendicular to the direction of propagation. The waves emerging from the hole will, in general, *not* form a section of a plane wave with a parallel bundle of rays, but will spread out more or less in all directions. As we shall see later, *if the wavelength of the waves is very small compared to the linear dimensions of the aperture*, this spreading effect, or *diffraction*, as it is called, becomes extremely small, and, just in the case of light waves. the wavelength is very small compared with the dimensions of ordinary objects. In this chapter we shall neglect diffraction effects and treat the bundle of light rays emerging from the aperture as strictly parallel. Similarly, we shall assume that an obstacle placed in the path of a beam of light casts a sharply defined geometrical shadow. The laws of optics and optical systems, to the approximation in which one can neglect typical wave effects such as diffraction and interference, comprise the subject of *geometrical optics,* and in this chapter we shall concern ourselves with this study.

1. Reflection of Light. We have derived the law of reflection, angle of incidence equals angle of reflection, for the case of plane waves reflected from a plane surface. It is justifiable, however, to use it for other types of waves, *e.g.,* spherical waves, reflected from curved surfaces. We can see this as follows: Consider an infinitesimal element of area on the wave surface of an arbitrary wave. The normal to this elementary area gives the direction of the ray at the point where the element is located, and since we are dealing with an infinitesimal area, it may be considered as plane. Now, if this wave impinges on a curved surface, our elementary area will come in contact with an infinitesimal section of the reflecting surface, and the latter may be considered as plane. Thus we can apply the law of reflection to this particular ray, and we must simply take into account the fact that different rays of the same beam have different directions and that the normal direction to the reflecting surface varies from point to point.

For example, consider a spherical wave diverging from a point source of light S and incident on a plane mirror. In Fig. 189 we show a diverging beam of rays from S incident on the mirror MM and the reflected beam of rays which appear to be diverging from a source S' in back of the mirror. This focal point S' of the reflected rays is called the image of the source S, and we say that it is a *virtual* image, since the rays do not actually pass through this point. There are cases where a pencil of rays actually do pass through a definite point in a medium and then diverge from that point. In such cases one speaks of a *real* image.

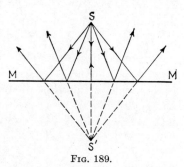

Fig. 189.

One can readily show that an object of finite size is imaged in a plane mirror in such a manner that each point of the image is just as far back of the surface as the corresponding point of the object is in front of it and that the linear dimensions of object and image are identical.   Thus the linear magnification, the ratio of linear dimension of image to object, is unity for a plane mirror.

An important case of reflection is that in which the reflecting surface is a portion of a spherical surface, a so-called spherical mirror. In the elementary discussion of spherical mirrors one learns that a bundle of rays parallel to the mirror axis (the normal to the mid-point of the mirror) is brought to a focus at a point halfway between the center of curvature of the mirror and the intersection of the mirror surface and the axis (the so-called vertex).   This statement is true only if the rays lie very close to the mirror axis, so that in practice it can be applied only to mirrors of small aperture, *i.e.*, when the mirror forms only a very small part of the whole spherical surface.   Let us examine the general case.   In Fig. 190 are shown the mirror and an incident ray parallel to the axis, which we call the *x*-axis.   The vertex of the mirror is taken as an origin, and we wish to find an expression for the distance *x*, the point *Q* being the

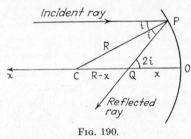

FIG. 190.

point where the reflected ray crosses the mirror axis.   In the triangle *CPQ* we have immediately from the law of sines

$$\frac{R - x}{R} = \frac{\sin i}{\sin (\pi - 2i)} = \frac{\sin i}{\sin 2i} = \frac{1}{2 \cos i}$$

and solving for *x*, we find

$$x = R \left(1 - \frac{1}{2 \cos i} \right) \tag{16.1}$$

Thus we see that the point at which a reflected ray crosses the axis depends on the angle of incidence of the ray, the value of *x* decreasing as the angle of incidence increases.   Only in the case of angles small enough so that we may place $\cos i = 1$ do we find the reflected rays all passing through a single point.   For this case we have from Eq. (16.1)

$$x_0 = R \left(1 - \frac{1}{2} \right) = \frac{R}{2} \tag{16.2}$$

and this point x_0 is called the *principal focus* of the mirror and the distance x_0 is called the *focal length* of the mirror.   The departure from sharp focusing of a bundle of paraxial rays coming from infinity by a mirror of large aperture is called *spherical aberration*. If the mirror surface is in the form of a paraboloid of revolution, objects very far from the mirror (at infinity) will be brought to a sharp focus. In astronomical mirrors one is always interested in imaging objects which are practically at infinity, so that paraboloidal mirrors are invariably used.

If we restrict ourselves to the case of spherical mirrors of such small aperture that all the rays diverging from an object (which may be at a finite distance from the mirror) make very small angles with the

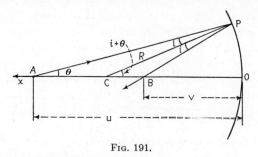

FIG. 191.

mirror axis, then the image will be sharp. We shall compute the position of the image by considering the object as a point on the mirror axis. First we note that a ray from the object coincident with the mirror axis is reflected on itself, so that the image must lie on the mirror axis.

In Fig. 191 we show an incident ray from the object A making an angle θ with the mirror axis, and the reflected ray intersecting this axis at B. The distance OA is denoted by u and is called the object distance, and $OB = v$ the image distance. In the triangle CPB we have from the law of sines

$$\frac{R - v}{R} = \frac{\sin i}{\sin [\pi - (2i + \theta)]} = \frac{\sin i}{\sin (2i + \theta)} \tag{16.3}$$

and using the triangle APC there follows

$$\frac{u - R}{R} = \frac{\sin i}{\sin \theta} \tag{16.4}$$

By eliminating the angle i from Eqs. (16.3) and (16.4), we can follow the reflected ray for every value of θ, and in general v will depend on θ. If the angles i and θ are small enough so that we may set $\sin i = i$ and $\sin \theta = \theta$, simultaneous solution of Eqs. (16.3) and (16.4) yields easily

$$\frac{1}{u} + \frac{1}{v} = \frac{2}{R} \qquad (16.5)$$

which is the usual expression relating image and object distances for a spherical mirror. Essentially the same formulas hold for the case of a convex mirror, and the derivations for this are left to the problems.

In any case it is clear that one may always find the image of any object by graphical construction, tracing a bundle of rays diverging from the object and, using the fact that the angle of incidence equals the angle of reflection, then tracing the corresponding reflected rays.

2. Refraction of Light at a Spherical Surface. The refraction of light at a spherical interface between two transparent media is fundamental in the study of optical instruments, since plane and spherical surfaces are the only ones which can be produced at sufficiently low cost for most practical purposes. In problems of this type, we have to do with incident light in a medium of refractive index n_1, let us say (the so-called *object* space), and refracted light in a medium of refractive index n_2 (the so-called *image* space). In order to minimize the chance of algebraic errors, it is essential to adopt a set of conventions for the coordinate systems to be employed and for the algebraic signs of the distances appearing in the calculations and to adhere rigidly to them. We shall adopt the following conventions:

1. Draw all figures with the light incident on the refracting surface from the left.

2. In object space, measure positive object distances to the *left* along the axis of the system from an origin which, in the case of a single refracting surface, is located at the vertex of the refracting surface.

3. In image space, measure positive image distances to the *right* along the axis of the system from an origin which, in the case of a single refracting surface, is located at the vertex of the refracting surface.

4. Treat radii of curvature as positive distances when the center of curvature lies to the *right* of the vertex and as negative when the center of curvature lies to the *left* of the vertex.

Consider the refraction of a pencil of rays diverging from an object point A on the axis of symmetry of a spherical refracting surface, as shown in Fig. 192.

Let AP be one of the rays intercepted by the refracting surface of radius R (positive for the case of Fig. 192), and let its direction relative to the axis be θ_1. The refracted ray crosses the axis at the point B, and the problem is to determine the position of this point for an arbitrary ray coming from the object A.   Applying the law of sines to the triangle APC, we have

$$\frac{u + R}{R} = \frac{\sin (\pi - i)}{\sin \theta_1} = \frac{\sin i}{\sin \theta_1} \tag{16.6}$$

and, using the triangle BPC,

$$\frac{v - R}{R} = \frac{\sin r}{\sin \theta_2} \tag{16.7}$$

If we divide Eq. (16.6) by Eq. (16.7) and use the law of refraction $(n_1 \sin i = n_2 \sin r)$, there follows

$$\frac{u + R}{v - R} = \frac{n_2}{n_1} \frac{\sin \theta_2}{\sin \theta_1} \tag{16.8}$$

Finally, the angle θ_2 may be expressed in terms of the angles θ_1, i, and r by equating the sum of the angles in the triangle APB to π.   If this

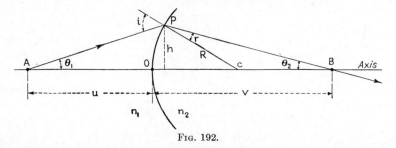

FIG. 192.

is done, we see in general that the image distance v will be different for different angles θ_1 of the incident ray, and this gives rise to spherical aberration of the same sort as we encountered in the case of reflection.

For the special but extremely important case that all the rays from A intercepted by the refracting surface make very small angles θ_1 with the axis (the so-called paraxial rays), we find that the image distance is the same for all rays coming from A.   In this approximation the object A is focused at B.   If the angles θ_1 and θ_2 are sufficiently small, we may write approximately (see Fig. 192)

$$\sin \theta_1 = \frac{h}{u}; \qquad \sin \theta_2 = \frac{h}{v}$$

so that

$$\frac{\sin \theta_2}{\sin \theta_1} = \frac{u}{v} \tag{16.9}$$

Substituting this value in Eq. (16.8), there follows

$$\frac{u + R}{R - v} = -\frac{n_2}{n_1}\frac{u}{v} \qquad (16.10)$$

an equation from which the angle θ_1 has disappeared. This equation, although derived for rays making small angles with the axis, is still valid for large angles when the surface has been corrected for spherical aberration, and is fundamental in geometrical optics. Equation (16.10) is usually written in the more convenient equivalent form

$$\frac{n_1}{u} + \frac{n_2}{v} = \frac{n_2 - n_1}{R} \qquad (16.11)$$

Although we have derived Eq. (16.11) for the case of a convex refracting surface (R positive), it holds equally well for a concave surface (R negative), as can be readily demonstrated. The convention as to

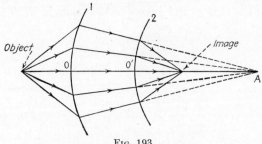

FIG. 193.

the algebraic signs of u and v must be kept in mind when applying Eq. (16.11).

In optical systems one is frequently confronted with a situation in which a series of refracting surfaces are employed. The method to be employed in computing, let us say, the position of the image of an object in such a case is to apply Eq. (16.11) successively to each refracting surface, treating the image formed by the first surface as the object for the second, etc. If the image which would be formed in the presence of the first refracting surface alone lies to the left of the second refracting surface (using our conventions), it acts as a *real* object for the second surface, whether it is a real or virtual image of the original surface. If, however, the second refracting surface is so placed that a converging pencil of rays from the first surface is intercepted before coming to a focus, the object distance for the second refracting surface is to be taken as negative and equal numerically to the distance from the vertex of the second refracting surface to the focal point of the pencil of rays from the first refracting surface. Such a case is shown in Fig. 193, in which $O'A$ is the object distance to be used in computing the refraction at surface 2. Concisely stated, we treat the image space of the nth surface as the object space of the $(n + 1)$st surface, using the appropriate indices of refraction in Eq. (16.11).

Consider an object of linear dimension y perpendicular to the axis of a single refracting surface, as shown in Fig. 194, and let the corresponding linear dimension of the image by y'. The linear dimension

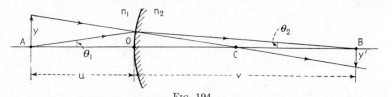

FIG. 194.

y' may be found by constructing the ray shown, which passes through the center of curvature C of the refracting surface. This ray is not refracted, as it is normally incident on the surface. We shall treat y as positive and y' as negative, corresponding to the ordinary conventions of coordinate geometry. Furthermore, we define the *linear magnification* (more precisely, the linear lateral magnification) m as the ratio of y' to y. From Fig. 194 it is evident that

$$- \frac{y'}{y} = \frac{BC}{AC} = \frac{v - R}{u + R}$$

and, using Eq. (16.8), we may write for the magnification

$$m = \frac{y'}{y} = - \frac{n_1 \sin \theta_1}{n_2 \sin \theta_2} \tag{16.12}$$

This equation is known as "Abbe's sine condition." To the approximation of paraxial rays, we may utilize Eq. (16.9) and obtain from Eq. (16.12)

$$m = \frac{y'}{y} = - \frac{n_1 v}{n_2 u} \tag{16.13}$$

3. Thin Lenses. By far the most important application of the results obtained in the preceding section is to the case of lenses in air. By a lens one means a portion of glass, or some other transparent substance, which is usually bounded by plane or spherical surfaces. It is assumed that the reader is familiar with the qualitative behavior of the different types of converging and diverging lenses. In our discussion of the behavior of lenses we shall assume that the apertures are sufficiently small or that aberrations have been corrected, so that Eqs. (16.11) and (16.13) may be used to describe the refraction at the lens surfaces.

For the sake of simplicity, we shall examine in this section the so-called *thin* lens, *i.e.*, one for which the thickness t between the vertices of the lens surfaces is small compared to the object and image distances entering into the discussion. In Fig. 195 is shown such a thin double-convex lens with surfaces of radii of curvature R_1 and R_2 as shown.

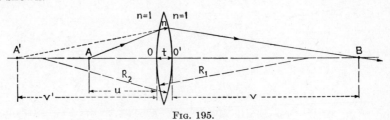

Fig. 195.

An object A will be imaged by the left-hand lens surface at the point A', and, according to Eq. (16.11), we have

$$\frac{1}{u} + \frac{n}{v'} = \frac{n-1}{R_1} \tag{16.14}$$

where v' is the image distance in the image space of index n for this surface and is negative as shown in the figure. This image A' now serves as the object for the right-hand lens surface in an object space of index n. The object distance $A'O' = u'$ is positive according to our conventions, and for a *thin* lens we may place it equal to $-v'$, neglecting t compared to v'. Thus, applying Eq. (16.11) to the second surface, we find

$$-\frac{n}{v'} + \frac{1}{v} = \frac{1-n}{R_2} \tag{16.15}$$

Since R_2 is negative and since $n > 1$, the right-hand side of Eq. (16.15) is positive. If we now add Eqs. (16.14) and (16.15), we find the usual equation for the object-image distances for a thin lens. This is

$$\frac{1}{u} + \frac{1}{v} = (n-1)\left(\frac{1}{R_1} - \frac{1}{R_2}\right) = \frac{1}{f} \tag{16.16}$$

where we have set

$$\frac{1}{f} = (n-1)\left(\frac{1}{R_1} - \frac{1}{R_2}\right) \tag{16.17}$$

and u and v are measured from either vertex or from the center of the lens. f is known as the *focal length* of the lens, and it depends only on the material and dimensions of the lens. Positive values of f correspond to converging lenses and negative values to diverging lenses. If an object is placed at a distance f to the left of the lens [$u = f$ in Eq. (16.16)], the emerging rays will form a parallel beam, and we say that an image is formed at infinity. This point is called a principal *focus* or *focal point* F_1 of the lens. Similarly, parallel rays

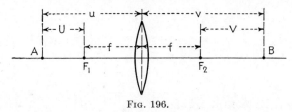

FIG. 196.

incident on the lens from the left (corresponding to an object at infinity) are focused at the second principal focus of the lens, F_2, a point which lies at a distance f to the right of the lens. These principal foci are shown in Fig. 196. Any corresponding object and image points, such as A and B, are called *conjugate points*.

There is an important and interesting way of rewriting Eq. (16.16) (the so-called Newtonian form) which, in many re pects, is more useful than the equation we have derived. This form of the equation is obtained by using the focal points of the lens as origins, F_1 for object space, and F_2 for image space, instead of the vertices of the refracting surfaces. If we denote by U the object distance measured from the first focal point and by V the image distance measured from the second focal point, we have from Fig. 196

$$\left.\begin{array}{l} U = u - f \\ V = v - f \end{array}\right\} \qquad (16.18)$$

Substituting in Eq. (16.16), we find

$$\frac{1}{U+f} + \frac{1}{V+f} = \frac{1}{f}$$

or simplified

$$UV = f^2 \qquad (16.19)$$

This is the Newtonian form of the lens equation.

The lateral magnification of a thin lens may be readily computed with the help of the results of the preceding section. If the linear dimension of an object at A in Fig. 195 is y, the corresponding linear dimension of the image formed by the first surface at A' is, according to Eq. (16.13),

$$y' = y\left(-\frac{v'}{nu}\right) = m_1 y$$

Similarly, the corresponding linear dimension y'' of the image of A' formed by the second surface at B is

$$y'' = y'\left(-\frac{nv}{A'O'}\right) = y'\left(\frac{nv}{v'}\right) = m_2 y'$$

Thus the magnification of the lens is

$$m = \frac{y''}{y} = -\frac{v}{u} \qquad (16.20)$$

In any case we have the relation

$$m = m_1 m_2 \qquad (16.21)$$

If we now express the magnification in terms of the focal distances U and V, we have from Eqs. (16.20) and (16.18)

$$m = -\frac{v}{u} = -\frac{V+f}{U+f}$$

or the more convenient form, using Eq. (16.19),

$$m = -\frac{f}{U} = -\frac{V}{f} \qquad (16.22)$$

It is customary in optometry to speak of the "power" of a lens instead of its focal length. The power of a lens is defined as the reciprocal of the focal length, and the conventional unit is called a *diopter*, which is 1 m^{-1}. Since the lens power $1/f$, according to Eq. (16.17), is the sum of two terms, each corresponding to one of the lens surfaces, one speaks also of the "power" of a lens surface. The sum of the surface powers is then the power of the lens in accordance with the above-mentioned equation.

4. The Thick Lens in Air. We shall now drop the restriction that the axial thickness of the lens be small compared to object and image distances from the lens vertices, and we shall analyze the behavior of a thick lens in air for paraxial rays. For convenience we redraw Fig. 195, relabeling the distances as shown in Fig. 197. The object distance from the vertex O of the left-hand lens surface (radius of curvature R_1) is now denoted by x_1, and the image distance from the vertex O' of the right-hand lens surface (radius of curvature R_2) is now x_2. The relation between the object distance x_1 and the image distance $d = A'O$ for the first lens surface is, according to Eq. (16.11),

$$\frac{1}{x_1} + \frac{n}{d} = \frac{n-1}{R_1} = \frac{1}{f_1} \tag{16.23}$$

where f_1 is used as an abbreviation for $R_1/(n-1)$. Using A' as an object for the second surface, the relation between d and x_2 is, using

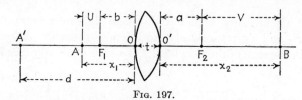

FIG. 197.

Eq. (16.11) again and remembering that d is negative for the case of Fig. 197,

$$\frac{n}{t-d} + \frac{1}{x_2} = \frac{1-n}{R_2} = \frac{1}{f_2} \tag{16.24}$$

where f_2 is defined as $R_2/(1-n)$. For the double-convex lens of Fig. 197 both f_1 and f_2 are positive, but our results will hold equally well for other types of lenses. Equations (16.23) and (16.24) may be written in the forms

$$d = \frac{nf_1x_1}{x_1 - f_1} \tag{16.23a}$$

$$t - d = \frac{nf_2x_2}{x_2 - f_2} \tag{16.24a}$$

Eliminating d between these equations, one finds readily

$$x_1x_2 - ax_1 - bx_2 - c = 0 \tag{16.25}$$

where we have placed

$$a = \frac{f_2\left(f_1 - \dfrac{t}{n}\right)}{f_1 + f_2 - \dfrac{t}{n}}; \qquad b = \frac{f_1\left(f_2 - \dfrac{t}{n}\right)}{f_1 + f_2 - \dfrac{t}{n}}; \qquad c = \frac{f_1f_2\dfrac{t}{n}}{f_1 + f_2 - \dfrac{t}{n}} \tag{16.26}$$

In these relations t is a positive quantity. Writing Eq. (16.25) in the form

$$(x_1 - b)(x_2 - a) = ab + c \tag{16.27}$$

we see that the first principal focus of the lens, F_1, lies at a distance

b to the left of the vertex O as shown in Fig. 197. For the object A placed at F_1, $x_1 = b$ and $x_2 = \infty$ according to Eq. (16.27). Similarly, the second principal focus F_2 lies at a distance a to the right of the vertex O', since an object at infinity ($x_1 = \infty$), corresponding to parallel rays incident on the left-hand lens surface, gives rise to an image at F_2 ($x_2 = a$). We have thus found the positions of the focal points of the thick lens. The planes perpendicular to the lens axis through these focal points F_1 and F_2 are called the *focal planes* of the lens.

Now let us measure object and image distances from the focal planes at F_1 and F_2, respectively, and denote them by U and V, just as we did in the case of the thin lens. We have evidently (see Fig. 197)

$$\left. \begin{aligned} U &= x_1 - b = x_1 - \frac{f_1[f_2 - (t/n)]}{f_1 + f_2 - (t/n)} \\ V &= x_2 - a = x_2 - \frac{f_2[f_1 - (t/n)]}{f_1 + f_2 - (t/n)} \end{aligned} \right\} \tag{16.28}$$

and Eq. (16.27) takes the familiar Newtonian form

$$UV = ab + c = \frac{f_1^2 f_2^2}{[f_1 + f_2 - (t/n)]^2} = f^2 \tag{16.29}$$

utilizing Eq. (16.26) and defining f^2 by this equation. The positive square root of this expression for f^2 is called the *focal length* of the lens, and we have

$$f = \frac{f_1 f_2}{f_1 + f_2 - (t/n)} \tag{16.30}$$

The Newtonian form of the lens equation which we have derived for the thick lens suggests strongly that it should be possible to obtain an equation of the form of Eq. (16.16) for the thick lens. This is possible by proper choice of origins, and these new reference points from which one may measure object and image distances are called the *principal points* of the lens and are denoted by H_1 and H_2, respectively. We determine the positions of these principal points as follows: Let U_1 and V_1 be the coordinates of the principal points H_1 and H_2 in object and image space, respectively, referred to the focal points as origins. If, then, u and v are object and image distances measured from the principal points, we have evidently

$$\left. \begin{aligned} u &= U - U_1 \\ v &= V - V_1 \end{aligned} \right\} \tag{16.31}$$

where U and V are the object and image distances from the focal points.   If now the thin-lens equation

$$\frac{1}{u} + \frac{1}{v} = \frac{1}{f}$$

is to be valid, we must have

$$\frac{1}{U - U_1} + \frac{1}{V - V_1} = \frac{1}{f}$$

or, rewritten,

$$fV - fV_1 + fU - fU_1 = f^2 - UV_1 - VU_1 + U_1V_1$$

where we have used the fact that $UV = f^2$.   This equation is evidently satisfied if we place

$$\left. \begin{array}{l} U_1 = -f \\ V_1 = -f \end{array} \right\} \qquad (16.32)$$

so that the principal points are also conjugate points of the lens.   We thus have the important result that the thin-lens equation holds equally well for a thick lens, provided the principal points H_1 and H_2 are used as origins for object and image distances, respectively. Clearly the separation between either focal point and the corresponding principal point is the focal length of the lens.

Let us compute the positions of the principal points (or planes) relative to the vertices of the lens surfaces, which we used originally as reference points. x_1 is the object distance from the left-hand vertex O, and u is the object distance from the first principal point H_1.   The relation between u and x_1 is given by

$$u = U - U_1 = x_1 - b + f = x_1 + \frac{f_1(t/n)}{f_1 + f_2 - (t/n)} \qquad (16.33)$$

using Eqs. (16.28), (16.30), and (16.32).

Similarly, the image distance v as measured from the second principal point H_2 is related to the image distance x_2 measured from the right-hand vertex O' by

$$v = V - V_1 = x_2 - a + f = x_2 + \frac{f_2(t/n)}{f_1 + f_2 - (t/n)} \qquad (16.34)$$

Note that for a thin lens $u = x_1$ and $v = x_2$, so that the principal points coincide and lie at the center of the lens.   Equations (16.33) and (16.34) locate the principal points of a thick lens with respect to its vertices.   Thus H_1 lies at a distance

$$h_1 = -\frac{f_1(t/n)}{f_1 + f_2 - (t/n)} \qquad (16.35)$$

from the left-hand vertex in object space (in our case to the right of O), and H_2 lies at a distance

$$h_2 = -\frac{f_2(t/n)}{f_1 + f_2 - (t/n)} \qquad (16.36)$$

from the right-hand vertex in image space (in our case to the left of O').

For the sake of completeness, we redraw the lens of Fig. 197, showing the principal points, focal points, focal length, and object and image distances (Fig. 198).

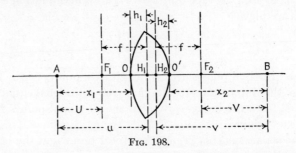

FIG. 198.

Not only the object-image distance equations but also the magnification formulas are identical in form for thick and thin lenses.   The magnification of the lens is the product of the magnifications of the two surfaces, and this is, using Eq. (16.13) (see Fig. 197),

$$m = \left(-\frac{d}{nx_1}\right)\left(-\frac{nx_2}{t-d}\right)$$

From Eqs. (16.23a) and (16.24a), we have

$$\frac{d}{t-d} = \frac{x_2 - f_2}{x_1 - f_1} \cdot \frac{f_1 x_1}{f_2 x_2}$$

so that

$$m = \frac{f_1}{f_2} \cdot \frac{x_2 - f_2}{x_1 - f_1} = \frac{f_1}{f_2} \frac{V + a - f_2}{U + b - f_1}$$

the last equality following from Eq. (16.28).

Using the definitions of a and b and of the focal length f [Eqs. (16.28) and (16.30)], one finds readily that

$$a - f_2 = -\frac{f_2}{f_1}f \qquad \text{and} \qquad b - f_1 = -\frac{f_1}{f_2}f$$

so that

$$m = \frac{f_1}{f_2} \cdot \frac{V - (f_2/f_1)f}{U - (f_1/f_2)f}$$

and, since $UV = f^2$ [Eq. (16.29)], this becomes

$$m = -\frac{f}{U} = -\frac{V}{f} \tag{16.37}$$

which is identical with Eq. (16.22). It immediately follows that Eq. (16.20) also holds for the thick lens, remembering that u and v are measured from the principal points. Equation (16.37) for the magnification holds for all object-image pairs, U and V being object and image distances as measured from the focal points F_1 and F_2. For the special case for which object and image lie at the principal points $U = V = -f$, we have unit magnification and a virtual image.

It is a property of the principal points that an incident ray through one of them emerges through the other parallel to the incident ray. The proof of this is left to a problem. Finally, it should be pointed out that all our results are valid for any lens or combinations of lenses, provided the object and image space have the same index of refraction. If this is not so, then only the form of the magnification formulas becomes modified, and the conjugate points for unit magnification (the so-called *nodal points*) no longer coincide with the principal points.

5. Lens Aberrations. Thus far our considerations have been restricted largely to what may be termed the "first-order" theory of the behavior of both thin and thick lenses. There have been two fundamental assumptions in the theory: (1) The objects and images have been treated as if they were situated on the axis of the lens, so that at best the theory gives a good approximation for objects and images, all the points of which lie very close to the axis; and (2) the rays from a point object on the axis have been considered as a very narrow pencil, so that the angular opening of the cone of rays is small enough to allow us to replace the sine of the angle by the angle. Thus we speak of "paraxial" rays.

In general, a lens must image points not on its axis, and the cone of rays from any point of the object will be of finite angular opening. Furthermore, even if individual object points were sharply focused at corresponding image points, we might still obtain distortion of the image in the sense that the geometrical shape of the image would not coincide with that of the object. Finally, we have dealt with the index of refraction as a constant. While this is true for light of a given frequency (monochromatic light), white light is a mixture of waves of many wavelengths, and the index of refraction of glass, for example, varies with wavelength (and frequency). Thus, even in the first-order theory, one encounters so-called *chromatic aberration*, variation of focal length with color of the light. The various defects of the image formed by a perfectly spherical lens are termed *aberrations*, and we shall briefly examine these various types of aberrations. A quantitative study of these aberrations and methods of minimizing them are far beyond the scope of this book. For the sake of simplicity we shall consider the aberrations for the case of a thin lens in air, although the same general considerations hold for thick lenses and combinations of lenses.

We classify the various aberrations as follows:

1. If a narrow pencil of rays (parallel or stigmatic) lies along the lens axis, we have the conditions of our first-order theory satisfied and have no aberration.

2. If a narrow pencil of rays passes *obliquely* through the lens, as does a portion of the cone of rays from a point object not located on the lens axis, this pencil becomes *astigmatic* after it passes through the lens. This astigmatic pencil does not focus at a point, but all the rays pass through two mutually orthogonal lines (focal lines) which are displaced from each other. This aberration is called *astigmatism*.

3. If a wide pencil of rays has its axis coincident with that of the lens or if we have a broad beam of parallel rays which are parallel to the lens axis, the rays of the pencil emerging from the lens will not pass through a single point. This aberration is called *axial spherical aberration*.

4. If a wide stigmatic pencil of rays (or broad parallel beam) passes obliquely through a lens, it becomes greatly confused upon emerging from the lens, and this type of aberration is denoted as *comatic aberration*, or simply as *coma*.

5. For objects of finite size, *e.g.*, an object in the form of a straight line perpendicular to the lens axis, there will result an image which is curved, and this aberration is known as *curvature of the field*. It is intimately connected with astigmatism, being essentially due to the astigmatic nature of the narrow pencils of rays from the various points of the object.

6. *Image distortion* is an aberration arising from a variation of magnification with distance of the various object points from the lens axis.

7. *Chromatic aberration*, as we have already mentioned, is due to the variation of index of refraction with the frequency of the light and results in the formation of a series of images at different distances and of different magnifications, one for each color present in the incident light.

We thus have classified six types of aberration of a simple thin lens. It should be kept in mind, however, that the monochromatic aberrations are classified into the types 2 to 6 for the sake of convenience, but they are not independent, and in general it is only approximately correct to consider any one type as being present to the exclusion of all the others. We shall now describe the above aberrations in more detail.

Astigmatism and Curvature of the Field. Let us first remind ourselves of the properties of an astigmatic pencil of rays. These rays are the normals to a small portion of a surface of constant phase which has two different radii of curvature in two mutually orthogonal directions. The pencil of rays is indicated in Fig. 199.   All the rays of the pencil pass through two focal lines, as shown in the figure.   The cross section of the pencil is in general elliptical for an elliptical boundary on the wave surface, the ellipse degenerating into straight lines at the positions of the focal lines.   Between these two positions there is a position where the cross section of the beam is circular, the major

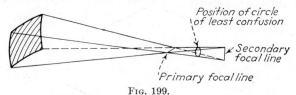

Position of circle
of least confusion

Secondary
focal line

Primary focal line

FIG. 199.

and minor axes of the ellipse becoming equal, and this circle is known as the *circle of least confusion,* giving the best image formed by an astigmatic pencil. As we have stated, a narrow pencil of rays passing obliquely through a thin lens gives rise to an astigmatic transmitted pencil.   In Fig. 200 are shown two views (top and side) of such a pencil of rays (exaggerated for the sake of clarity) from the tip of an arrow used as an object for a thin lens. A' and A''

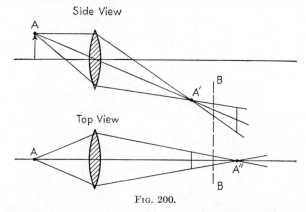

Side View

Top View

FIG. 200.

are the locations of the focal lines of the pencil, and BB is the location of the circle of least confusion. A' and A'' are often called the primary and secondary images of A.

If one considers all the points of the arrow, instead of only the tip, the locus of all the primary images will form a curve, as will the locus of the secondary images.   These two curves will be tangent to each other at the axis, and somewhere between them lies a surface containing the circles of least confusion for all the points of the object.   This is the surface of *best focus,* and in general it is not a plane, giving rise to the curvature of the best possible image of the object.   The shape of the image surfaces depends on the shape of the lens and on the positions of stops or apertures on the lens axis. It is not possible to eliminate both curvature of the field and astigmatism with a single lens, but either may be readily corrected. A narrow aperture lens corrected for astigmatism is called *anastigmatic*.

Spherical Aberration. In Fig. 201 is shown the effect of spherical aberration. A finite cone of rays from a point A on the lens axis is not imaged at a single point. All the rays making a given angle with the axis are imaged at

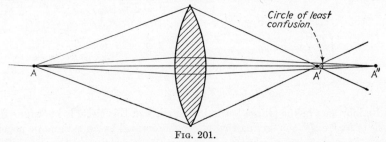

Fig. 201.

the same point, the widest angle rays at A' and the small-angle, or paraxial, rays at A''. The cross section of the beam is everywhere circular, and the circle of least radius is the circle of least confusion, the best image of A. Spherical aberration may be reduced by "stopping down" the lens (using only the central portion), but only at the expense of the amount of light transmitted by the lens. A lens of given focal length may be designed for mini-

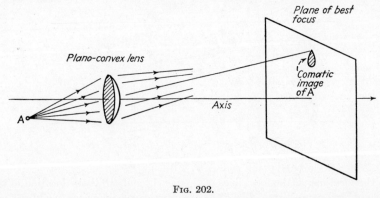

Fig. 202.

mum spherical aberration by choosing appropriate radii of curvature for the two surfaces. In general, this type of aberration is cut down by dividing the deviation of the rays equally between the two surfaces.

Coma. The image of a point object not on the lens axis, when the lens intercepts a cone of rays of large angle, is very confused and is called comatic. Let us assume that astigmatism may be neglected, so that there is a well-defined plane of best focus. The finite cone of rays from the point object may be considered as a sum of very narrow pencils with a common focal point. As we have seen, each of these narrow pencils gives a best image in the form of a circle of least confusion. In general, the centers and radii of these circles of least confusion will be different for the different narrow pencils making up the cone of rays, so that the final image may be thought of as a superposition of circles of different radii and centers. The resultant figure is shaped somewhat like a comet (hence the name coma) and is illustrated in Fig. 202. Coma may be eliminated completely for a single thin lens for *one pair* of object-image points by proper choice of the radii of curvature of the lens surfaces. Such a lens will then necessarily show axial spherical aberration, since the condition for no coma is not the same as for minimum spherical aberration. A very-wide-aperture lens may be corrected for axial spherical aberration and for coma for slightly oblique rays. It is then said to be *aplanatic*, and the single pair of object and image points for which this correction is valid are called the *aplanatic points* of the lens.

Image distortion, caused by the variation of magnification with lateral distance of an object point from the lens axis, may be of two types, depending on

Object   Image   Image
           (pin cushion   (barrel distortion)
           distortion)

Fig. 203.

whether the magnification increases or decreases with distance from the axis. In the former case the distortion is known as "pincushion" distortion and in the latter case as "barrel" distortion. A rectangular object will give rise to the two images shown in Fig. 203 for these two types of distortion.

Chromatic aberration and the methods of minimizing it will be discussed in the chapter on dispersion of light.

It is clear that it is impossible to eliminate or even to minimize simultaneously all the aberrations discussed above for a single lens, but it is possible, by combining a number of lenses to form a *compound lens*, to balance the aberrations of one part of the system against the other. The larger the number of elements of a compound lens, the higher the degree of correction which may be obtained. In practice, attention is directed toward correcting those aberrations which would be most disturbing for the particular purpose to which the lens is put. When we discuss chromatic aberration, we shall illustrate the manner in which a compound lens may be designed to compensate for chromatic aberration.

6. The Eye. The essential parts of the human eye, treated as an optical instrument, are shown in Fig. 204. The eye is roughly spherical, the front surface of the eyeball being somewhat more sharply curved and covered with a tough transparent membrane *C*, the *cornea*.

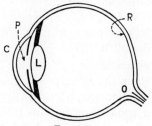

Fig. 204.

Between the cornea and the *lens L* is a watery liquid known as the *aqueous humor*. The remainder of the eyeball is filled with a transparent viscous liquid, known as the *vitreous humor*. The front surface of the cornea and the lens surfaces are nearly spherical and constitute essentially a compound lens which projects images of external objects upon a sensitive membrane, the *retina R*, in which terminate the ends of a great many nerve fibers entering the eye at *O*, the nerve bundle being known as the optic nerve. The *pupil P* is an aperture in a muscular membrane called the *iris* and serves to cut down or increase the amount of light entering the eye.

The lens of the eye may be compressed into a more nearly spherical shape by the action of a muscle attached to it and thus may have its focal length varied. The process of focusing the eye on objects at varying distance from it is called *accommodation*, and the range over which distinct vision is possible determines the so-called *near* and *far points* of the eye. For the normal eye the far point may be taken as infinity. The position of the near point depends on how much the curvature of the lens may be increased by accommodation, and the power of accommodation diminishes with increasing age. For the normal eye we shall take the near point as about 15 cm, and the distance of *most distinct vision* as 25 cm (or 10 in.).

7. The Simple and the Compound Microscope. When looked at directly with the eye, an object seems large when the retinal image is

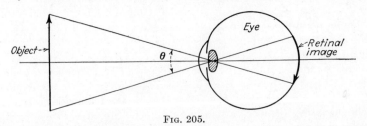

FIG. 205.

large, and the angle subtended at the eye by the object (the so-called *visual angle*) is a measure of the apparent size of the object. In Fig. 205 the angle θ is the visual angle. In order to examine an object in detail, it is brought as near to the eye as possible to obtain a large visual angle. Since the eye cannot focus sharply on objects closer than the near point, the maximum visual angle obtainable by the unaided eye is limited by the power of accommodation. By placing a converging lens in front of the eye, one can in effect increase its effective accommodation. The eye then looks at an enlarged virtual image as indicated in Fig. 206. Such a device is known as a magnifying glass or simple microscope. *The magnifying power M of a magnifying glass is defined as the ratio of the angle subtended at the eye by the image to that subtended by the object when the latter is placed at the distance of most distinct vision d_0, which we shall take as 25 cm.*

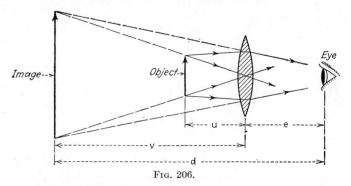

Fig. 206.

If θ is the angle subtended at the eye by the image of Fig. 206 and y_i its length, we have

$$\frac{y_i}{2} = d \tan\left(\frac{\theta}{2}\right) \qquad (16.38)$$

If the object has a length y_0 and is located at the distance of most distinct vision d_0, it subtends an angle θ_0 at the eye, where

$$\frac{y_0}{2} = d_0 \tan\left(\frac{\theta_0}{2}\right) \qquad (16.39)$$

For small angles we may replace the tangents of the angles by the angles and have for the magnifying power

$$M = \frac{\theta}{\theta_0} = \frac{y_i}{y_0}\frac{d_0}{d} \qquad (16.40)$$

We have further from Fig. 206

$$\frac{y_i}{y_0} = \frac{d - e}{u} \qquad (16.41)$$

so that Eq. (16.40) becomes

$$M = \left(1 - \frac{e}{d}\right)\frac{d_0}{u} \qquad (16.42)$$

In general, the eye is placed close enough to the magnifier that the distance e in Eq. (16.42) may be neglected compared with d, and hence we have simply

$$M = \frac{d_0}{u} \qquad (16.43)$$

If the image is formed at the distance of most distinct vision, we have $v = -d_0$, and from the lens equation we have

$$\frac{1}{u} - \frac{1}{d_0} = \frac{1}{f}$$

so that the magnifying power becomes for this case

$$M = \frac{d_0}{u} = \frac{d_0}{f} + 1 \qquad (16.44)$$

If the image is formed at infinity, we have $1/u = 1/f$, so that for this case

$$M = \frac{d_0}{f} \qquad (16.45)$$

Thus the magnifying power is somewhat greater when the image is formed at the point of most distinct vision.

According to the above results, a high-power magnifying glass must have a very short focal length, and it must be held close to the object

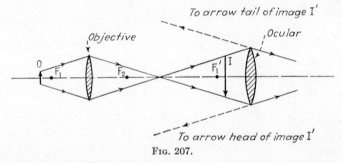

Fig. 207.

under examination and near to the eye. The difficulty of accurately grinding a lens of small focal length and freeing it as far as possible from aberrations, in addition to the inconveniences of operation just mentioned, place a practical upper limit of about $20 \times$ on the magnifying power of a simple microscope. For higher powers one utilizes a *compound microscope*, consisting essentially of a lens, called the *objective*, which produces a real enlarged image of the object, and a magnifying glass or ocular for viewing this image. The arrangement is shown in Fig. 207 in which both objective and ocular are treated as simple lenses, although in an actual microscope both would be highly corrected compound lenses. The object O is placed just outside the first focal point F_1 of the objective, yielding an enlarged real image I. This image lies just inside the first focal point F_1' of the ocular, giving rise to a virtual enlarged image I' of I (not shown in the figure). The position of I' may be taken at the point of most distinct vision of the eye.

The magnifying power of the compound microscope is the product of the magnifying powers of the objective and ocular. Since the objective forms a real image which is examined by the ocular, its magnifying power is just the linear magnification m_1, which, according to Eq. (16.37), may be written as

$$m_1 = -\frac{V}{f_1} \tag{16.46}$$

where V is the focal distance of the image I (the distance from F_2 to I) and f_1 the focal length of the objective. The magnifying power of the ocular is, according to Eq. (16.44),

$$M_1 = \frac{d_0}{f_2} + 1 \tag{16.47}$$

where f_2 is the focal length of the ocular. Thus the magnifying power of a compound microscope is

$$M = m_1 M_1 = \left(-\frac{V}{f_1}\right)\left(\frac{d_0}{f_2} + 1\right) \tag{16.48}$$

or

$$M = m_1 M_1' = -\left(\frac{V}{f_1}\right)\left(\frac{d_0}{f_2}\right) \tag{16.48a}$$

the latter equation being valid when I' is formed at infinity. It has become standard practice to make $V = 18$ cm, so that, using the value of 25 cm for d_0, we may write in place of Eq. (16.48a)

$$M = -\left(\frac{18}{f_1}\right)\left(\frac{25}{f_2}\right) \tag{16.49}$$

where f_1 and f_2 are expressed in centimeters.

8. Oculars. In actual practice the magnifying glass shown in the compound microscope of Fig. 207 is replaced by a compound lens. When a compound lens is used to examine the image formed by a system of lenses (or mirrors), it is called an *ocular*, or *eyepiece*. In addition to the primary purpose of magnification, a well-designed ocular increases the *field of view* and, of course, lends itself to a better reduction of aberrations than a simple lens. The fundamental difference between a real object and an image used as an object lies in the fact that the rays from the former diverge in all directions, whereas in the latter the pencil of rays from any point forms a cone of limited

opening.   This is illustrated in Fig. 208, in which are indicated the
cone of rays coming from the head and tail of an image which is being
examined by a simple magnifier.   If the eye is placed at A, it is clear
that none of the rays from the arrowhead reach it, so that the arrowhead lies outside the field of view.   Similarly at B the tail of the arrow

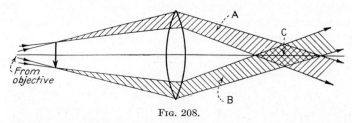

Fig. 208.

is not visible.   By placing the eye at C, one can see the whole arrow,
but in most instruments it is desirable to have the eye close to the
eyepiece.

The method employed to increase the field of view for an eye placed
near the eyepiece consists essentially in the use of two lenses in the
ocular.   The function of the first lens, called the *field lens*, is to alter
the direction of the rays from the various points of the image under

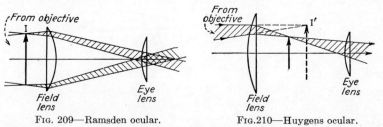

Fig. 209—Ramsden ocular.   Fig. 210—Huygens ocular.

examination, so that pencils of rays from each of these points pass
through the central portion of the second or *eye lens* and hence can all
enter the pupil of an eye placed near this eye lens.   Two common
types of oculars are shown in Figs. 209 and 210.   In the Ramsden
ocular the lenses are of equal focal length, and the image is formed in
front of the field lens as shown.   If cross hairs or a scale are to be
mounted in the ocular so that measurements can be made, they should
be placed in the plane of the image I.   In the Huygens ocular the field
lens intercepts the rays from the objective before the image is formed,
and thus we have a virtual object I' for this field lens, giving rise to the
image I, which is then examined with the help of the eye lens.   Clearly
the Ramsden ocular can be used to examine a real object, but the
Huygens ocular cannot be so employed.

9. Telescopes. The simple astronomical telescope consists essentially of an objective converging lens of long focal length and an ocular for examining the image of a distant object formed by the objective. A schematic sketch of the optical system is given in Fig. 211, in which no attempt has been made to show the paths of the rays. Since the object is practically at infinity, the image I is formed at the second focal point of the objective, and if the image formed by the ocular of I is also at infinity, I lies at the first focal point of the ocular. The angles

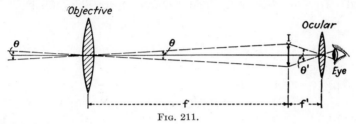

Fig. 211.

θ and θ' are the angles subtended by the object at the objective and by the image at the ocular. *The magnifying power M of a telescope is defined as the ratio of these angles*, and since in the telescope shown we have an inverted image, we write

$$M = -\frac{\theta'}{\theta}$$

and because in general the angles are small, this can be written in the form

$$M = -\frac{f}{f'} \qquad (16.50)$$

as is evident from Fig. 211, where f is the focal length of the objective and f' that of the ocular.

The inverted image formed by the simple telescope described above is not disadvantageous for astronomical work, but for terrestrial

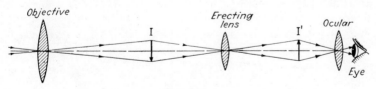

Fig. 212.

purposes it is desirable to have an upright image. This can be accomplished by the addition of an erecting lens to the astronomical telescope, as shown in Fig. 212, to form a *terrestrial telescope* or *spyglass*.

The disadvantage of this arrangement is that the length of the instrument becomes unwieldy.   Since the shortest object-image distance for a thin convex lens which forms a real image is four times its focal length, the minimum length of the telescope tube becomes the sum of the focal lengths of objective and ocular and four times the focal length of the erecting lens.

This disadvantage can be overcome by using a diverging instead of a converging lens for the eyepiece, and a telescope so constructed is called a *Galilean telescope.*   The ordinary opera glass is such a tele-

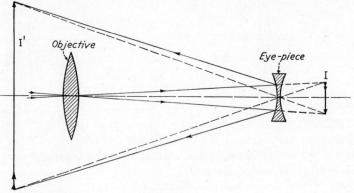

Fig. 213.

scope.   Figure 213 shows a diagram of the elements.   It is readily seen that the magnifying power M is given by Eq. (16.50) ($M = -f/f'$), and since f' is negative, this indicates the upright image.   The length of the telescope is the difference of the focal lengths of the two lenses instead of the sum, as in the case of the astronomical telescope, thus yielding a compact instrument.

10. The Projection Lantern.   Figure 214 shows the essential parts of the optical system of a projection lantern.   The condensing lens C,

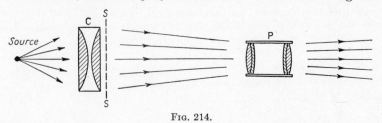

Fig. 214.

usually consisting of a pair of plano-convex lenses as shown, serves to deviate the rays from the source through the lantern slide SS so that they are all intercepted by the projection lens P.   Its function is thus very similar to that of the field lens in an ocular. The projection lens usually consists of two separate lenses as shown, each of which is a compound lens with two kinds of glass (to correct for chromatic aberration as we shall see later) and must be corrected for curvature of the field and for image distortion. Since the final image is produced by the projection lens only, it is not necessary to correct for aberrations in the condensing lens.

The simple optical instruments which we have discussed are all of the image-forming type, and we postpone discussion of the so-called analyzing instruments, *i.e.*, those employed to determine the spectral composition or intensity of a beam of light, until we have occasion to study the results obtained by their use.

Problems

1. What is the apparent depth of a swimming pool in which there is water of depth 9 ft,

a. When viewed at normal incidence?

b. When viewed at an angle of 60° with the surface? The refractive index of water is 1.33.

2. An observer looking through a small vertical glass window in the side of a swimming pool wishes to see an object on the bottom of the pool, 6 ft below the window and 8 ft from the near edge of the pool. At what angle with the horizontal must the observer look to see the object through the window if the refractive indices of the window glass and water are 1.50 and 1.33, respectively?

3. A layer of ether ($n = 1.360$) 2.0 cm deep floats on water ($n = 1.330$) 4.0 cm deep. What is the apparent distance from the ether surface to the bottom of the water when viewed at normal incidence?

4. To measure the refractive index of a crystal in the form of a flat plate 12.62 mm thick, a microscope is focused on a scratch on the top surface and then lowered a distance of 5.43 mm to focus on a scratch on the bottom surface.

Compute the index of refraction of the crystal.

5. A cube of glass of refractive index 1.50 is 1 in. on a side and has a small bubble at its center. What is the minimum radius of circular opaque disks which, when pasted on the six cube faces, will prevent the bubble from being seen?

6. Compute the angular deviation (the angle between the incident and emergent ray) of the ray incident as shown on the prism of Fig. 215. The refractive index of the prism material is 1.532.

7. Light is deviated by a glass prism of index n as shown in Fig. 216. The ray in the prism is parallel to the base. Show that the refractive index is related to the deviation angle δ and the prism angle ϕ by the equation

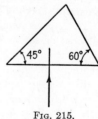

FIG. 215.

$$n \sin \frac{\phi}{2} = \sin \left(\frac{\phi + \delta}{2}\right)$$

for this angle of incidence.

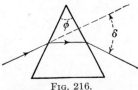

FIG. 216.

The deviation angle δ is a minimum for this angle of incidence and is known as the angle of minimum deviation.

8. What is the relation between the size of an observer and the minimum size of a plane mirror if the observer is to see his complete image?

9. Derive the appropriate form of Eq. (16.5) of the text for the case of a convex mirror.

10. A concave spherical mirror has a radius of curvature of 50 cm. Find two positions of an object such that the image will be four times as large as the object. What is the position of the image in each case? Is it real or virtual?

11. A convex mirror has a focal length of 10 in. Compute the position of the image of an object 6 in. in front of the mirror. What is the magnification for this case?

12. A point source of light is 15 cm above the silvered bottom of a flat glass dish, in which water stands to a depth of 10 cm. Find the position of the image of the light source formed by the complete optical system if the refractive index of the water is 1.33.

13. A narrow pencil of parallel light rays is normally incident on a solid glass sphere of radius R and refractive index n. How far from the center of the sphere are the rays brought to a focus?

14. Prove that Eq. (16.11) of the text is valid for refraction at a surface of negative radius of curvature (concave toward the object).

15. A glass rod, index of refraction n, has its ends ground spherically, the radii being R_1 and R_2, as shown in Fig. 217. The length of the rod is $l = 2R$, and a small object is placed at A.

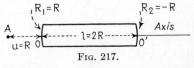

FIG. 217.

Show that the image of A lies at a distance $R[(4 - n)/(3n - 4)]$ from the right-hand vertex O'. (Assume small angles of incidence.)

16. A narrow pencil of parallel light rays is normally incident on a hollow glass sphere of inner radius 2.0 in. and outer radius 2.5 in. If the refractive index of the glass is 1.60, where will these rays be brought to a focus? Make a careful sketch of the pencil of rays.

17. A glass hemisphere 20 cm in diameter and of refractive index 1.50 is silvered on its spherical surface. A small object is located at a distance of 20 cm from the plane surface on the perpendicular to this plane through the center of the sphere. Find the position of the final image of the object.

18. A glass "sphere" with a flat polished bottom rests on the drawing of an arrow 1.0 cm long, as shown in Fig. 218. The radius of the spherical surface is $R = 3.0$ cm, and the refractive index of the glass is 1.50. Where does the

arrow appear to be located for an observer looking vertically down into the "sphere"? What is the magnification? Is the image erect or inverted?

19. A small air bubble inside a glass
sphere (index of refraction = 1.50) of
radius 6.0 cm appears to be 4.0 cm
from the surface and to be of 2.0 mm
diameter when viewed along a diameter passing through the center of the
bubble.

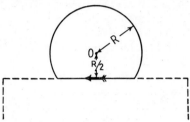

Fig. 218.

What is the true diameter of the
bubble and where is it located relative to the center of the sphere?

20. A glass hemisphere of radius 4.0 cm and refractive index 1.50 is silvered
on its plane surface. Find the position of the image of an object located at a
distance of 12 cm from the vertex of the curved surface on the axis. Is the
image real or virtual?

21. The focal length of a thin lens is determined as 25 cm by using a lamp
as an object, placing the lamp far from the lens, and measuring the image-lens
separation. How far away must the lamp be placed to attain a precision of
3 per cent?

22. A thin glass lens of focal length 12 in. and refractive index 1.52 is
immersed in water of refractive index 1.33. What is the focal length in water?

23. Prove that if two thin lenses are placed in contact, they are equivalent
to a single lens of focal length

$$f = \frac{f_1 f_2}{f_1 + f_2}$$

where f_1 and f_2 are the focal lengths of the two thin lenses.

24. Prove that the focal length of a double-convex thin lens of diameter d
and axial thickness t is given by

$$f = \frac{d^2}{8(n - 1)t}$$

when n is the refractive index of the lens material.

25. Derive the appropriate form of Eq. (16.16) of the text for a double-
concave lens.

26. The radii of curvature of a thin double-convex lens are 20 and 30 cm.
The lens forms an image of an object 40 cm to the left of the lens at a position
48 cm to the right of the lens.

a. What is the focal length of the lens?

b. What is the index of refraction of the lens material?

c. An object is placed 16 cm from the lens. Find the position of the image
and check by graphical construction.

27. A thin convex lens of focal length 15 cm and refractive index 1.53 is
immersed in water of index 1.33. Where is the image of an object placed
100 cm from the lens, the whole system being in water?

28. A thin double-convex glass lens ($n = 1.50$) has a focal length of 3.00 cm and a diameter of 2.00 cm.   An object in the form of an arrow 2.00 cm long is placed perpendicular to and bisecting the lens axis at a distance of 5.00 cm to the left of the lens.

Locate the image, and construct a careful diagram of the pencil of rays intercepted by the lens.

What fractional part of this image will be visible to an eye on the lens axis at a point 22.5 cm to the right of the lens?

29. Make a careful plot of image distance as a function of object distance

a. For a thin converging lens.

b. For a thin diverging lens.

30. The radii of curvature of a double-convex thin lens have magnitudes of 20 and 30 cm.   The glass of which the lens is made has a refractive index of 1.52.   Find the focal length of the lens.

What is the focal length of a convex meniscus lens with the same radii of curvature and made of the same glass?

31. A thin convex lens of focal length f produces a real image of magnification m.   Show that the object distance is

$$u = \frac{m+1}{m} f$$

32. An image of height a is formed on a screen by a thin convex lens.   It is found by moving the lens toward the screen that there is a second lens position at which a second sharp image of height b is formed on the screen.

Show that the height of the object is $\sqrt{ab}$.

33. A thin convex lens is used to form an image on a screen 7 ft from an object.   The distance between the two possible lens positions is found to be 1 ft, and the height of the *larger* of the two images is 8 in.

a. Find the focal length of the lens.

b. How high is the object?

34. A thin lens of focal length f is used to form an enlarged real image of an object on a screen.   The separation of the screen and object is s.

a. Deduce an expression for the distance between the object and the lens.

b. What is the minimum ratio s/f for the formation of a real image?

35. Prove that the distance between an object and its real image formed by a thin convex lens is always greater than four times the focal length of the lens.

36. Parallel light from a distant object falls on the front surface of a thin double-convex lens (each radius of curvature is 10.0 cm).   The back surface of the lens is silvered to form a mirror so that the light coming through the front surface is reflected by the back surface.   If the refractive index of the glass is 1.50, find the image position.

37. A thin convex and a thin concave lens, each of 20 cm focal length, are placed coaxially at a separation of 6.0 cm.   Find the position of the image formed by this lens system of an object at a distance of 30 cm

a. Beyond the convex lens.

b. Beyond the concave lens.

38. Each of two similar converging lenses has a focal length of 10 in. They are mounted coaxially with a separation of 10 in. Find the positions of the images of a small object placed on the axis at a point 20 in. to the left of the first lens.

39. An object is placed 30 cm in front of a thin convex lens of focal length 18 cm. A thin concave lens of focal length 18 cm is placed 6.0 cm behind the convex lens. Where is the final image formed by this optical system?

40. A point object is displaced a small distance du along the axis of a lens. Find an expression for the corresponding image displacement dv. Treating du as an object length along the axis and dv as the corresponding image length, the ratio dv/du is called the *longitudinal magnification*. Prove that it is equal to the square of the ordinary lateral magnification.

41. A thin plano-convex lens is made of glass of refractive index 1.50, and the radius of the curved surface is 6.0 cm. It is used to form an image in air of an object in water of index 1.33, the flat lens surface being in contact with the water.

a. Find the positions of the principal focal points of the lens.

b. Using these focal points as origins for object and image distances U and V respectively, show that $UV = f^2$ and find the focal length f of the lens.

42. Solve Prob. 41 when the curved lens surface is in contact with the water.

43. A thin glass lens of refractive index n and radii of curvature R_1 and R_2 is used to form images in air of objects in water of index n_0. The surface of radius R_1 is in contact with the water.

a. Find expressions for the positions of the two principal focal points of the lens, measured from the lens center.

b. Derive an equation relating object and image distance for this system, using either the lens as an origin *or* the focal points as origins.

44. A plano-convex glass lens of refractive index 1.50 and radius of curvature 24 cm is 2.0 cm thick along its axis. Calculate its focal length, and find the position of the image of an object 50 cm from the convex surface:

a. When on the convex side.

b. When on the plane side.

What is the magnification in each of the above cases?

45. A thick lens is made by grinding each of the ends of a glass rod 16 cm long into a spherical surface of radius 12 cm. Both spherical surfaces are convex to the left, and the refractive index of the glass is 1.60.

a. Find the focal length of the lens.

b. Find the positions of the focal points and of the principal points of the lens.

46. A thick, double-convex glass lens $(n = \frac{3}{2})$ has radii of curvature $R_1 = R$, $R_2 = -2R$, the left-hand surface being of curvature R_1. The axial thickness of the lens is $3R/2$.

a. Locate the focal points and the principal points.

b. Find the image of a point P at a distance $2R$ to the left of the vertex of the left-hand lens surface.

47. Prove that if an incident ray on a thick lens is directed so that it will pass through one of the principal points, the emergent ray has a direction which is parallel to the first and passes through the other principal point.

48. A glass hemisphere of radius 5.0 cm and refractive index 1.50 is used as a lens, rays passing through it very nearly coinciding with its axis. Where are the principal points of this lens, and what is its focal length?

49. Sketch the lenses described below and locate the positions of their principal planes. The radii R_1 and R_2 are of the left-hand and right-hand surfaces, respectively, and t is the thickness. Take $n = 1.50$.

	Lens a	Lens b	Lens c	Lens d	Lens e
R_1, cm..............	+10	−10	∞	+5	−10
R_2, cm..............	−10	+10	+10	+10	−5
t, cm..............	2	2	1.5	1.5	1.5

50. An image is formed in a space of refractive index n_2 of an object in a space of index n_1 by a thick lens of index n. Prove that the lateral magnification is given by

$$m = -\sqrt{\frac{n_1}{n_2}}\frac{f}{U}$$

where f is the focal length of the lens and U is the object distance measured from the first principal focus of the lens.

51. Prove that if an object is located inside a transparent sphere of radius R and index n at a distance R/n from the center, the lens is free from spherical aberration. Derive a formula for the position of the image. Is it real or virtual?

52. Prove that the focal length f of a compound lens consisting of two coaxial thin lenses of separation d is given by

$$\frac{1}{f} = \frac{1}{f_1} + \frac{1}{f_2} - \frac{d}{f_1 f_2}$$

where f_1 and f_2 are the focal lengths of the two thin lenses.

53. Derive expressions for the positions of the principal points and of the principal focal points for two coaxial thin lenses of separation d and focal lengths f_1 and f_2.

54. Two thin lenses A and B of focal lengths +15.0 in. and −5.00 in. are mounted coaxially with a separation of 5.0 in. The lens A is to the left of lens B.

Treating the two thin lenses as the elements of a single compound lens, find the positions of the principal points and of the focal points of this lens.

If x_1 and x_2 are object and image distances in inches measured from lens A and lens B, respectively, show that

$$x_1 x_2 + 10 x_1 + 30 x_2 + 75 = 0$$

for the above compound lens.

55. Two thin convex lenses of focal lengths 30 and 10 cm are mounted coaxially, the lens of 30 cm focal length being on the left. Compute the positions of the principal points and of the principal foci for the following separations: 5 cm, 15 cm, 25 cm, 40 cm, 55 cm, and 70 cm.

Construct a diagram in which these points are located approximately to scale, plotting the six configurations one under the other with the left-hand lens always at the same position.

56. A lens system has its principal and focal points as shown in Fig. 219.

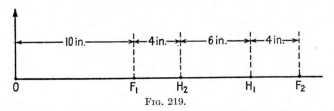

Fɪɢ. 219.

An object O is placed 10 in. from F_1 as shown. Find the image position and the magnification of the system. Show the image on a sketch.

57. A photographic objective consisting of several elements forms an image of the sun 10 cm from the nearest surface A. When the objective is turned around, the image is 12 cm from the nearest surface B.

A scale 1.0 cm long and 30 cm from surface B is photographed with this objective. If the length of the image is 9.0 mm, what is the focal length of the objective? How far is the image from the nearest lens surface?

58. Discuss the axial spherical aberration of a convex mirror for a wide beam of parallel rays which are parallel to the mirror axis, computing the length of that part of the axis which is crossed by the reflected rays.

59. *a.* If the near point of an eye is 100 cm, what sort of lenses are needed in spectacles for reading? What focal length should these lenses have?

b. If spectacles with diverging lenses of focal length 40 cm are prescribed to correct defective vision, what is the far point of the eye?

60. A person with normal vision has a range of accommodation from 25 cm to infinity. Over what range would he be able to see objects distinctly when wearing spectacles of focal length −4.0 m?

61. A magnifying glass has a focal length of 4.0 cm. How far from the lens should an object be placed so that it is seen clearly by an observer whose eye is accommodated for a distance of 25 cm? What is the magnifying power of the glass?

62. What is the magnifying power of a glass ball 2.0 cm in diameter if the glass has in index of refraction of 1.50?

63. A compound microscope comes equipped with objectives of focal lengths 2.0 and 6.0 mm and with oculars of magnifying power 4× and 16×. Find the magnifying powers obtainable. What are the focal lengths of the oculars?

64. A compound microscope has an objective of focal length 4.5 mm and an ocular of focal length 5.0 cm.

a. Find the magnifying power if the image is formed at infinity.

b. How far should the ocular be moved if it is to form a real image on a screen 2 m from the microscope?   Find the lateral magnification.

65. A compound microscope has an objective of focal length 0.40 cm and an ocular of magnifying power 10×.

a. What is the magnifying power of the microscope?

b. With the objective set for visual observation ($V = 18$ cm), the ocular is moved until a sharp image is obtained on a screen at a distance of 20 cm from the ocular.   What is the true length of a microscope object which appears on the screen 9.45 mm long?

66. A properly focused telescope is sighted at the sun.   How far and in what direction must the eyepiece be moved to project a sharp image of the sun on a screen 2 m back of the eyepiece?   The focal length of the eyepiece is 5.0 cm.

67. The objective of a field glass has a focal length of 24 cm.   When used to examine an object 2 m away, its magnifying power is 2.5.   What is the focal length of the ocular?   What will the magnifying power be when viewing an object at infinity?

68. The objective of an astronomical telescope has a focal length of 40 cm and the ocular a focal length of 5.0 cm.   Plot the magnifying power as a function of object distance if the latter varies from 5 m to infinity.   Through what distance must the ocular be moved to maintain a sharp focus for this variation of object distance?

69. The objective of a telescope is a thin lens of focal length f_1 and the ocular a thin lens of focal length f_2, the two being separated by a distance equal to the sum of the focal lengths.

a. Prove that the *linear magnification* of this instrument is given by $-f_2/f_1$, independent of object and image positions.

b. Show that the object-image distance relation for this telescope is given by

$$\frac{f_2}{f_1} x_1 + \frac{f_1}{f_2} x_2 = f_1 + f_2$$

where x_1 is the object distance from the objective and x_2 the image distance from the ocular.

70. A projecting lens of what focal length is required to enlarge a 3- by 4-in. lantern slide to a 3- by 4-ft image on a screen 25 ft from the lens?   Where should the slide be placed?

CHAPTER 17

DISPERSION AND SCATTERING

In this chapter we shall examine the question of the variation of the velocity of sinusoidal electromagnetic waves in dielectrics with the frequency of these waves. In the realm of optics, this effect is called the dispersion of light and results in the variation of refractive index (and hence of the velocity of light) with wavelength or color. This study, when undertaken from an atomic viewpoint, will lead us to the understanding of another phenomenon, the so-called scattering of light, as well as to a deeper insight into the physical nature of the refracted light wave, both in isotropic and in crystalline bodies. In Chap. 13 we have presented an atomic explanation of the electrostatic behavior of dielectrics, and we now must extend the ideas presented there to the case of electromagnetic fields varying rapidly with time. We have seen that the polarization of a dielectric by an electrostatic field resulted either from the orientation of permanent molecular dipoles or from atomic dipole moments induced by the field. Let us now inquire as to how one would expect these effects to vary as the frequency of an impressed alternating field is increased. For both types of polarization one may introduce the idea of a natural frequency (or frequencies). For the permanent dipoles the effect of thermal agitation is to tend to restore a random orientation, very much as the restoring torque of a torsion pendulum tends to restore the pendulum to its equilibrium orientation. For the induced dipoles, as we have seen in Sec. 5, Chap. 13, the restoring force is linear, as if we had springs holding the electrons to the atoms.

In both the above cases the natural frequencies will depend on the stiffness coefficients of the force (or torque) and on the masses involved. In the case of the permanent dipoles the masses are extremely large compared to the electronic mass, and consequently the natural frequencies for these dipoles are very much smaller than for the elastically bound electrons. For frequencies low compared to the natural frequencies, the steady-state motions of the permanent dipoles or of the electrons will be sinusoidal with amplitudes practically equal to the static displacements, as is always true when a system is set into forced vibration by an external force of frequency very much below its natural frequency.   As the frequency increases, the induced moments increase slowly until one reaches frequencies not far from the lowest natural frequency.   Here one encounters the phenomenon of resonance, a sharp increase in the amplitude of the forced motion with friction alone limiting the motion.   In this range there is absorption of energy from the electromagnetic field; this absorbed energy heats the substance, and one has an *absorption band* in the neighborhood of this natural frequency.   The dielectric constant behaves "anomalously" in this frequency region, and if these frequencies lie in the optical region, the substance is no longer transparent, the energy of the electromagnetic field being constantly dissipated.   Consider now a further increase in frequency, passing well beyond the natural frequencies of the permanent dipoles.   In this case these permanent dipoles no longer contribute to the dielectric constant (or index of refraction) since they cannot follow the rapid variations of the field.   For a substance such as water, for which the abnormally high static dielectric constant of 80 is due to the permanent dipole moment of the water molecule, the permanent dipole moments are completely ineffective at optical frequencies, with the result that the dielectric constant is very much the same as for nonpolar substances at these frequencies.

With further increase of frequency, one must get into the infrared, visible, and ultraviolet region of the spectrum before the natural frequencies of the electrons which are responsible for the *induced* dipole moments become evident.   We then have resonance phenomena again, strong absorption of the electromagnetic waves at one or more frequencies, and regions of "normal" transparent behavior of the substance between these absorption frequencies.   This is the region of the electromagnetic spectrum which is of concern in the study of optics, and the effects of the permanent dipoles can be disregarded entirely in this connection.   Our problem becomes then a study of the motion of bound electrons under the influence of a sinusoidal electromagnetic wave.   From the motion we can calculate the induced dipole moment as a function of the time, from this the polarization vector and the dielectric constant, leading to a theory of the variation of refractive index with frequency or wavelength.

1. Dispersion in Gases.   In the case of a gas, in which the atoms are relatively far enough apart at moderate pressures so that one may neglect the interactions between particles, the calculation outlined above may be carried out readily.   For solids and liquids, the resultant external force on an electron is the sum of the force due to the incident wave and the forces exerted by the neighboring induced dipoles; hence the calculation becomes more complicated. If an electromagnetic wave travels in a gas, the electrons in an atom are set into forced motion, and the resultant force acting on an electron is given by $e[\mathcal{E} + (v \times B)]$, where e is the charge on the electron, v is its velocity, and $\mathcal{E}$ and B are the electric field intensity and magnetic induction vectors of the electromagnetic wave at the point where the electron is located. Since the electron velocities are very small compared to the velocity of light in the case at hand, and since the magnitude of B in a plane wave is $1/c$ times that of $\mathcal{E}$, one may neglect the magnetic force.

For the sake of simplicity, consider a plane electromagnetic wave, linearly polarized so that the electric vector is directed along the x-axis, traveling in the z-direction. We have

$$\mathcal{E}_x = \mathcal{E}_0 \sin \omega \left(t - \frac{z}{v_0} \right) \tag{17.1}$$

where $\omega = 2\pi\nu$ is the angular frequency, ν the frequency, and v_0 the phase velocity of the wave. If we consider an atom located at $z = 0$, let us say, the force acting on an electron in this atom will be

$$F_x = e\mathcal{E}_x = e\mathcal{E}_0 \sin \omega t \tag{17.2}$$

Here we have assumed that the phase of the electromagnetic wave is essentially constant (at a definite instant of time) over the region of space occupied by the atom. Since the diameter of an atom is of the order of 10^{-10} m $= 1$ A and the wavelength of light is about

$$5 \times 10^{-7} \text{ m} = 5,000 \text{ A}$$

in the visible, we see that this is a justifiable procedure. It would be incorrect, however, to proceed as above for the case of short X rays. Let us suppose that we are not in the immediate neighborhood of an absorption band (the natural frequency of the electron) and can therefore neglect "friction" effects. If the electron is displaced a distance x from its normal position, there will be a restoring force $-kx$ acting on it in addition to the force given by Eq. (17.2), and its equation of motion is

$$m \frac{d^2x}{dt^2} + kx = e\mathcal{E}_0 \sin \omega t \tag{17.3}$$

This is the equation of the forced motion of a simple harmonic oscillator, and we are interested only in the *steady-state* motion, which ensues with the same frequency as that of the external force. To find this motion, we try a solution of the form[1]

$$x = A \sin \omega t \tag{17.4}$$

being prepared to reject it if it fails, *i.e.*, if A does not turn out to be independent of t. From Eq. (17.4) we have for the acceleration

$$\frac{d^2x}{dt^2} = -\omega^2 A \sin \omega t \tag{17.5}$$

and substituting the values of x and d^2x/dt^2, as given by Eqs. (17.4) and (17.5), back into Eq. (17.3), there follows readily

$$A = \frac{e\mathcal{E}_0/m}{\omega_0^2 - \omega^2}$$

where $\omega_0 = 2\pi\nu_0 = \sqrt{k/m}$ is the natural angular frequency of the electron. Thus the required solution is

$$x = \frac{e\mathcal{E}_0 \sin \omega t}{m(\omega_0^2 - \omega^2)} = \frac{e/m}{\omega_0^2 - \omega^2}\mathcal{E}_x \tag{17.6}$$

The dipole moment of the atom, due to this motion of the electron, is then

$$ex = \frac{e^2\mathcal{E}_x}{m(\omega_0^2 - \omega^2)}$$

and the total induced dipole moment of the atom, p_x, is given by

$$p_x = \sum ex = \left(\sum \frac{e^2/m}{\omega_0^2 - \omega^2}\right)\mathcal{E}_x \tag{17.7}$$

where the summation is over all the electrons in the atom, different electrons having in general different natural frequencies. For simplicity, consider only one electron contributing appreciably to the induced dipole moment. There follows for the polarizability of the atom [see Eq. (13.22)],

$$\alpha = \frac{p_x}{\mathcal{E}_x} = \frac{e^2/m}{(\omega_0^2 - \omega^2)} \tag{17.8}$$

Note that for electrostatic fields ($\omega = 0$), this is the same result as that expressed in Eq. (13.22). If there are N atoms per unit volume (or, more precisely, N electrons of natural angular frequency ω_0 per unit volume), the polarization vector P has the magnitude

$$P = N\alpha\mathcal{E}$$

---

[1] Compare the following discussion with that in Frank's "Introduction to Mechanics and Heat," pp. 116–119.

so that

$$D = \epsilon \mathcal{E} = \epsilon_0 \mathcal{E} + N\alpha \mathcal{E}$$

from which

$$\frac{\epsilon}{\epsilon_0} = \kappa = n^2 = 1 + \frac{N\alpha}{\epsilon_0} \tag{17.9}$$

[compare Eq. (13.23)]. Using the value of α given by Eq. (17.8), there follows

$$\kappa = n^2 = 1 + \frac{Ne^2/m\epsilon_0}{\omega_0^2 - \omega^2} \tag{17.10}$$

which predicts the variation of refractive index with frequency ($\omega/2\pi$) when only one type of electron plays an essential role. For the more general case, one has a sum of terms, each similar to the last term of Eq. (17.10), instead of this single term. For the case of gases, n is very nearly equal to unity (for air, $n = 1.0003$), so that we may replace Eq. (17.10) by

$$n - 1 = \frac{Ne^2/m\epsilon_0}{2(\omega_0^2 - \omega^2)} \tag{17.11}$$

In Fig. 220 is shown a plot of Eq. (17.11). According to this equation, $n - 1$ becomes infinite for $\omega = \omega_0$, but as we have stated, in this range strong absorption takes place; consequently our equation is essentially correct for angular frequencies less than about ω_A and greater than about ω_B, as indicated in the figure, but not in between. Notice that in the range where Eq. (17.11) is expected to be valid, the index of refraction *increases with increasing frequency*, i.e., with decreasing wavelength. This is the so-called *normal dispersion*, whereas the behavior in the immediate neighborhood of $\omega = \omega_0$ is called *anomalous*, since it can be shown that the re-

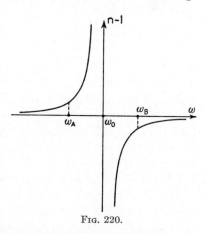

FIG. 220.

fractive index decreases with increasing frequency in this region. It is customary for experimentalists to write formulas for dispersion in terms of wavelength rather than frequency. One of the common empirical formulas, known as the Cauchy formula, is

$$n = A + \frac{B}{\lambda^2} + \frac{C}{\lambda^4} \tag{17.12}$$

One can show easily that Eq. (17.11) or (17.10) leads to this formula for $\omega \ll \omega_0$, *i.e.*, when the absorption is in the ultraviolet region of the spectrum.

2. Dispersion in Solids and Liquids; the Prism Spectroscope.   The theory of dispersion in solids and liquids proceeds along the lines of that for gases, except that Eq. (17.2) for the force on an electron must be extended to include the effects of the neighboring atoms.   We shall not carry this through but should point out that the empirical formula (17.12), which works well for ordinary optical materials in the visible

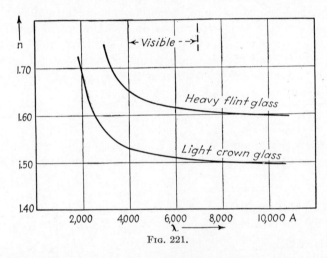

FIG. 221.

region of the spectrum, can be justified on theoretical grounds.   In Fig. 221 is shown the variation of index of refraction with wavelength for two common types of optical glass, both showing normal dispersion. As a general rule, the rate of increase of n with decreasing wavelength is larger at shorter wavelengths; and for different substances, the curve is usually steeper at a given wavelength, the larger the value of n.

The dispersion of optical materials is utilized in analyzing the spectral composition of light in the instrument known as the *prism spectrometer*.   A beam of light, in general, consists of an electromagnetic wave field which is the superposition of many elementary waves of different frequencies (colors), amplitudes, and polarization, and the study of the wavelengths of the different component waves is fundamental for obtaining nformation concerning the structure of atoms and molecules.   We start with the problem of the deviation of a very narrow pencil of light rays by a prism of angle A, as shown in Fig. 222.   Let us suppose that we have monochromatic light of a single color or frequency. For a fixed prism angle A, the deviation angle varies with the angle of incidence i_1, and there is one angle of

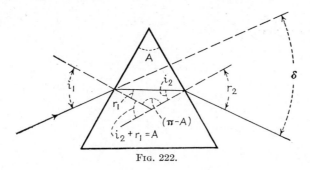

FIG. 222.

incidence for which this deviation is a minimum. From the figure it is clear that

$$\delta = i_1 - r_1 + r_2 - i_2 = i_1 + r_2 - A \qquad (17.13)$$

If the deviation δ is to be a minimum, we must have $d\delta/di_1 = 0$, or from Eq. (17.13)

$$dr_2 = -di_1 \qquad (17.14)$$

so that we must express r_2 in terms of i_1. This is done most easily in differential form and suffices for the condition required by Eq. (17.4). At each surface of the prism, we have from the law of refraction

$$\left. \begin{array}{c} \sin i_1 = n \sin r_1 \\ n \sin i_2 = \sin r_2 \end{array} \right\} \qquad (17.15)$$

Differentiating these expressions, one obtains

$$\cos i_1 \, di_1 = n \cos r_1 \, dr_1$$
$$n \cos i_2 \, di_2 = \cos r_2 \, dr_2$$

and since $r_1 + i_2 = A$, we have also $dr_1 = -di_2$. Thus there follows

$$dr_2 = n \frac{\cos i_2}{\cos r_2} \, di_2 = -n \frac{\cos i_2}{\cos r_2} \, dr_1 = -\frac{\cos i_2}{\cos r_2} \frac{\cos i_1}{\cos r_1} \, di_1$$

and Eq. (17.14) requires that

$$\frac{\cos i_1}{\cos r_2} \frac{\cos (A - r_1)}{\cos r_1} = 1 \qquad (17.16)$$

where we have used the relation $r_1 + i_2 = A$. Equation (17.16) is evidently satisfied if $i_1 = r_2$ and $r_1 = A/2$, *i.e.*, if the ray passes symmetrically through the prism. When this condition is satisfied, Eq.

(17.13) gives

$$i_1 = \frac{A + \delta}{2}$$

and from the first of Eqs. (17.15) we have finally

$$\sin\left(\frac{A + \delta}{2}\right) = n \sin \frac{A}{2} \qquad (17.17)$$

as the condition relating the *angle of minimum deviation* δ to the prism angle A and the refractive index n. For small-angle prisms, we may replace the sines of the angles in Eq. (17.17) by the angles and have

$$n = \frac{A + \delta}{A}$$

or

$$\delta = (n - 1)A \qquad (17.18)$$

which is a convenient approximation. Note that the deviation

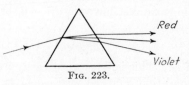

Fig. 223.

increases with increasing refractive index, so that the shorter the wavelength, the greater the deviation for a given prism. If the light incident on the prism is natural white light, a mixture of all visible wavelengths, the emergent light will be spread or "dispersed" into a spectrum, as indicated in Fig. 223.   One defines the *angular dispersion D* as the rate of change of the deviation δ with wavelength, *i.e.*, by

$$D = \frac{d\delta}{d\lambda} = A \frac{dn}{d\lambda}$$

where the last equality holds for small-angle prisms. The actual dispersion of a prism spectroscope (see below) is measured by the separation in angstroms per millimeter in the field of the observing telescope or on the photograph of the spectrum. This quantity depends not only on the angular dispersion D but also on the focal length of the telescope or camera objective.

It is customary to define the *dispersive power d* of a small-angle prism as the ratio of the difference in deviation for two extreme colors in the visible spectrum to the mean deviation for the spectrum as a whole.   In this connection, it has become common practice to utilize the following wavelengths as reference wavelengths.

$$\lambda_1 = 6{,}560 \text{ A} \qquad \text{(the Fraunhofer C line; red)}$$
$$\lambda_2 = 4{,}860 \text{ A} \qquad \text{(the Fraunhofer F line; blue)}$$
$$\lambda_0 = 5{,}890 \text{ A} \qquad \text{(the Fraunhofer D line; yellow)}$$

Using Eq. (17.18), one finds immediately for the dispersive power of a small-angle prism

$$d = \frac{\delta_2 - \delta_1}{\delta_0} = \frac{n_2 - n_1}{n_0 - 1} \tag{17.19}$$

where the n's are the refractive indices for the above colors. The refractive indices and dispersive powers are given for two kinds of glass:

Kind of glass	n_0	n_1	n_2	d
Silicate flint..............	1.620	1.613	1.632	0.031
Silicate crown............	1.508	1.504	1.513	0.018

Since, in general, the dispersive power of various optical materials is not proportional to the mean refractive index, it is possible to combine

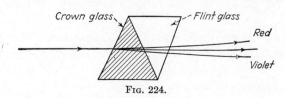

FIG. 224.

two or more prisms to obtain zero net deviation for a given wavelength, such as the D line, and yet to obtain a spectrum. Such a device is known as a *direct-vision prism* (Fig. 224) and is used in the direct-vision spectroscope, a convenient small instrument which may be held in the hand and pointed directly at a light source.

It is also possible to combine two prisms so that the dispersions are compensated (strictly speaking, for two wavelengths only), but the deviations are not. Such a prism is called *achromatic*. This principle is utilized in designing achromatic lenses, and we shall illustrate the method in the next section.

The ordinary form of the prism spectroscope is shown in Fig. 225. The essential parts are as follows: A narrow slit S illuminated by the light to be examined; a collimating lens C, which produces a parallel beam of light incident on the prism P; a telescope lens T, which produces a real image of the slit at the first focal point of the eyepiece E. The observer sees a series of images of the slit side by side, each of different color. If white light is used, the images overlap, and a *continuous spectrum* is observed. If the incident light is a mixture of a finite number of wavelengths, a series of bright lines, one of each color present in the incident light, will appear, and a *line spectrum* is observed.

A stigmatic pencil incident on a prism becomes astigmatic upon emergence unless the angle of incidence is that for minimum deviation, so that the collimating lens is necessary to produce sharp images. This lens must be achromatic (corrected for chromatic aberration).

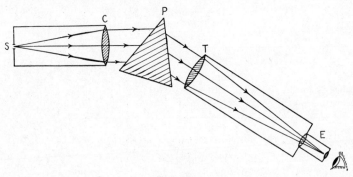

FIG. 225.

3. Chromatic Aberrations and Their Correction. The chromatic aberration of simple lenses, referred to in the last chapter, is the result of dispersion. Since the focal length of a lens depends on its refractive index, a single lens will produce a series of colored images of an object at different positions and of different magnifications. One can design a lens which will have the same focal length for two wavelengths, and it is then said to be "achromatized" for these two colors. The following method illustrates how an "achromatic doublet," consisting of two thin lenses of different kinds of glass in contact, may be designed to be achromatic for the C and F Fraunhofer lines. Now the reciprocal focal length of a thin lens is proportional to $n - 1$, and the reciprocal focal length of a pair of thin lenses in contact is the sum of the reciprocal focal lengths of the two lenses. If we use subscripts 1, 2, and 0 to refer to the two reference wavelengths λ_1 and λ_2 and the intermediate wavelength λ_0 and use primes and double primes to indicate the two different lenses, we have for the reciprocal focal length of the system

$$\frac{1}{f} = c'(n_1' - 1) + c''(n_1'' - 1) = c'(n_2' - 1) + c''(n_2'' - 1) \quad (17.20)$$

since the focal length f is to be the same at the two wavelengths λ_1 and λ_2. c' and c'' are the values of $[(1/R_1) - (1/R_2)]$ for the two lenses. From (17.20) there follows

$$\frac{c'}{c''} = -\ \frac{n_2'' - n_1''}{n_2' - n_1'} \tag{17.21}$$

The focal lengths of the two lenses at the intermediate wavelength λ_0 are given by $1/f_0' = c'(n_0' - 1)$ and $1/f_0'' = c''(n_0'' - 1)$, so that

$$\frac{c'}{c''} = \frac{n_0'' - 1}{n_0' - 1} \frac{f_0''}{f_0'} \tag{17.22}$$

Equating (17.21) and (17.22) and using Eq. (17.19), there follows

$$\frac{f_0''}{f_0'} = -\ \frac{d''}{d'} \tag{17.23}$$

where d' and d'' are the dispersive powers of the two kinds of glass employed.   Since d' and d'' are positive quantities, the doublet must consist of one positive and one negative lens.   If the faces of the lenses in contact are to be cemented together, then $R_2' = R_1''$, where R_2' and R_1'' are the radii of curvature of the right face of the first lens and the left fact of the second lens.   Two other conditions as given by Eqs. (17.20) and (17.23) must also be satisfied by the four radii of curvature of the lens surfaces.   Thus we must have

$$\left.\begin{array}{c} R_2' = R_1'' \\[2mm] \dfrac{1}{f} = (n_1' - 1)\left(\dfrac{1}{R_1'} - \dfrac{1}{R_2'}\right) + (n_1'' - 1)\left(\dfrac{1}{R_1''} - \dfrac{1}{R_2''}\right) \\[4mm] \dfrac{f_0''}{f_0'} = -\ \dfrac{d''}{d'} = \dfrac{(n_0' - 1)}{(n_0'' - 1)}\dfrac{[(1/R_1') - (1/R_2')]}{[(1/R_1'') - (1/R_2'')]} \end{array}\right\} \tag{17.24}$$

A fourth condition may be imposed arbitrarily and may be used for other corrections such as minimizing spherical aberration.   For sim-

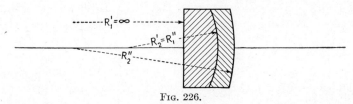

FIG. 226.

plicity, let us choose $R_1' = \infty$, making the first lens plano-convex with the plane side toward the light source; we then obtain the lens shown in Fig. 226.   Numerical examples are left to the problems.

One can achromatize a compound lens by using two simple lenses of the same kind of glass separated by an appropriate distance a. The focal length f of this compound lens is given by

$$\frac{1}{f} = \frac{1}{f'} + \frac{1}{f''} - \frac{a}{f'f''}$$

with f' and f'' the focal lengths of the two simple lenses. Using the above notation, we have [$1/f' = c'(n-1)$ and $1/f'' = c''(n-1)$]

$$\frac{1}{f} = (n-1)(c' + c'') - ac'c''(n-1)^2 \qquad (17.25)$$

and if f is to be independent of wavelength, $\dfrac{d}{d\lambda}\left(\dfrac{1}{f}\right)$ must vanish. Accordingly

$$[c' + c'' - 2ac'c''(n-1)]\frac{dn}{d\lambda} = 0$$

and since $dn/d\lambda \neq 0$, we must have

$$a = \frac{c' + c''}{2c'c''(n-1)} = \frac{(1/f') + (1/f'')}{2/f'f''} = \frac{f' + f''}{2} \qquad (17.26)$$

so that the separation of the lenses should equal one-half the sum of their focal lengths. The correction can be made exactly for only one wavelength, viz., for that wavelength to which f' and f'' refer. However, the departure from perfect achromatization is small for wavelengths not far from the one for which Eq. (17.26) is satisfied, and this method is employed in many types of oculars.

4. The Scattering of Light; Scattering Cross Section. In our calculation of the index of refraction of a gas as a function of frequency in Sec. 1 of this chapter, we were concerned solely with the magnitudes of the dipole moments induced by a light wave traveling through the gas. We must now consider the fact that the induced oscillating dipoles are themselves radiators of electromagnetic waves, and these secondary waves are responsible for the so-called scattering of light by matter. Consider a linearly polarized monochromatic wave incident on an electron bound to a gas atom. The electron performs forced simple harmonic motion and gives rise to an oscillating dipole moment given by Eq. (17.6), viz.,

$$p = ex = \frac{e^2\mathcal{E}_0}{m}\frac{\sin \omega t}{\omega_0^2 - \omega^2}$$

where e and m are the electronic charge and mass, respectively, and $\mathcal{E}_0$ is the amplitude of the electric vector of the incident wave. ω_0 is the angular natural frequency of the oscillating dipole. Absorption is neglected as before. This oscillating dipole will radiate according to Eq. (11.18), and the light emitted by all the induced dipoles constitutes the scattered light. The amplitude p_{max} of the oscillating dipole is evidently

$$p_{max} = \frac{e^2 \mathcal{E}_0 / m}{\omega_0^2 - \omega^2} \qquad (17.27)$$

so that the average rate of emission of energy of this electron (the average power radiated) is, using Eq. (11.18),

$$\bar{P}_s = \frac{e^4 \mathcal{E}_0^2}{12\pi\epsilon_0 m^2 c^3} \frac{\omega^4}{(\omega_0^2 - \omega^2)^2} \qquad (17.28)$$

This scattered power $\bar{P}_s$ is the average rate at which energy is abstracted from the incident plane wave, and it is proportional to the power density or intensity of this wave. Owing to the random thermal motion of the atoms of a gas and to the consequent random positions of these atoms, there will be no fixed phase relations among the secondary waves emitted by the various atoms—with the important exception of the light emitted *in* the direction of the incident wave—so that the scattered light intensity will be the sum of the intensity contributions from the individual atoms. Thus *the scattered light is incoherent,* and if there are n dipoles per unit volume of the scattering substance, the intensity of the light scattered per unit volume is $n\bar{P}_s$, where $\bar{P}_s$ is given by Eq. (17.28).

As a measure of the scattering "power" of an electron, one uses the so-called *scattering cross section.* This is defined as follows: *The scattering cross section is that cross section of the incident plane wave such that the energy traversing it per unit time is equal to the energy scattered per unit time.* If σ is this cross section and $\bar{S}$ the average value of the Poynting vector of the incident wave, then the definition of σ is

$$\sigma = \frac{\bar{P}_s}{\bar{S}} \qquad (17.29)$$

Since, for a plane wave, $\bar{S} = \frac{1}{2}\mathcal{E}_0 H_0 = \frac{1}{2}\sqrt{\epsilon_0/\mu_0}\,\mathcal{E}_0^2 = c\epsilon_0\mathcal{E}_0^2/2$, insertion of $\bar{P}_s$ from (17.28) into (17.29) yields

$$\sigma = \frac{e^4}{6\pi\epsilon_0^2 m^2 c^4} \frac{1}{[(\omega_0^2/\omega^2) - 1]^2} \qquad (17.30)$$

The factor $e^4/6\pi\epsilon_0^2 m^2 c^4$ has the dimensions of the square of a length, and this length is of the order of magnitude of the "classical" radius of an electron. This classical radius can be estimated by considering an electron as a sphere of radius r_0, carrying its charge e uniformly distributed over its surface, calculating the energy stored in its electro-static field, and equating this to mc^2 (compare Prob. 28, Chap. 4). The result is

$$r_0 = \frac{e^2}{8\pi\epsilon_0 mc^2} \qquad (17.31)$$

In terms of this electron radius, Eq. (17.30) becomes

$$\sigma = \frac{32\pi r_0^2}{3} \frac{1}{[(\omega_0^2/\omega^2) - 1]^2} \qquad (17.32)$$

This formula shows that the scattering cross section of an electron is proportional to its classical geometrical cross section, but that the proportionality factor depends on frequency. There are three cases of interest: First, if the natural frequency ω_0 lies in the ultraviolet, as it does in a normal atom, then for visible light we may set $\omega_0^2/\omega^2 \gg 1$, and Eq. (17.32) takes the form

$$\sigma = \frac{32\pi r_0^2}{3} \frac{\omega^4}{\omega_0^4} = \frac{32\pi r_0^2}{3} \frac{\lambda_0^4}{\lambda^4} \qquad (17.33)$$

where λ is the wavelength of the light and λ_0 the wavelength cor-responding to the natural frequency. This is the basis for the so-called Rayleigh scattering formula, which predicts that blue light is scattered much more intensely than red light because of the inverse dependence on the fourth power of the wavelength. This provides an explanation of the blue color of the sky, the air molecules scattering the blue light much more than the red. The transmitted light is correspondingly deficient in blue light, as is evidenced by the red color of the sun at sunset, when the sunlight reaches us through a long air path.

For high frequencies when $\omega^2 \gg \omega_0^2$, Eq. (17.32) becomes

$$\sigma = \frac{32\pi r_0^2}{3} \qquad (17.34)$$

independent of wavelength. This is essentially the Thomson scatter-ing formula, and it finds important application in the study of X rays. Finally, if ω is almost equal to ω_0, the cross section becomes very large, and the scattered light is very intense, and then we may no longer neglect absorption (frictional effects). This scattering is called *resonance scattering*.

Since all the induced dipoles vibrate in the direction of the electric vector $\mathcal{E}_0$ of the incident light, the scattered light will be linearly polar-ized if the incident light is so polarized. There will be zero intensity of scattered light in the direction of the vector $\mathcal{E}_0$ and a maximum at right angles to this direction, both directions being normal to the direction of propagation of the incident wave. If the incident light is unpolarized, the light scattered in a direction perpendicular to the direction of propagation of the incident light will be linearly polarized; of the electric vectors of the elementary waves of which unpolarized light is composed, only those components normal to both the above directions are effective in producing scattered light in this given direction. The fundamental experiments performed by *Barkla*, which demonstrated that X rays are electromagnetic waves, depended on these facts.

We have already pointed out that the atoms of a substance scatter independently of one another (so that intensities rather than amplitudes are to be added), in all directions except that of the incident wave, because of the random positions of these atoms; this excludes crystals in which the atoms have fixed positions relative to each other. In the forward direction the scattered light combines with the incident light to form the refracted light wave. Evidently the relative phase of the incident wave and the wave scattered by a given atom at a point lying ahead of this atom does *not* depend on the exact position of the scattering atom, so that there are *fixed* phase relations between the incident wave and the secondary waves scattered in the forward direction. Thus one must add amplitudes rather than intensities; the scattering in the forward direction is coherent with the incident wave and interference effects become important. Owing to the phase retardations of the secondary scattered waves relative to the primary incident wave, the resultant refracted wave suffers a phase retardation relative to the primary wave proportional to the distance traversed, *i.e.*, to the number of scattering atoms in this path. Consequently the resultant wave travels with a phase velocity less than that of electromagnetic waves in empty space. This yields a simple and effective physical picture of the manner in which the refracted wave is generated and of the reason for the reduced velocity of light in a material body.

To clarify the preceding statements, consider a simple idealized model in which we take the atoms arranged in layers perpendicular to the direction of propagation of the incident plane wave WW in Fig. 227. This incident wave excites the electrons in the layer AA, and they emit a secondary plane wave out of phase with the primary wave. We can find the phase of this secondary wave by a simple vector diagram. At the point B the electric field vector oscillates sinusoidally with time, so that we can use the vector diagram of a-c circuits. Furthermore, the amplitude of the secondary wave emitted by a single layer of atoms is exceedingly small compared to that of the primary wave, and since there is no absorption, the amplitude of the resultant wave must equal the amplitude of the incident wave. In Fig. 228 $\mathcal{E}_p$ represents the primary-wave amplitude at the point B, assuming no layer of atoms AA. $\mathcal{E}_s$ is the amplitude of the secondary wave at B emitted by the layer of atoms AA, and this amplitude can

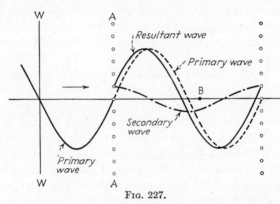

FIG. 227.

be taken as infinitesimal. The sum of these two yields $\mathcal{E}_r$, the amplitude of the resultant wave. Since $\mathcal{E}_p$ and $\mathcal{E}_r$ are equal in magnitude, the vector $\mathcal{E}_s$ must be practically at right angles to either, so that the secondary wave is very nearly 90° out of phase with the primary wave. This result is not in conflict with the fact that the secondary wave radiated by a *single* atom is 180° out of phase with the primary wave (the acceleration of the electron being 180° out of phase with its displacement), since we are considering the contribution at point B of all the atoms in the layer AA, and the individual secondary waves arriving at B from the individual atoms have

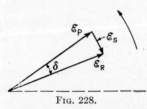

FIG. 228.

different amplitudes and phases. The superposition of these individual spherical waves then yields the plane secondary wave of the phase obtained above. In Fig. 227 are shown the relations among primary, secondary, and resultant waves. The phase lag shown in Fig. 228, produced by *one* layer of atoms, is proportional to the amplitude of the secondary wave, and as the wave progresses through the medium, the total phase lag in a distance x will be proportional to the number of atomic layers in this distance and hence to the distance x in a homogeneous substance.

Summarizing, we have the result that the refracted wave in a material body is the superposition of the incident wave and the light scattered coherently in the forward direction, whereas in other directions one has the ordinary incoherent scattered light as expressed in Eq. (17.28).

5. The Propagation of Light in Crystals; Double Refraction. In isotropic media the velocity of light is independent of the direction of propagation and of the polarization of the light waves. According to the theory set forth in this chapter, this fact indicates that the natural frequencies of the electrons which are set into oscillation in such bodies are independent of the direction in which these oscillations occur. The dependence of refractive index on these natural frequencies is given essentially by the right-hand term in Eq. (17.10) (the equation itself must be modified for the case of solids), and in the region of normal dispersion the velocity of light should increase with increasing ω_0, *i.e.*, the stronger the binding forces acting on the electrons. There exist many transparent crystals which are *anisotropic*, the binding forces and natural frequencies of the electrons being different in different directions, and a number of remarkable and important optical phenomena occur when light passes through such crystals.

We shall confine our attention to the case for which there is *one* preferred direction in the crystal, let us say the x-axis, so that all directions in planes normal to this x-axis (the y-z planes) are equivalent. Thus, if the electrons are set in motion along the x-axis, they will behave as simple harmonic oscillators of angular natural frequency ω_{ox}, whereas, if they are set into motion in any direction in a y-z plane, they behave as harmonic oscillators of a different natural frequency $\omega_{oy} = \omega_{oz}$. Crystals for which there is *one* preferred direction are called *uniaxial*, and this preferred direction is called the *optic axis* of the crystal. Consider a linearly polarized plane light wave traveling in the direction of the optic axis, *i.e.*, along the x-axis. Since the electric vector oscillates in the y-z plane, the amplitudes of the induced oscillating dipoles and consequently the velocity of propagation of the wave do not depend on the direction of polarization. Hence we may introduce an ordinary index of refraction n_0 (depending on ω_{oy}) for propagation along the optic axis, and the velocity of propagation v_0 for this case is given by

$$v_0 = \frac{c}{n_0}.$$ (17.35)

Thus if light is normally incident on a crystal surface which is perpendicular to the optic axis, it propagates through the crystal with a velocity v_0 independent of the state of polarization of the light, and the crystal behaves like an isotropic substance, such as glass.

The state of affairs is quite different, however, if the direction of propagation is not along the optic axis. Consider a plane wave propagating in a direction perpendicular to the optic axis, let us say along the z-axis, such as one may obtain by allowing parallel light to fall at normal incidence on a crystal surface which has been ground parallel to the optic axis. In this case it is evident that the state of polarization of the wave plays an important role in determining the nature of the refracted wave. First, let us consider the case for which

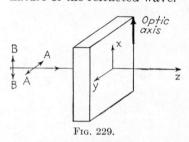

the incident wave is linearly polarized, the direction of oscillation of the electric vector being along the y-axis (the direction AA in Fig. 229) perpendicular to the direction of the optic axis. The electrons in the crystal are set into oscillation in the y-direction, and the phase velocity of this wave inside the crystal depends on the natural fre-

FIG. 229.

quency ω_{oy}, in accordance with the foregoing discussion. Evidently this wave will propagate with the velocity v_0 given by Eq. (17.35).

On the other hand, if the incident wave is polarized along the optic axis (the direction BB in Fig. 229), the electrons in the crystal are set into oscillation along the x-axis. Thus the phase velocity of this wave inside the crystal depends on the natural frequency ω_{ox}, which is different from ω_{oy}. We may now introduce a second index of refraction n_e for this type of wave, so that its velocity v_e is given by

$$v_e = \frac{c}{n_e} \qquad (17.36)$$

n_0 and n_e are called the *principal indices of refraction* of the crystal. If $v_0 > v_e$ ($n_0 < n_e$), the crystal is called *positive uniaxial*, whereas, if $v_0 < v_e$ ($n_0 > n_e$), it is called *negative uniaxial*. For the crystal calcite ($CaCO_3$), a crystal important in many applications to optical instruments, the principal indices have the values (for the sodium D lines)

$$n_0 = 1.6584$$
$$n_e = 1.4864$$

so that calcite is a negative uniaxial crystal.

Now let the incident light have an arbitrary direction of polarization relative to the optic axis, as indicated in Fig. 230. We can resolve

the electric vector of the incident wave into x- and y-components
(Fig. 230), and these oscillate in phase for the linearly polarized wave
under discussion. [For elliptically (or circularly) polarized light we
would have the same vector diagram as in Fig. 230, but the two components would then oscillate out of phase with each other.] After
passing through the crystal the x- and y-components of $\mathcal{E}$ will no longer
be in phase because of the different velocities of propagation for these
two types of polarization. The phase difference thus obtained depends
on the thickness of the crystal, and in general the emergent light

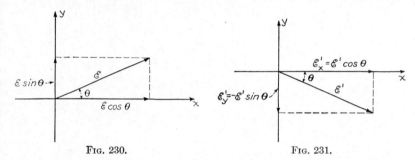

Fig. 230.　　　　　　　　　　　　　Fig. 231.

will be polarized differeutly from the incident light. Suppose, for
example, that the crystal of Fig. 229 is just thick enough to produce
a phase difference of 180° between the x- and y-components of $\mathcal{E}$.
For the emergent light we then can construct the vector diagram
corresponding to Fig. 230 for the incident light. This is shown in
Fig. 231. The resultant $\mathcal{E}'$ of the emergent light now makes a negative
angle θ with the optic axis. The effect of the crystal has been to
rotate the direction of polarization through an angle of 2θ. We can
readily derive a formula for the thickness of such a *half-wave* plate.
The phase lag for the y-component of $\mathcal{E}$ produced by a plate of thickness
d is given by

$$\frac{\omega d}{v_0} = \frac{\omega d n_0}{c}$$

whereas for the x-component it is

$$\frac{\omega d}{v_e} = \frac{\omega d n_e}{c}$$

Remembering that $2\pi c/\omega$ is the wavelength of the light (in vacuum),
the relative phase retardation between these two components of $\mathcal{E}$
becomes

$$\delta = \frac{2\pi d}{\lambda} (n_0 - n_e) \qquad (17.37)$$

For a half-wave plate we set $\delta = \pi$ and have from Eq. (17.37)

$$d = \frac{\lambda}{2}\frac{1}{n_0 - n_e}$$

Evidently the same results would be obtained for a given wavelength if the phase retardation is an odd number of half wavelengths. In the special case of $\theta = 45°$ in Fig. 230, a quarter-wave plate will produce circularly polarized emergent light. Further details are left to the problems.

There are a number of uniaxial crystals, such as tourmaline, which, when used as in Fig. 229, have the remarkable property of absorbing light polarized along the y-axis and transmitting light polarized along the x-axis (the optic axis). Such crystals are called *dichroic*. A tourmaline plate used as indicated in Fig. 232 forms a simple polarizer.

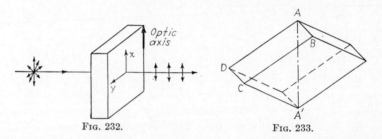

FIG. 232.   FIG. 233.

Incident natural unpolarized light falling on the plate emerges as linearly polarized light, as indicated. Although the resultant electric vector of unpolarized light may be represented by two equal components at right angles, it must be remembered that since the electric vector is the sum of many elementary vectors of random orientation and phases, there are no fixed phase relations between these two components. The commercial material "Polaroid," composed of many small dichroic crystals which are lined up, acts in the above manner and provides a very useful and simple polarizer.

Finally, we must consider what happens when light is incident on a crystal surface which is neither parallel to nor perpendicular to the optic axis. For simplicity, we shall consider the case of normal incidence on one of the natural cleavage planes of calcite. The natural cleavage planes of calcite yield a rhombohedral crystal as shown in Fig. 233, in which AA' gives the direction of the optic axis when the crystal is of such a length BC that AA' makes equal angles with the three edges at A. If a narrow beam of natural unpolarized light falls at normal incidence on the face $ABCD$ of the crystal, one observes that *two* refracted beams are formed inside the crystal and two parallel beams emerge from the opposite face, and these two beams are linearly polarized at right angles to each other.

This phenomenon of *double refraction*, or *birefringence*, is illustrated in Fig. 234.   The incident beam I is normally incident on the left-hand face at C.   Inside the crystal it breaks up into two beams, one of which, O, traverses the crystal without being bent; the other, E, is refracted

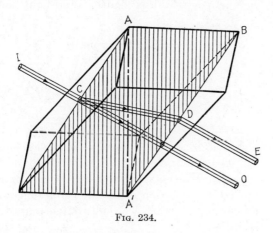

FIG. 234.

upon entrance in the direction CD and emerges parallel to the first beam.   The ray O which goes straight through behaves inside the crystal, in this experiment and in any others which one may perform, just as if it were in an isotropic medium.   It is called the *ordinary ray* and obeys Snell's law when the light is not normally incident on the surface.   Its velocity is v_0 as given by Eq. (17.35) and is independent of its direction of propagation.   On the other hand, the ray E evidently does not follow Snell's law, as it is refracted for normal incidence.   It is called the *extraordinary ray*, and its velocity may have any value between v_0 and v_e as given by Eqs. (17.35) and (17.36).   To answer the question as to the direction in which the extraordinary ray is refracted, one observes that if the

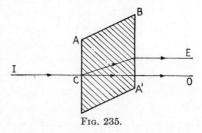

FIG. 235.

crystal in Fig. 234 is rotated about ICO as an axis, the position of the ordinary ray O is unaltered, but the ray CDE rotates about this axis. Hence *CD* is fixed in the crystal in the shaded plane which contains the optic axis and the incident ray. This plane is called a *principal section* of the crystal for this ray, and the extraordinary ray lies in this plane. Figure 235 indicates the process somewhat more simply than Fig. 234, and in it the plane of the page is chosen to coincide with the principal section. The ordinary ray is polarized in a direction perpendicular to the principal section, *i.e.*, to the plane of the page, whereas the extraordinary ray is polarized in the plane of the page in this figure. For light not normally

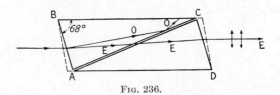

Fig. 236.

incident on the surface of a crystal, one obtains a very similar picture to the one which we have discussed, the ordinary ray obeying Snell's law with an index n_0 and the extraordinary ray behaving anomalously. Since a quantitative investigation of double refraction would lead us far beyond the scope of this book, we shall content ourselves with the above brief description.

The Nicol Prism. A beam of linearly polarized light may be obtained conveniently with the help of a Nicol prism, or "Nicol," which is constructed from a long calcite rhombohedron as follows: In

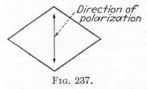

Fig. 237.

the principal section of a calcite crystal (Fig. 236) the angles at *B* and *D* are 71°. The two end faces *AB* and *CD* are cut down so that these angles are reduced to 68°. The crystal is sliced along *AC* in a plane perpendicular to the ends and to the plane of the paper (the principal section), and the two surfaces thus formed are cemented together with canada balsam of refractive index 1.55, which is less than that for the ordinary ray in calcite and greater than that for the extraordinary ray shown in the figure. The passage of a ray of light through the prism is shown in Fig. 236, the ordinary ray being totally reflected from the canada balsam and the extraordinary ray being transmitted with but small loss in intensity. The emergent light is linearly polarized in the plane of the paper, as indicated, and the direction of oscillation is along the short diagonal of the diamond-shaped end face of the Nicol prism (Fig. 237).

Problems

1. The observed values of $n - 1$ for hydrogen at a number of wavelengths are as follows:

λ, A..............	5,460	4,080	3,340	2,890	2,540	2,300	1,900
$(n - 1) \times 10^7$.......	1,400	1,426	1,461	1,499	1,547	1,594	1,718

Construct a plot of these data, and from two points on this curve compute the values of N and ω_0 (or the corresponding wavelength λ_0) of Eq. (17.11). How does this value of N compare with the number of hydrogen molecules per unit volume under standard conditions?

2. Show that the Cauchy dispersion formula [Eq. (17.12)] follows from Eq. (17.11) if $\omega \ll \omega_0$. Prove that the Cauchy formula is valid for a gas with more than one kind of electron per atom (different ω_0's) providing all the ω_0's are larger than ω.

3. A prism of angle $A = 60°$ gives a minimum deviation of $30°$ for monochromatic light of wavelength 6,800 A. What is the index of refraction of the glass at this wavelength?

4. A parallel beam of light from a mercury arc passes through a slit and is then incident on a $10°$ glass prism at an angle corresponding to minimum deviation.

a. What is the angular separation of the violet line (4,050 A) and the red line (6,230 A)?

b. Can the unaided eye, or the eye aided by a single lens, *see* the spectrum? Explain.

c. If a lens of focal length 1 m, placed next to the prism, projects these lines on a screen, what is their linear separation on the screen?

The refractive index of the glass is 1.636 at $\lambda = 4,050$ A and 1.616 at $\lambda = 6,230$ A.

5. An $8°$ crown-glass prism has an angular dispersion $D = -0.36 \times 10^{-4}$ degrees/A in the neighborhood of the sodium D doublet, $\lambda_1 = 5,890$ A and $\lambda_2 = 5,896$ A. Find the angular separation of these two lines when the prism is used at minimum deviation. Calculate the difference of the refractive indices of this glass between the two wavelengths λ_1 and λ_2.

6. Compute the prism angle for a crown-glass prism needed to construct a direct-vision prism in conjunction with an $8°$ flint-glass prism, if the Fraunhofer D line is to have no net deviation.

Find the angular separation of the Fraunhofer C and F lines. Use the data given in the text for the refractive indices of crown and flint glass.

7. What is the proper angle for the crown-glass prism of Prob. 6 if, when used with the $8°$ flint-glass prism, there is to be no net dispersion (angular separation) of the C and F lines? Compute the net deviation of the F, D, and C lines.

8. The following table gives the index of refraction as a function of wavelength for two types of optical glass:

Wavelength, A	n (light crown glass)	n (heavy flint glass)
4,000	1.5238	1.8059
4,500	1.5180	1.7843
5,000	1.5139	1.7706
5,500	1.5108	1.7611
6,000	1.5085	1.7539
6,500	1.5067	1.7485
7,000	1.5051	1.7435
7,500	1.5040	1.7389

Using these data, compute the design of an achromatic doublet of focal length −20.0 cm, achromatized in focal length for wavelengths of 4,500 and 6,500 A. Take one of the lens surfaces as plane.

Compute and plot the focal length of the lens so designed as a function of wavelength from 4,000 to 7,500 A.

9. A compound lens consisting of two identical thin lenses is achromatized in focal length at 5,000 A. The thin lenses are each constructed of the light crown glass of the table in Prob. 8.

a. If the focal length of the compound lens is to be 10.0 cm at 5,000 A, what must be the focal lengths of the thin lenses at this wavelength and what must be their separation?

b. For the separation computed in part *a,* find and plot the focal length of the compound lens as a function of wavelength from 4,000 to 7,500 A.

10. Prove that two simple harmonic motions at right angles to each other, of arbitrary amplitudes and phases, but of the same frequency, yield elliptical motion. Under what conditions does this ellipse become a circle? A straight line?

11. Show that a linearly polarized light beam can be represented as the superposition of two circularly polarized beams of opposite rotation. If the phase of one of the component beams is altered by 45°, what is the nature of the resultant light beam?

12. Compute the thickness of a quarter-wave plate of calcite and of quartz for the wavelength $\lambda = 5,893$ A (the D line). The principal indices of refraction for quartz at this wavelength are $n_0 = 1.5443$ and $n_e = 1.5534$.

13. Light, polarized linearly at an angle of 30° with the optic axis of a quartz plate 0.43 mm thick, is normally incident on a surface which is parallel to the optic axis. If the light is monochromatic of wavelength 5,893 A,

a. Find the phase retardation in degrees caused by the plate for the components of the electric vector parallel to and perpendicular to the optic axis.

b. What is the polarization of the emergent light?

14. Prove that light, linearly polarized at 45° with the optic axis, normally incident on a quarter-wave plate becomes circularly polarized upon emergence. What factors determine whether the light becomes right- or left-handed circularly polarized?

15. The electric vector of a monochromatic light wave of wavelength 6,000 A has the following components:

$$\mathcal{E}_y = 1.5 \sin \left(\omega t - \frac{2\pi x}{\lambda} + \frac{2\pi}{3} \right) \qquad \text{(volts/meter)}$$

$$\mathcal{E}_z = 3.0 \sin \left(\omega t - \frac{2\pi x}{\lambda} \right) \qquad \text{(volts/meter)}$$

This wave is normally incident on the surface of a sheet of mica with its optic axis along the y-direction and emerges from the sheet as a linearly polarized wave. Micrometer measurements show that the mica is approximately 0.004 cm thick. Compute the exact thickness of the mica if its principal indices of refraction are $n_y = 1.5226$ and $n_z = 1.5106$.

16. If two Nicols or Polaroids are mounted as polarizer and analyzer with their principal sections at an angle ϕ with each other, prove that the ratio of the intensities of light emerging from each is given by $\cos^2 \phi$.

17. Two Nicols are used as a polarizer and analyzer with their principal sections at an angle of 10° with each other.

a. What is the relative change in transmitted light intensity if the angle is changed to 75°?

b. What is the change in transmitted light intensity on rotating the polarizer by 10° each way?

18. On passing a beam of monochromatic light through a Polaroid and rotating the Polaroid axis through 360°, it is found that the transmitted intensity goes through two maxima and two minima which are in the ratio of 4:1. How can you tell whether the incident light is partially linearly polarized or elliptically polarized? What additional equipment would you use?

19. Light of intensity I_0 from a steady source passes successively through three polarizers, A, B, and C. The principal section of A is horizontal, that of C vertical, and that of B is rotated with a constant angular velocity ω so that $\theta = \omega t$. θ is the angle between the principal section of B and the horizontal.

Derive expressions for the intensity of the light emerging from the three polarizers, A, B, and C.

20. Two light sources are observed in sequence with a polarizer and an analyzer. The emergent light is found to have the same intensity for angles of 30 and 60° between the principal sections of the polarizer and analyzer, respectively.

Compute the relative intensities of the two sources.

21. Linearly polarized light of amplitude $\mathcal{E}_0$ from a Nicol prism falls normally on a quartz quarter-wave plate with the direction of $\mathcal{E}_0$ making an angle of 30° with the optic axis of the plate. The light then passes through a second Nicol oriented at 60° relative to the first Nicol.

a. What is the polarization of the light emerging from the quarter-wave plate?

b. What are the intensity and polarization direction of the beam from the second Nicol?

22. *a.* Find the minimum thickness of a quartz half-wave plate for light of wavelength 5,000 A. $n_e = 1.5534$; $n_0 = 1.5443$.

b. The half-wave plate is introduced between crossed Nicols (principal planes at 90°) so that the optic axis is at an angle of 60° with the direction of polarization of the incident linearly polarized light.   What is the polarization of the light emerging from the half-wave plate?   Find the ratio of the intensity of light emerging from the analyzer to that of the light emerging from the polarizer.

23. Monochromatic light passes successively through a polarizer, a quarter-wave plate, and a crossed analyzer.   The quarter-wave plate is rotated in its plane at 50 rps about the axis of the system.   Find the variation of the intensity of the light transmitted by the analyzer if the incident light is natural unpolarized light of intensity I_0.

24. A quartz half-wave plate is used in conjunction with a polarizer and an analyzer to rotate the plane of polarization of linearly polarized light of 5,000 A wavelength.   Since a plate only one-half wave thick would be too fragile, one is used which corresponds to a $5\frac{1}{2}$-wavelength difference between the ordinary and extraordinary ray.

a. Find the thickness of the quartz plate ($n_e - n_0 = +0.0091$ for quartz).

b. If the principal sections of polarizer and analyzer are at 60°, find the ratio of light intensity from the analyzer to that from the polarizer.   If the half-wave plate is now inserted with its optic axis between the principal sections of polarizer and analyzer, and at 15° with that of the polarizer, find the new ratio of intensities.

25. A quartz plate of unknown thickness, with its optic axis parallel to its surface, is placed in a beam of linearly polarized light.   The optic axis makes an angle of 45° with the direction of polarization of the incident beam.   The light emerging from the plate is analyzed with a Nicol prism, and it is found that no setting of the prism causes the light to vanish but that the intensity is maximum at a certain angle θ.

a. What is the state of polarization of the light emerging from the plate?

b. For what angle of the Nicol will the emergent light have minimum intensity?

c. As a result of these measurements it is concluded that the plate introduces a phase difference of 120° between the ordinary and extraordinary ray. What is the minimum thickness of the plate?   ($n_e = 1.5534$; $n_0 = 1.5443$.)

26. A parallel beam of white light of spectral range 4,500 to 7,500 A passes successively at normal incidence through a Polaroid, a crystal plate, and a second Polaroid.   The transmission axis of each Polaroid is vertical.   The crystal plate is 10^{-2} cm thick, and its birefringence Δn (difference of its principal indices of refraction) is the same for all wavelengths.   The optic axis of the crystal is parallel to its surface and at 45° with the vertical.   Light of wavelengths 5,000 and 7,000 A is found missing from the transmitted light.

a. What is the birefringence Δn of the crystal?

b. If the second Polaroid is rotated by 90°, what wavelength will be missing from the spectrum of the transmitted light?

CHAPTER 18

INTERFERENCE

We now turn our attention to a number of optical phenomena which are entirely foreign to those which can be described with the help of geometrical optics, and these require for their explanation a more exact theory, *viz.*, the electromagnetic theory of light. In particular, experiments performed before the time of Maxwell involving interference effects (the superposition of two light beams to produce darkness or a greater intensity of light than the sum of the intensities of the two original beams) made it evident that some sort of wave theory was required for their explanation. We shall attack these problems from the standpoint of the electromagnetic theory of light and at least indicate, in those cases for which the analysis becomes prohibitively involved, how these phenomena can be understood with the help of electromagnetic laws.

Fundamental in the study of wave optics is the *principle of superposition*, according to which the various wave trains which, in their totality, make up a light beam may be considered as mutually independent. The behavior of the beam as a whole may then be computed as the sum of the effects of the elementary waves, treating the latter as if each were present alone. This is characteristic of all wave motion and follows from the fact that the equations for wave motion are *linear* equations. The sources of electromagnetic waves of optical wavelengths are atoms, and a light beam is a complicated wave field involving the superposition of many millions of elementary wave trains emitted by the atoms in the source. The time during which an atom radiates light is of the order of 10^{-8} sec; hence even a nearly monochromatic beam of light consists of multitudinous elementary wave trains, each about 1 m long, of *random* polarizations and phases. In particular, the randomness of the phases of these elementary waves is characteristic of any electromagnetic radiation emitted by atomic or molecular sources, and such radiation is called *incoherent*, in contrast to the so-called *coherent* radiation in which the phases of the elementary waves have fixed values relative to one another.

We have already pointed out that one may follow the propagation of electromagnetic waves with the help of *Huygens' principle*, and we must formulate this principle (which can be derived from the funda-mental electromagnetic equations) in a more precise form than we have done hitherto. In its most naïve form, Huygens' principle states that if one knows the shape of a constant-phase surface or of a wave front of a wave, the position of this wave front at a later time Δt may be obtained by treating each point of the wave front as a source of secondary spherical wavelets. The wave front at time Δt is obtained

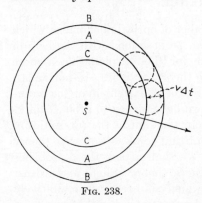

by constructing spheres of radii $v\,\Delta t$ (with v the velocity of the waves), using each point of the original wave surface as a center. The en-velope of these wavelets then gives the wave surface at time Δt. In this form there is obviously a serious defect, inasmuch as one finds a wave traveling backward as well as one traveling forward, although the former does not exist. This is illus-trated in Fig. 238, in which is shown

FIG. 238.

a wave front AA of a wave emitted by a source S, the outward-traveling wave front BB at a later time Δt, and also the inward-traveling wave front CC, as given by Huygens' construction.

The correct formulation of Huygens' principle states that one can obtain the electromagnetic field at any point of space by considering each point on any *closed* surface (it may be taken as a wave front for convenience) as a source of secondary wavelets and superposing the effects of these secondary waves at the point in question. These secondary waves, however, have different amplitudes in different directions, and when one takes into account the proper phases and dependence of amplitude on direction of these secondary waves, it turns out that the "back" wave has zero amplitude. We shall not attempt a rigorous formulation of this principle but shall employ an approximate form which is justifiable for optical wavelengths, since they are always very small compared to the dimensions of the appa-ratus employed in the experimental study of optical phenomena.

The fact that the resultant amplitude at a given point of an electro-magnetic field is obtained by adding the amplitudes of the various waves which pass through the point in question gives rise to the possi-bility of *constructive* or *destructive* interference, just as one encounters in acoustics. Thus, for example, two sinusoidal waves of the same frequency will yield constructive interference if they are in phase at the point in question and destructive interference if they are 180° out of phase with each other and of equal amplitudes. It is usual to divide phenomena of this sort into two classes, denoted by *diffraction* and *interference*. In diffraction effects one is concerned with the interference effects produced by a limitation of the cross section of a wave front. The effects arise from the fact that, in directions other than that of the primary wave, the mutual cancellation by destructive interference of the secondary Huygens' wavelets is not complete. On the other hand, if one causes two (or more) beams of light from *two separate portions* of the wave front to recombine, the resulting variations of intensity with position are termed *interference* effects. It must be remembered, however, that both these phenomena are fundamentally ascribable to the same process, the addition of wave amplitudes. In this chapter we shall concern ourselves with interference effects and postpone the treatment of diffraction to the next chapter.

1. Conditions for Interference. There are certain fundamental conditions which must be satisfied to obtain the phenomenon of interference; some of these are inherent in the nature of light and others are necessary if the effects are to be observable experimentally. For simplicity consider two sinusoidal electromagnetic waves which are to produce destructive interference at a given point of space which is traversed by both waves. If a steady interference pattern is to exist, *i.e.*, if in our example the resultant intensity is to be zero for all values of time at the point in question, then the following conditions must be satisfied:

1. The waves must have the same frequency and wavelength.
2. The phase difference between the waves at a fixed point must not change with time (in our example this difference must be 180°).
3. The amplitudes of the two waves must be equal or very nearly so.
4. The waves must have the same polarization.

Thus for light waves it is essential that the two waves which combine to produce interference must originate in the *same* source. This follows from the incoherent nature of light waves. *Light from two different sources can never give interference patterns.*

For successful observation of interference patterns produced by light, there are two more conditions to be satisfied:

5. The difference of optical path length between the two beams which combine must be very small (of the order of the wavelength), unless the light is monochromatic or very nearly so.

6. The directions of propagation of the two interfering waves must be almost the same; *i.e.*, the wave fronts must make a very small angle with each other.

These two conditions are imposed because one deals in general with beams of light which are a mixture of waves of many wavelengths, and it is necessary that the destructive interference for any one wavelength not be masked by the partial or complete constructive interference of other wavelengths in the same beam. In Fig. 239 are shown two wave fronts traveling to the right, inclined at a slight angle to each other. Both waves have come from the same source, and let us suppose that we are dealing with a mixture of wavelengths. Suppose now that the optical path from the source to the point A is the same for both waves. At this point there is constructive interference for all wavelengths, since the phase difference between any two elementary waves of the same wavelength is zero. At a point B the optical difference in path will be $\lambda/2$ for some wavelength and the corresponding phase difference of $(2\pi/\lambda)(\lambda/2) = \pi$; hence there will be partial constructive interference for other wavelengths at this point, but this will not amount to much for waves of wavelength nearly equal to λ. On the other hand, if the path difference $B'B$ is a large odd integer times $\lambda/2$, there will still be destructive interference for the color λ, but the waves of wavelength almost equal to λ now reinforce each other strongly and mask the effect.

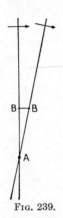

Fig. 239.

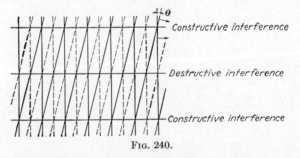

Constructive interference

Destructive interference

Constructive interference

Fig. 240.

Condition 6 may be understood more clearly with the help of Fig. 240. In this figure are shown two plane waves traveling to the right with a small angle θ between them. The solid lines represent crests and the dotted lines troughs of these waves. The horizontal solid lines show the regions of complete constructive and destructive interference, *i.e.*, the width of the so-called *interference fringes*. The larger the angle θ, the narrower becomes the spacing of the fringes until they cannot be separated even when magnified.

There are two general types of devices utilized in producing interference phenomena: (1) There are those which change the propagation directions of two separate parts of the same wave front so that they recombine at a small angle. In all such devices diffraction will be present, since limited portions of the wave fronts are employed. (2) There are devices which divide the amplitude of a wave front into two

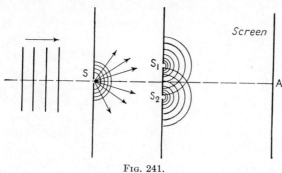

Fig. 241.

(or more) parts and later reunite these parts to produce interference. These devices may employ a large section of a wave front and minimize diffraction effects.

2. Interference of Two Beams; Young's Experiment. The first experiment showing interference of light was performed by Young about 1800. The apparatus is shown schematically in Fig. 241. Sunlight was allowed to pass through a pinhole S and then through two pinholes S_1 and S_2 in opaque screens. The two spherical waves emerging from S_1 and S_2, in accordance with Huygens' principle, then interfere with each other to form an interference pattern on the observing screen, symmetrical about the point. A. The first pinhole S serves as the common source for the two interfering beams. In accordance with modern technique we shall consider the pinholes replaced by very narrow parallel slits and assume that a plane wave of monochromatic light is incident on the slits. We now proceed to a calculation of the intensity of light at the point P of the screen as shown in Fig. 242. The slit separation d is always very small compared to D, as are the coordinates x of the points P at which the pattern is observed. Thus we have $d \ll D$ and $x \ll D$. If the plane wave is normally incident on the screen containing the slits, then the electric vectors at these slits will be in phase and of equal amplitude. Either is of the form $A \sin \omega t$, with ω the angular frequency of the light waves. The electric vector at P will be the sum of the electric vectors at P of the two spherical waves coming from S_1 and from S_2 according to Huygens' principle. Thus we have

$$\mathcal{E}_P = \mathcal{E}_1 \sin\left(\omega t - \frac{2\pi r_1}{\lambda}\right) + \mathcal{E}_2 \sin\left(\omega t - \frac{2\pi r_2}{\lambda}\right) \quad (18.1)$$

Now since r_1 and r_2 are practically equal and are very large compared to all values of x in which we are interested, we may place $\mathcal{E}_1 = \mathcal{E}_2 = \mathcal{E}$, thus neglecting the variation of *amplitude* of the Huygens' wavelets with direction and with the difference of the distances r_1 and r_2, a procedure which is justifiable in this case. We are then left with the problem of adding two sinusoidal functions of equal amplitudes and frequencies but with a phase difference $\phi = (2\pi/\lambda)(r_2 - r_1)$ at

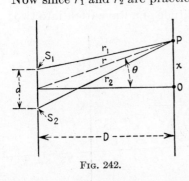

FIG. 242.

the observation point P. This is just the same problem as that of adding two sinusoidal alternating currents of equal amplitude but of different phases, and we shall employ the familiar vector diagram of a-c circuits. This vector diagram with the phase difference $\phi = (2\pi/\lambda)(r_2 - r_1)$ and the resultant amplitude $\mathcal{E}_0$ is shown in Fig. 243. As one moves the point P along the screen, starting from O (Fig. 242), the phase lag ϕ increases from zero and is proportional to $(r_2 - r_1)$. When we reach the point where ϕ has increased to π, the resultant is zero, and there is destructive interference. When we

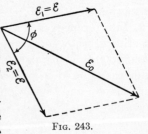

FIG. 243.

reach the point where ϕ has increased to 2π, there is constructive interference and the same intensity as at O. One thus obtains alternate light and dark bands on the screen, and this is the interference pattern.

The resultant amplitude $\mathcal{E}_0$ is clearly given by (Fig. 243)

$$\mathcal{E}_0^2 = \mathcal{E}^2(1 + \cos\phi)^2 + \mathcal{E}^2 \sin^2\phi$$

or

$$\mathcal{E}_0^2 = 2\mathcal{E}^2(1 + \cos\phi) = 4\mathcal{E}^2 \cos^2\frac{\phi}{2} \quad (18.2)$$

Since the light intensity I at P is proportional to $\mathcal{E}_0^2$, we may rewrite Eq. (18.2) in the following form, calling I_1 the intensity due to one slit alone,

$$\frac{I}{I_1} = 4 \cos^2 \frac{\phi}{2} = 4 \cos^2 \left[\frac{\pi}{\lambda} (r_2 - r_1) \right] \tag{18.3}$$

There remains the task of expressing $(r_2 - r_1)$ in terms of the distances shown in Fig. 242. We have

$$r_2^2 = D^2 + \left(x + \frac{d}{2} \right)^2 \quad \text{and} \quad r_1^2 = D^2 + \left(x - \frac{d}{2} \right)^2$$

so that

$$r_2^2 - r_1^2 \cong 2r(r_2 - r_1) = 2xd \tag{18.4}$$

where we have set $r_1 + r_2 = 2r$. Since $x/r = \sin \theta$, we have

$$r_2 - r_1 = d \sin \theta \tag{18.5}$$

so that Eq. (18.3) becomes

$$\frac{I}{I_1} = 4 \cos^2 \left(\frac{\pi d}{\lambda} \sin \theta \right) \tag{18.6}$$

and if we wish to express the intensity variation with position along the x-axis on the screen, we set $\sin \theta = x/r \cong x/D$ and have

$$\frac{I}{I_0} = 4 \cos^2 \left(\frac{\pi d}{\lambda D} x \right) \tag{18.6a}$$

The intensity is maximum in the directions θ given by

$$\frac{\pi d \sin \theta}{\lambda} = n\pi$$

or

$$\sin \theta = \frac{n\lambda}{d} \qquad (n = 0, 1, 2, \ldots) \tag{18.7}$$

or at the points

$$x_n = \frac{n\lambda D}{d} \qquad (n = 0, 1, 2, \ldots) \tag{18.7a}$$

so that the maxima are uniformly spaced.

The minima of intensity are of intensity zero and lie at the positions given by

$$\frac{\pi d}{\lambda D} x = \left(n + \frac{1}{2} \right)$$

or

$$x_n = \left(n + \frac{1}{2} \right) \frac{\lambda D}{d} \qquad (n = 0, 1, 2, \ldots) \tag{18.8}$$

The integer n is called the *order* of the interference. The distance between two adjacent maxima (or minima) gives the linear spacing

s of the fringes and is equal to

$$s = \frac{\lambda D}{d} \tag{18.9}$$

This affords a direct method of determining the wavelength of monochromatic light.

The maxima and minima may be located by a somewhat simpler argument. Maxima will occur whenever the phase difference ϕ is an integer times 2π, or when $(r_2 - r_1)$ equals a whole number of wavelengths. Thus we must have $(r_2 - r_1) = n\lambda$, or, using Eq. (18.5),

$$\sin \theta = \frac{n\lambda}{d}$$

in agreement with Eq. (18.7). The location of the minima proceeds in exactly the same manner, setting $(r_2 - r_1)$ equal to an odd number of half wavelengths to attain destructive interference.

3. Interference by Many Beams. The interference effects produced by two interfering beams can be enhanced greatly by the use of a large number of interfering beams, *i.e.*, by the use of many slits instead of the two employed in Young's experiment, and by an appropriate modification of the experimental arrangement. In this section we shall discuss only the general nature of the interference pattern thus produced, deferring a more detailed discussion to the next chapter when we consider the problem of the diffraction grating. The principal features of the pattern can be obtained most simply with the help of a vector diagram similar to that of Fig. 243. Suppose that at a given observation point P the resultant wave is the superposition of N waves of equal amplitudes but of different phases. Furthermore, if we number the N waves 1, 2, 3, . . . , N and denote the phases of these waves by P by ψ_1, ψ_2, . . . , ψ_N, we consider the case that

$$(\psi_2 - \psi_1) = (\psi_3 - \psi_2) = \cdots = (\psi_N - \psi_{N-1}) = \phi$$

Thus there is an equal phase difference between adjacently numbered waves, as there would be if they originated at N equally spaced slits in an arrangement essentially similar to that of Young's experiment. The characteristic phase difference ϕ depends on the position of the observation point but has a definite fixed value at a given point P. The total spread in phase between waves 1 and N is thus $(N - 1)\phi$.

Consider first an observation point P_1 such that all the N waves are in phase, *i.e.*, $\phi = 0$. If $\mathcal{E}$ is the common amplitude of the electric vector of all the N waves, and $\mathcal{E}_0$ the amplitude of the electric vector of the resultant wave, then evidently the value of $\mathcal{E}_0$ is $N\mathcal{E}$, and the intensity of the light at this point P_1 is N^2 times the intensity due to a single beam. The vector diagram at this observation point is trivial, all the N vectors $\mathcal{E}$ coinciding. Now suppose we move the point of observation, the value of ϕ increasing as we move from P_1. The vector diagram now fans out into N equiangular vectors, of total angular spread $(N - 1)\phi$. This is indicated in Fig. 244. Evidently the magnitude of the resultant $\mathcal{E}_0$ decreases steadily as ϕ increases until ϕ becomes equal to $2\pi/N$. For this condition the vector diagram is

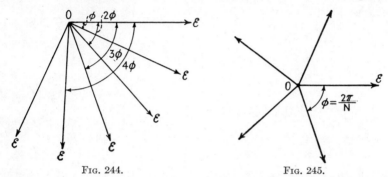

FIG. 244.   FIG. 245.

shown in Fig. 245, and evidently the resultant $\mathcal{E}_0$ is zero. At this point of observation one then has complete destructive interference and hence darkness. Further increase of ϕ now results in an initial increase in intensity, owing to partial constructive interference, and then a decrease to zero when $\phi = 2(2\pi/N)$. The maximum which occurs between $\phi = 2\pi/N$ and $\phi = 2(2\pi/N)$ is evidently considerably weaker than that for $\phi = 0$, since there is still partial destructive interference. Evidently one proceeds through alternate minima and maxima, the minima occurring for $\phi = 2\pi/N, 2(2\pi/N), \ldots ,(N - 1)(2\pi/N)$, the maxima being relatively small compared to the *principal maximum* at $\phi = 0$. Finally when $\phi = 2\pi$, all the N vectors line up again and a *principal* maximum occurs again, with $\mathcal{E}_0^2 = N^2\mathcal{E}^2$. As ϕ increases further, the whole cycle of minima and secondary maxima occurs again until $\phi = 2(2\pi)$, when we again have a principal maximum. Thus the principal maxima of the interference pattern occur whenever

$$\phi = 2\pi n \qquad (n = 0, 1, 2, \ldots) \qquad (18.10)$$

or when the optical path length between *any* two of the interfering beams equals a whole number of wavelengths. Thus we are led to the following general picture: The interference pattern consists of a series of intense (principal) maxima between which there are a number of minima and secondary maxima. The intensity of a principal maximum is N^2 times that of a single beam. The real advantage gained lies not so much in the intensity of the principal maxima as in their sharpness. The separation between a principal maximum and the adjacent minimum is evidently $\phi = 2\pi/N$, and this can be made very small by employing a large number N of interfering beams. Note that the locations of the principal maxima (determined by the values $\phi = 2\pi n$) are independent of the number of interfering beams.

The analytic formulation of the foregoing results can be obtained simply as follows: The square of the amplitude of the electric field vector at an observation point corresponding to a definite value of ϕ is given by (see Fig. 244)

$$\mathcal{E}_0^2 = \mathcal{E}^2\{[1 + \cos\phi + \cos 2\phi + \cdots + \cos(N-1)\phi]^2 + [\sin\phi + \sin 2\phi + \cdots + \sin(N-1)\phi]^2\}$$

or, written more concisely,

$$\frac{\mathcal{E}_0^2}{\mathcal{E}^2} = \frac{I}{I_1} = \left(\sum_{n=0}^{N-1}\cos n\phi\right)^2 + \left(\sum_{n=0}^{N-1}\sin n\phi\right)^2 \qquad (18.11)$$

Since the evaluation of these sums is somewhat unwieldly unless complex numbers are used, we omit the details and simply give the end result. This turns out to be

$$\frac{I}{I_1} = \frac{\sin^2(N\phi/2)}{\sin^2(\phi/2)} \qquad (18.12)$$

Note that this checks Eq. (18.6) for $N = 2$ if we set $\phi = 2\pi d \sin\theta/\lambda$ as it is in Young's experiment.

All our previous results as obtained from the vector-diagram discussion can now be readily obtained from Eq. (18.12). For $\phi = 0$ we find a *principal* maximum as before with $I/I_1 = N^2$, since

$$\lim \frac{\sin^2 Nx}{\sin^2 x} = N^2 \qquad \text{as } x \to 0$$

As ϕ increases, I/I_1 decreases from this value until $N\phi/2 = \pi$, or $\phi = 2\pi/N$, when it becomes zero. This locates the first minimum. Further increase of ϕ leads to an initial increase in I/I_1 and then a decrease until I/I_1 vanishes again when ϕ reaches the value $2(2\pi/N)$. Between these two minima lies the first secondary maximum, and if $N \gg 1$, it lies very nearly halfway between these minima, *i.e.*, at $\phi = \frac{3}{2}(2\pi/N)$. For this value of ϕ we have

$$\frac{I}{I_1} = \frac{\sin^2(3\pi/2)}{\sin^2(3\pi/2N)} \cong \left(\frac{2N}{3\pi}\right)^2 = \frac{4}{9\pi^2}N^2$$

Thus the intensity of the first secondary maximum is about 4 per cent of the intensity of the principal maximum, which is small but not entirely negligible. Now as ϕ increases further, I/I_1 goes through successive maxima and minima, the latter occurring at $\phi = 3(2\pi/N)$, $4(2\pi/N)$, . . . , $(N - 1)(2\pi/N)$. When ϕ becomes equal to 2π, we again find a principal maximum, and the whole cycle of secondary maxima and minima repeats itself with further increasing values of ϕ. The *least* intense of the secondary maxima occurs about halfway between two principal maxima, since there the denominator of Eq. (18.12) reaches its maximum value of unity.[1] Thus the least intense secondary maximum has a value essentially equal to I_1, the intensity of a single beam.[1]

4. Interference in Thin Films; Newton's Rings. The brilliant colors of a thin film of oil floating on water or of a thin soap film are due to interference effects of the type where the amplitude of the incident wave is divided by reflection and refraction at the boundaries of the film. Consider the light reflected from such a film when a plane monochromatic wave is incident on it. The reflected wave can be considered as the superposition of *two* beams, one arising from the reflection of the incident wave at the first film surface and the other the wave emerging through this first film surface which originated in the reflection occurring at the second interface. This apparently simple picture is complicated by the fact that the relative *amplitudes* as well as the phases of these two beams depend on the film thickness, so that the problem is more subtle than that of the superposition of two beams of equal amplitudes and different phases (as in Young's experiment). Since we

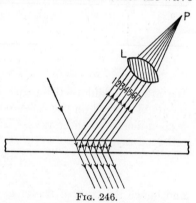

FIG. 246.

have already examined the problem of reflection and refraction of a plane wave at a *single* interface in Chap. 15, we shall adopt the following equivalent procedure which allows the direct application of those results: Suppose the incident plane monochromatic wave is traveling in air. Part of this wave is reflected at the first interface and part transmitted. This latter wave is partially reflected (inter-

---

[1] These statements are true exactly for N odd and are very nearly true, if N is large compared to unity, for even values of N.

nally) at the second interface and partially transmitted through the film. When the internally reflected wave impinges on the first surface, part of it is transmitted and part internally reflected, etc. The phase differences between the first reflected wave and those emerging from the top surface after successive internal reflections give rise to interference patterns. The multiple reflections between the boundaries of a thin film with parallel surfaces is illustrated in Fig. 246, the various reflected rays being focused at P by the lens L.

To find the phase difference between these reflected waves, we must compute the path difference for a pair of successive waves, such as 1 and 2 of Fig. 246. In so doing, we must remember that there is a phase difference of 180° between the electric vectors of the incident and reflected waves when a wave is reflected at the surface of an optically denser medium and a zero phase difference between these vectors when reflection occurs at the surface of an optically rarer medium see Eq. (15.25)]. Thus we understand why a very thin soap film (of thickness small compared to the wavelength of the light) appears black by reflected light.

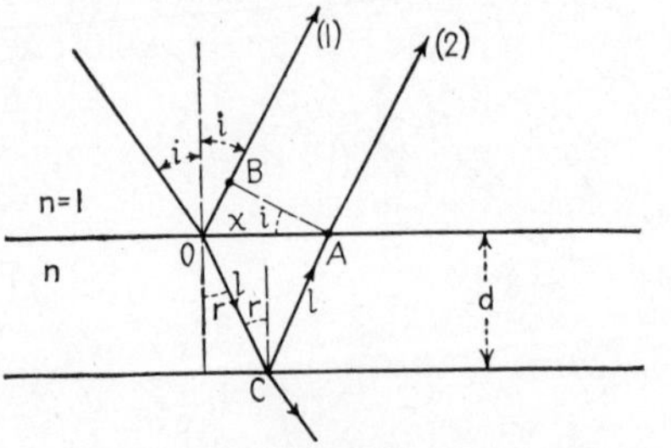

FIG. 247.

In Fig. 247, let d be the thickness of the film of refractive index n, and let i and r be the angles of incidence and refraction, as shown. We are to calculate the phase difference between the corresponding points A and B on the reflected rays (2) and (1), where AB is drawn perpendicular to these rays. The distance traveled by the internally reflected ray OCA is

$$2l = \frac{2d}{\cos r}$$

and hence the time of traversal of this path is

$$t_2 = \frac{2l}{c/n} = \frac{2nd}{c \cos r}$$

The time of traversal of the distance $OB = x \sin i$ is

$$t_1 = \frac{x \sin i}{c} = \frac{2l \sin i \sin r}{c}$$

The difference of traversal time gives rise to a phase difference $\omega(t_2 - t_1)$, with $\omega = 2\pi\nu$, from which we must subtract an angle π since the electric vector undergoes this latter phase change at reflection for ray (1), whereas there is no such change at point C for internal reflection. The difference in time is thus

$$t_2 - t_1 = \frac{2l}{c}(n - \sin i \sin r)$$

or, since $\sin i = n \sin r$,

$$t_2 - t_1 = \frac{2nl}{c}(1 - \sin^2 r) = \frac{2nl}{c}\cos^2 r = \frac{2nd}{c}\cos r$$

and the phase difference becomes

$$\phi = \frac{2nd\omega}{c}\cos r - \pi$$

or, since $\omega/c = 2\pi/\lambda$ (λ is the wave length in air),

$$\phi = \frac{4\pi nd}{\lambda}\cos r - \pi \qquad (18.13)$$

Since for a maximum in the reflected interference pattern we must have $\phi = 2\pi k$ with k an integer, these maxima occur when

$$\frac{4\pi nd}{\lambda}\cos r - \pi = 2\pi k$$

or

$$2nd \cos r = (k + \tfrac{1}{2})\lambda \qquad (18.14)$$

whereas for minima

$$2nd \cos r = k\lambda \qquad (18.15)$$

In Eqs. (18.14) and (18.15), k is any integer or zero.

If Eq. (18.15) is satisfied, so that the electric vectors of rays 1 and 2 are 180° out of phase, it is easy to see that the other reflected rays 3, 4, 5, etc., of Fig. 246 emerge with their electric vectors in phase with that of ray 2. This follows from the fact that the phase difference between any succeeding rays, such as 2 and 3, is evidently equal to $(2\pi/\lambda)2nd \cos r$, and if Eq. (18.15) is satisfied, this is $2\pi k$. On the other hand, when the condition of constructive interference, as given by Eq. (18.14), is satisfied for rays 1 and 2, we see that rays 2, 4, 6, etc., will be in phase with 1, whereas rays 3, 5, 7, etc., will be a half wave-length out of phase with 1. Since the amplitude drops off sharply on successive reflections, there will still be a maximum intensity under these conditions. For the intensity minima, ray 2 is considerably weaker than ray 1, so that it alone cannot completely annul ray 1. However, one can show that the sum of the amplitudes of all the successive waves 2, 3, 4, etc., is just equal to the amplitude of the incident wave, so that one obtains complete darkness for the minima.

Equations (18.14) and (18.15) show that for normal incidence (cos $r = 1$) strong reflection occurs when the film thickness is an odd multiple of a quarter wavelength *in the film* (λ/n), whereas no reflection occurs if the thickness is an even number of quarter wavelengths in the film. This is the principle underlying the behavior of so-called "invisible" glass made by evaporating a thin transparent film on its surface.

If the convex surface of a plano-convex lens is placed in contact with a plane, optically flat, glass plate, a thin film of air of varying

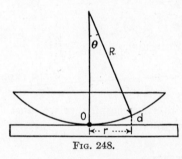

FIG. 248.

thickness will be formed between the surfaces. The loci of points of equal film thickness will be circles concentric with the point of contact. Such an air film shows circular interference bands, known as *Newton's rings*. When viewed by reflected light, the center of the pattern is black, and when viewed by transmitted light, it is white. To obtain a relation between the radii of the interference rings, the wavelength, and the curvature of the lens surface, we have from Fig. 248

$$d = R(1 - \cos \theta) = 2R \sin^2 \frac{\theta}{2}$$

For small angles θ, we may set $\sin^2 (\theta/2)$ equal to $\theta^2/4$ and set $\theta = r/R$, so that d is given very nearly by

$$d = \frac{r^2}{2R} \tag{18.16}$$

Hence we shall observe a dark ring by reflected light if, according to Eq. (18.15) ($n = 1$ for the air film)

$$2d \cos r = k\lambda$$

Using Eq. (18.16) and placing cos $r = 1$, since the angle r as measured with the normal to the film surface is very small, we find

$$\frac{r^2}{R} = k\lambda$$

or

$$r_k^2 = kR\lambda \qquad (k = 0, 1, 2, \ldots) \tag{18.17}$$

giving the radii of the dark rings.   Similarly, the radii of the bright fringes are given, according to Eq. (18.15), by

$$r_k^2 = (k + \tfrac{1}{2})R\lambda \qquad (k = 0, 1, 2, \ldots) \qquad (18.18)$$

5. Interferometers.   The *Michelson interferometer* is an instrument which can be used to measure exceedingly small distances in terms of the wavelength of light.   The essential parts are shown in Fig. 249. Light from a source S is collimated by lens L and falls on a plate P_1,

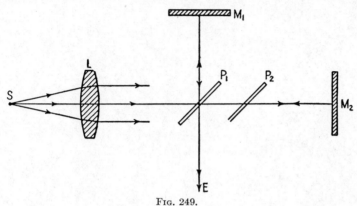

Fig. 249.

which is inclined at an angle of 45° with the beam and is lightly coated with silver on its back surface, so that approximately half the light is transmitted to mirror M_2 and the other half is reflected to mirror M_1. The plate P_2 is identical with and parallel to plate P_1, except that it is not silvered.   It is used so that the optical paths $P_1M_1P_1$ and $P_1M_2P_1$ contain the same thickness of glass.   This is important whenever light of many wavelengths is used, because of the dispersion of glass.

The interference pattern is observed at E with the help of a telescope. One sees the surface of the mirror M_1 through the half-silvered plate P_1 and the surface of the mirror M_2 reflected in P_1.   If the distances from P_1 to the two mirrors are exactly equal and if the mirrors M_1 and M_2 are exactly at right angles to each other and at 45° with P_1, the image of M_2 coincides with the surface of M_1.   If the adjustment is not exact, then in effect a thin air film exists between the surface of M_1 and the image of M_2 and causes the interference pattern observed. As the mirror M_2, let us say, is moved, the system of fringes is displaced, and a displacement of the mirror of one-half wavelength causes each fringe to move to the position formerly occupied by an adjacent fringe.   Thus, by counting fringes, extremely small distances may be measured.

The Fabry-Perot interferometer utilizes the fringes produced in the light transmitted by an air film between two lightly silvered surfaces of plane-parallel plates P_1 and P_2 of Fig. 250. The separation d between the reflecting surfaces is of the order of 1 cm, and the observations are made near normal incidence. To observe the fringes, monochromatic light from an extended source, of which S is one point, is made parallel by the lens L_1, and the transmitted light is brought

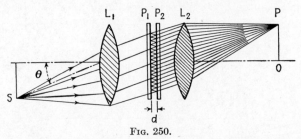

FIG. 250.

together to produce interference by the lens L_2. In Fig. 250 a ray from S is incident at an angle θ, producing a series of parallel rays at the same angle, which are focused at P by the lens L_2. The condition for constructive interference will be the same for all points on a circle of radius OP, so that circular fringes will be observed. In the actual instrument one of the plates is fixed and the other may be moved toward or away from it to vary the distance d.

Problems

1. Two plane waves, each of wavelength 6,000 A, travel at an angle θ, as shown in Fig. 240, and form interference fringes. If the smallest separation between neighboring light and dark fringes is to be 0.01 mm, what is the largest angle θ allowable if the fringes are to be observed?

2. In a radio navigation system two vertical transmitting antennas, separated on a north-south line by a distance of 100 m, are excited by the same transmitter so that they are 180° out of phase with each other. A navigator is located initially 200 km due east of the mid-point of the line joining the antennas.

  a. Does his receiver indicate a maximum or minimum response?

  b. After proceeding 5.0 km due north, he again finds the same response. What is the wavelength of the radio waves?

3. Two vertical antennas are excited in phase at a frequency of 1,000 kc and are 24 km apart on an east-west line. Derive and plot the curves in the horizontal antenna pattern along which a minimum signal is received.

4. In Young's experiment the slit separation is 0.20 mm, and the distance from the slits to the screen is 2.0 m. Compute the distance between neighboring dark fringes,

a. For blue light of wavelength 4,000 A.

b. For red light of wavelength 7,000 A.

5. Monochromatic light is used to illuminate two parallel slits 0.40 mm apart. Interference fringes are produced on a screen 200 cm from the slits and parallel to the plane of the slits. If the third bright fringe (beyond the central fringe of the pattern) is 7.5 mm from the central fringe, find the wavelength of the light.

6. Plot the relative intensity of light on the screen in Young's experiment as a function of x, the coordinate of the point P of Fig. 242. Prove that the average intensity is the same as would exist in the absence of interference, so that there is no violation of the law of conservation of energy.

7. Suppose that the light employed in a Young's experiment consists of a mixture of two wavelengths λ_1 and λ_2, almost equal to each other. Derive an expression for the difference of these wavelengths if one of the maxima for one wavelength is located at the position of a neighboring intensity minimum of the other wavelength.

8. In one modification of Young's experiment, known as the Fresnel double-mirror experiment, light from a source S is reflected at nearly grazing

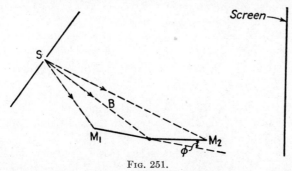

Fig. 251.

incidence from two plane mirrors making a small angle ϕ with each other, as shown in Fig. 251. The source is a thin slit, parallel to the line of intersection of the two mirrors and at a distance B from this line.

a. Find the locations of the virtual sources (in back of the two mirrors) from which the light incident on the screen seems to come.

b. If the distance between the line of intersection of the mirrors and the position of the zero-order maximum on the screen is D, show that (assuming all angles small) the separation of adjacent fringes of the interference pattern for a monochromatic source of wavelength λ is

$$x = \frac{B + D}{2B\phi} \lambda$$

9. Two similar ships with antennas 20 m above the water surface communicate at a frequency of 300 megacycles. As the two ships approach each other, the signal strength received by one from the other goes through a succession of maxima and minima.   This is due to the interference between the direct beam and the beam reflected from the surface of the water with a phase change of 180°.   As the two ships approach each other from a large distance, find their separation for the first minimum.

10. A radar antenna operating on a wavelength of 10.0 cm is located 8.0 m above the water line of a torpedo boat.   Treat the reflected beam from the water as originating in a source 8.0 m below the water directly under the radar antenna.   What is the altitude of an airplane 12 km from the boat if it is to be in the first interference minimum of the radar signal?

11. Find the thickness of a plane soap film of refractive index 1.33 for a strong first-order reflection of the red hydrogen line of wavelength 6,563 A at normal incidence.   What is the wavelength of the light inside the film?

12. Light containing a mixture of all wavelengths from $\lambda = 4,900$ A to $\lambda = 6,300$ A is normally incident on an air film of thickness d formed between two parallel glass plates.

a. What must be the film thickness if only the blue light of wavelength 4,900 A and the red light of wavelength 6,300 A are strongly reflected by the film, but none of the colors between these two?

b. If white light of spectral range 4,000 to 7,000 A is employed, what other wavelengths (if any) will be strongly reflected?

13. White light of spectral range 4,000 to 7,000 A is normally incident on a soap film of uniform thickness 4.0×10^{-5} cm and of refractive index 1.3. What wavelengths of the white light will be strongly reflected?   State the order of interference for each such wavelength.

14. A water film of refractive index 1.33 and uniform thickness 4.5×10^{-5} cm lies on a flat glass plate (refractive index of the glass $= 1.50$) and is illuminated at normal incidence by white light of spectral range 3,500 to 7,500 A.   What wavelengths will be reflected strongly?

15. Some of the earlier attempts to determine the order of magnitude of molecular dimensions consisted in measuring, by interference methods, the thickness of oil films floating on water.   Suppose oil of refractive index 1.40 is used, and a parallel light beam of wavelength 5,000 A, incident at an angle of incidence of 20°, gives a first-order reflection maximum.   What is the thickness of the oil film?

16. A plane wave of blue light ($\lambda = 4,500$ A) is normally incident on a thin plastic film of index 1.50 suspended in air.   The film is of a thickness to produce the first-order reflection maximum.   The electric vector of the incident wave is 0.10 volt/m (rms).   Considering only one internal reflection at each surface of the film, compute

a. The intensity (average value of the Poynting vector) of the reflected wave.

b. The intensity of the wave transmitted into the air beyond the film.

c. The thickness of the plastic film.

17. Light of frequency ν traveling in a medium of refractive index n is incident on a uniform thin film of thickness d and refractive index n_1.   The light transmitted through the film travels in the medium of index n. Derive an equation for the angles of incidence of the light incident on the film which give rise to maxima in the intensity of the reflected light.

18. Two pieces of plane plate glass are placed together with a piece of paper between the two at one edge. When viewed at normal incidence with sodium light ($\lambda = 5,893$ A), eight interference fringes per centimeter are observed. Find the angle of the wedge-shaped air film between the plates.

19. A glass surface is to be made "invisible" for normally incident light of wavelength 5,800 A by evaporating on its surface a thin film of index of refraction 1.55. What is the smallest film thickness if the refractive index of the glass is 1.50? If this latter index is 1.60?

20. If the radius of curvature of the convex surface of the plano-convex lens used in producing Newton's rings is 5.0 m, what will be the diameters of the fifth and tenth bright rings in the reflected pattern for the red hydrogen line, $\lambda = 6,563$ A?

21. Newton's ring experiment is performed with violet light using a convex lens surface of radius 10.0 m. The radius of the kth dark fringe is 4.0 mm and that of the $(k + 5)$th dark fringe is 6.0 mm. Find the wavelength of the light used and the ring number k.

22. A plano-convex lens is to be tested for curvature by means of Newton's rings, as shown in Fig. 252. Light of wavelength 6,000 A in air is used at normal incidence, and 25 bright concentric circles are seen by reflected light. The center appears dark.

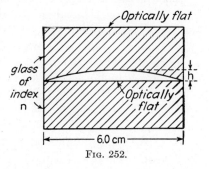

Fɪɢ. 252.

a. What is the height h?

b. If the lens diameter is 6.0 cm, what is the radius of curvature of the concave face?

23. Prove that the sum of the amplitudes of all the reflected rays excepting the first in Fig. 246 is equal to the amplitude of the first reflected ray. Assume normal incidence.

24. The Michelson interferometer has been used to compare the length of the standard meter in Paris with the wavelength of the cadmium red line by counting the number of fringes which cross the center of the field of view as one arm of the interferometer is moved from one end of the standard meter to the other. This number turned out to be 3,106,327. What is the wavelength of the cadmium red line in angstrom units?

CHAPTER 19

DIFFRACTION

When the cross section of a beam of light is limited by allowing the light to pass through one or more openings in an opaque screen, the distribution of intensity in the transmitted beam as observed on another screen or with the help of a telescope is called a *diffraction pattern*. If the diffracting screen (or obstacle) is placed between source and observation screen and *no* lenses or mirrors are employed, the resulting diffraction pattern on the observing screen is called a *Fresnel diffraction* pattern. For this case both source and observation screen lie at finite distances, in general, from the diffracting screen. If, on the other hand, one employs a plane wave of incident light, either from a distance source or collimated with the help of a lens, and the diffracted waves are observed on a very distant screen (at infinity) or with the help of a telescope focused on infinity, the resulting pattern is known as a *Fraunhofer diffraction pattern*. This Fraunhofer pattern may be observed on a screen in practice by placing a lens directly in back of the diffraction apertures and placing the screen in the focal plane of the lens. Fundamentally, both types of diffraction are but different aspects of the same basic phenomenon and are explicable in terms of Huygens' principle. Our first task, then, is to examine this principle more closely than we have done so far and to see how it describes the rectilinear propagation of light for unobstructed waves.

1. The Rectilinear Propagation of Light; Fresnel Zones. Consider a monochromatic spherical wave diverging from a source O, and suppose we wish to utilize Huygens' principle to compute the amplitude of this wave at a point P which lies at a distance R from the source O. First we construct a spherical surface of radius $r' < R$ with its center at O. This is a wave front, and we must consider each element of area dS on this surface as a source of secondary waves, which in their totality combine at P to give the resultant wave motion at P (Fig. 253). The relative phases of the secondary waves arriving at P may be obtained readily by noting that it takes a time r/c for a disturbance originating at dS to reach point P. Thus the relative phases of these waves are given by $2\pi r/\lambda$. It is not evident, however, when the relative amplitudes of these waves will be. We would expect them to be

374

proportional to dS, the area of the elementary source on the wave front, and inversely proportional to r, and this is true. In addition, however, it turns out that they depend on the angle θ in Fig. 253 in the form $(1 + \cos \theta)$, where θ is the angle between the outer normal to the spherical surface and r, so that $\cos \theta$ varies from $+1$ to A to -1 at B. This so-called *obliquity* factor eliminates the "back" wave in the elementary Huygens' construction.

As we shall see presently, for an unobstructed wave the secondary waves from all the elements of area dS mutually destroy each other

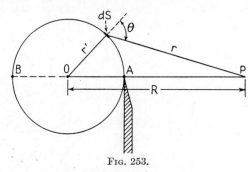

Fig. 253.

by interference at P, *except* for those originating in a very small region around the point A; hence, to all intents and purposes, the net effect is the same as if the light traveled in a straight line from O to P.

If now some sort of obstacle, such as the opaque screen indicated in Fig. 253, is inserted between O and P, we no longer have the possibility of the mutual cancellation of the secondary waves from various elements of area, since the screen prevents the secondary waves originating on the lower hemisphere from reaching P. This gives rise, then, to diffraction effects, and one may obtain even larger intensities at P than without the screen, depending on the location of the latter. Since each secondary wave is of infinitesimal amplitude (being proportional to dS), the task of computing the resultant amplitude at P is that of carrying out an integration over all the source elements of area dS. *Fresnel* has given an ingenious method of computing approximately the contributions of the various secondary waves to the resultant amplitude, which enables one to obtain the essential results without complicated integrations. Let us present this method for the case of a plane wave to compute the amplitude produced at a point P lying ahead of a given wave front (Fig. 254).

On a plane wave front we describe a series of circles about O as a center (Fig. 254) of radii r_1, r_2, r_3 etc., such that the distances from P

to these various circles increase by one-half wavelength as we go from one circle to its neighbor.   The line $PO = d$ is perpendicular to the plane.   We have thus divided the wave front into zones called *Fresnel zones, or half-period elements,* and a similar construction may be carried out readily for the spherical wave of Fig. 253.   Note that the location of these Fresnel zones depends on the point of observation P.   Now the phase difference between the waves arriving at P from O and from the edge of the first zone (at r_1) is just $(2\pi/\lambda)[d + (\lambda/2) - d] = \pi$, so that all the waves originating at points within this first zone give contributions, at a definite instant of time, of the same algebraic sign (let us say positive).   Similarly, the phases of the waves coming from

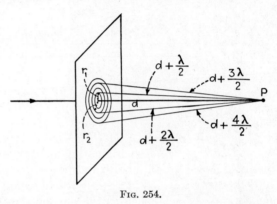

Fig. 254.

points in the second zone (relative to that coming from O) lie between π and 2π, and these waves give negative contributions, those from the third zone positive contributions, etc.   The resultant amplitude A at the point P will then be the sum of the contributions from the various Fresnel zones, a sum of terms of the form

$$A = a_1 - a_2 + a_3 - a_4 + \cdots + a_n \qquad (19.1)$$

where successive terms alternate in sign and have magnitudes which decrease very slowly, as we shall see, as one proceeds from one term to the next.   The magnitudes a_n will vary in general because of three effects: (1) the zone areas change slightly from zone to zone; (2) the distance from the zones to the observation point increases slightly with increasing zone number; and (3) the angle θ of the obliquity effect increases slowly with increasing zone number.   The net effect is that there is a slow decrease of magnitude of a_n with increasing n.

Let us compute the areas of these zones for the plane-wave case of Fig. 254.   From the figure we see that, for the nth circle,

$$d^2 + r_n^2 = \left(d + \frac{n\lambda}{2}\right)^2 = d^2 + n\lambda d + \frac{n^2\lambda^2}{4}$$

or

$$r_n^2 = nd\lambda + \frac{n^2\lambda^2}{4} \tag{19.2}$$

and for the $(n-1)$st circle

$$r_{n-1}^2 = (n-1)d\lambda + \frac{(n-1)^2\lambda^2}{4}$$

The area of the nth zone is accordingly

$$S_n = \pi r_n^2 - \pi r_{n-1}^2 = \pi d\lambda + \frac{\pi}{2}\left(n - \frac{1}{2}\right)\lambda^2$$

or

$$S_n = \pi d\lambda \left(1 + \frac{2n-1}{4}\frac{\lambda}{d}\right) \tag{19.3}$$

Now, in general, $\lambda \ll d$, so that one may neglect the second term inside the parentheses of Eq. (19.3), and one has very nearly

$$S_n = \pi d\lambda \tag{19.4}$$

independent of zone number for the plane-wave case.

We now return to the question of the amplitude A as given by Eq. (19.1). If we consider the vector diagram of the electric field at P, we note that the individual terms a_n of Eq. (19.1) represent the resultant vectors of all the infinitesimal waves coming from the points in the nth zone. These vectors are alternately 180° out of phase with each other, and hence the vector addition becomes a simple algebraic process. We shall now show that the amplitude A of Eq. (19.1) is very nearly given by

$$A = \tfrac{1}{2}(a_1 + a_n) \tag{19.5}$$

i.e., that the sum of an alternating series is approximately half the sum of the first and last terms if the magnitudes of successive terms are about equal. To see this, we rewrite Eq. (19.1) in the form

$$A = \frac{a_1}{2} + \left(\frac{a_1}{2} - a_2 + \frac{a_3}{2}\right) + \left(\frac{a_3}{2} - a_4 + \frac{a_5}{2}\right) + \cdots$$

$$+ \left(\frac{a_{n-2}}{2} - a_{n-1} + \frac{a_n}{2}\right) + \frac{a_n}{2}$$

and since the amplitude from any zone is nearly equal to the average of those of the preceding and following zones, we may write

$$a_2 = \tfrac{1}{2}(a_1 + a_3), \qquad a_4 = \tfrac{1}{2}(a_3 + a_5), \ldots$$

so that all the terms in the parentheses vanish, and we are left with Eq. (19.5). Evidently the result as written holds for n odd. If n is

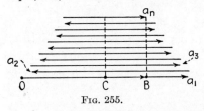

FIG. 255.

even, it is clear that one need merely replace a_n by $-a_n$ in Eq. (19.5). The vector diagram illustrating the foregoing results is shown in Fig. 255, where we have placed the n vectors a_n side by side for clarity instead of trying to show them on the same straight line. The sum of the vectors is OB; OC is one-half of a_1; and CB is one-half of a_n, as indicated in the figure.

If we are concerned with a problem where a very large number of zones contribute, the effect of the last zone becomes negligible in general, and we have

$$A = \frac{a_1}{2} \tag{19.5a}$$

showing that the amplitude at the observation point P is essentially one-half the contribution from the first zone. This is OC in Fig. 255. Thus, for example, for the unobstructed spherical wave of Fig. 253, the amplitude at P may be taken as originating practically at the point A of that figure, so that the concept of rays is justified from the standpoint of wave theory.

2. Application of Fresnel Zones to Fresnel Diffraction. The general method of calculation of the diffraction pattern produced by interposing a plane opaque screen, containing one or more apertures, between the source and the observation screen is to assume that the amplitude of the light wave at all points of the apertures is the same as if the diffracting screen were absent and then to integrate the contributions at the observing screen of the infinitesimal Huygens' secondary waves emitted from the points within the apertures. For Fresnel diffraction this is a relatively complicated task, and we shall not attempt quantitative solutions but shall examine the qualitative nature of the phenomena with the help of Fresnel zones. Suppose that there is a single aperture in the diffracting screen in the form of a rectangular slit. For a given point of observation, we imagine the Fresnel zones constructed on the diffracting screen and then can examine the diffraction pattern as one moves the point of observation and correspondingly the system of Fresnel zones. The nature of the diffraction pattern will depend on which zones are uncovered and can transmit light and on which zones are obscured by the screen. Suppose first that the center of the zone system lies well within the aperture, corresponding to an observation point P, which should be fully illuminated according to geometrical optics. The central zone is fully uncovered as well as a number of others, but as we proceed to larger zones, they become partially covered and finally completely covered. This is indicated in Fig. 256. The amplitude A at the observation point is the sum of the contributions from the various exposed zones, and while the areas decrease somewhat more rapidly than for an unobstructed wave, we may still use the result that A is given approximately by half the sum of the first and last zones. Since the last zone is almost entirely covered, its contribution to A is negligible (remember also that the re-

sultant of the Huygens' secondary waves from this partially covered zone is neither in phase nor 180° out of phase, in general, with the contribution from the central

FIG. 256.

zone), and we are left essentially with half the contribution from the first zone. Thus the intensity on the screen at this point is the same as if the diffracting screen were absent.

As a second case, suppose the observation point P is near the edge of the geometrical shadow, making the center of the zone system near the edge of the aperture. If the first zone is completely uncovered but the next ones partially obscured, the contributions a_2, a_3, etc., may vary so rapidly and have phases relative to the contribution a_1 quite different from 180° or 0°, that it would be incorrect to take half the sum of the contributions from the first and last zones. In such a case, one might well obtain an amplitude A greater than $a_1/2$, so that the intensity would be greater than in the absence of the screen. As one moves past the edge, successive zones become covered, and there is a periodic variation of intensity; these are the diffraction fringes.

Finally, if we move the point P well into the geometrical shadow, then a number of zones starting with the first will be obscured. A certain zone is partially uncovered, and succeeding zones become more uncovered to a considerable extent. The larger zones again become more and more obscured, and in the sum of the contributions from all the zones, the first and last terms are zero. Thus there is darkness at this observation point. This is well within the geometrical shadow, and, speaking physically, the waves from the partially uncovered zones mutually cancel by interference.

Having now obtained a general picture, let us examine a few special cases more closely. Consider first the diffraction pattern formed by a circular opening in the diffracting screen of Fig. 257. Suppose that the size of the circular opening is such that only the first zone (the point P being on the axis) is uncovered. The amplitude at P is then a_1, or *twice* the amplitude with no diffracting screen present. Thus the intensity is four times as great. If we imagine the opening now increased until two zones are uncovered, the amplitude becomes $a_1 - a_2$, and this is practically zero since a_1 and a_2 are almost equal to

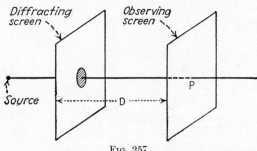

FIG. 257.

each other. Thus it is clear that the intensity at P is a maximum if an *odd* number of zones is uncovered and a minimum when an *even* number of zones is uncovered. The same effect is obtained by moving the observation screen with a *fixed* aperture rather than by increasing the aperture with a fixed distance D. We have seen [Eq. (19.2)] that the radius of the first zone is given by λD, and as D is varied, one can obscure or uncover a larger number of zones, leading to alternating intensities along the axis. Similarly, one can follow the alternations of intensity as the point P moves laterally into the geometrical shadow. One can also discuss the diffraction pattern caused by a circular obstacle by exactly the same scheme. One obtains the surprising result that if the obstacle obscures only a few Fresnel zones, a bright spot should appear at the center of the geometrical shadow. This has been observed experimentally and provides a most convincing argument in favor of a wave theory of light. Diffraction by a straight edge may be examined with the help of an appropriate Fresnel zone construction, differing only in detail from the examples given above. Details are left to the problems.

3. Fraunhofer Diffraction by a Single Slit. We shall now examine the Fraunhofer diffraction pattern produced by a single rectangular slit. For the sake of simplicity let the diffracting screen containing the slit be perpendicular to the incident plane wave of monochromatic light. The pattern is observed on a screen very far from the slit (at infinity) or with the help of a telescope focused on infinity, or by placing a lens in back of the diffracting slit and observing the pattern on a screen placed in the focal plane of the lens (Fig. 258). Thus the intensity at any point P of the pattern is due to the superposition of all the diffracted rays leaving the various points of the aperture *in a given direction*. Thus in Fig. 258 all the rays leaving the aperture at an angle θ with the normal to the plane of the slit are brought to a focus at the point P on the observation screen as shown.

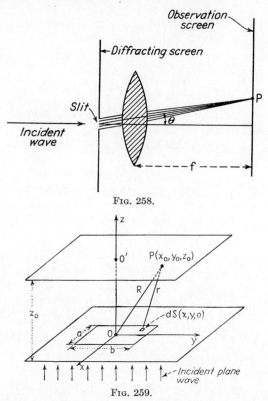

Fig. 258.

Fig. 259.

Let us choose a coordinate system, as shown in Fig. 259, with the origin at the center of the rectangular slit of width a and length b. We start with the observation screen at a finite distance z_0 from the slit and consider the wave arriving at P (coordinates x_0, y_0, z_0) as the superposition of elementary waves coming from the various infinitesimal elements of area dS of the aperture. Since we are interested only in the limiting case of infinite distance from slit to P, we may set the amplitudes of the various waves arriving from the elementary areas dS (of equal size) equal to each other. In so doing, we neglect the slight variation with angle (the obliquity effect); consequently our results will hold for small angles, *i.e.*, near the center of the pattern O'. *The variations of intensity in the pattern are thus due practically only to the relative phase differences among the various waves.* The contribution du to one of the components of the electric field, let us say, at P from the wave coming from dS is

$$du = A \, dS \cos (\omega t - kr) \qquad (19.6)$$

with $\omega = 2\pi\nu$ and $k = 2\pi/\lambda$, corresponding to an oscillation $A' \, dS \sin \omega t$ at dS, and the sum of the contributions from the various elementary areas dS of the aperture is evidently

$$u = \iint A \cos (\omega t - kr) \, dS \qquad (19.7)$$

where the integration is to be carried out over the whole slit area. In order to evaluate the integral, we must express r, the distance from dS to P, in terms of the coordinates of dS and of P. We have

$$r^2 = (x - x_0)^2 + (y - y_0)^2 + z_0^2$$

or, expanding and placing $x_0^2 + y_0^2 + z_0^2 = R^2$ (see Fig. 259),

$$r^2 = R^2 - 2xx_0 - 2yy_0 + x^2 + y^2 \qquad (19.8)$$

Now x_0/R is the cosine of the angle between R and the x-axis, which we denote by l, and $y_0/R = m$ is the cos ne of the angle between R and the y-axis. Using this notation, Eq. (19.8) becomes

$$r^2 = R^2 \left(1 - \frac{2lx + 2my}{R} + \frac{x^2 + y^2}{R^2} \right) \qquad (19.9)$$

Now x/R is very small compared to unity if R is very large (the Fraunhofer case), so that we may neglect terms of the order of x^2/R^2, y^2/R^2, and higher powers. Therefore we drop the last term on the right of Eq. (19.9), take the square root, and expand according to the binomial theorem. There follows

$$r = R - (lx + my) \qquad (19.10)$$

Setting $dS = dx \, dy$ and inserting Eq. (19.10) into Eq. (19.7), we have

$$u = A \int_{-a/2}^{+a/2} \int_{-b/2}^{+b/2} \cos [\omega t - kR + k(lx + my)] \, dx \, dy \qquad (19.11)$$

If we denote $(\omega t - kR)$ by ϕ, the integrand may be written in the form

$$\cos [(\phi + klx) + kmy] = \cos (\phi + klx) \cos kmy$$
$$- \sin (\phi + klx) \sin kmy \qquad (19.12)$$

When integrated with respect to y, the second term on the right-hand side of Eq. (19.12) gives zero, since

$$\left[\cos kmy \right]_{y=-b/2}^{y=+b/2} = 0$$

The first term on the right-hand side of Eq. (19.12) may similarly be written as

$$\cos (\phi + klx) \cos kmy = \cos \phi \cos klx \cos kmy$$
$$- \sin \phi \sin klx \cos kmy \quad (19.13)$$

and the second term is zero when integrated with respect to x, since

$$\left[\cos klx \right]_{x=-a/2}^{x=+a/2} = 0$$

Thus we are left with the first term of Eq. (19.13), which, when reinserted into Eq. (19.11), yields

$$u = A \cos (\omega t - kR) \int_{-a/2}^{a/2} \cos klx \, dx \int_{-b/2}^{b/2} \cos kmy \, dy \quad (19.14)$$

the product of two identical integrals. The integral with respect to x is

$$\frac{1}{kl} \left[\sin klx \right]_{-a/2}^{+a/2} = \frac{2}{kl} \sin \frac{kla}{2}$$

and since $k = 2\pi/\lambda$, this can be written as $(\lambda/\pi l) \sin (\pi la/\lambda)$. Similarly the integral with respect to y is $(\lambda/\pi m) \sin (\pi mb/\lambda)$, so that Eq. (19.14) becomes

$$u = Aab \cos (\omega t - kR) \frac{\sin (\pi la/\lambda)}{\pi la/\lambda} \frac{\sin (\pi mb/\lambda)}{\pi mb/\lambda} \quad (19.15)$$

Since the light intensity is proportional to the square of u, we may write

$$\frac{I}{I_0} = \frac{\sin^2 \alpha}{\alpha^2} \cdot \frac{\sin^2 \beta}{\beta^2} \quad (19.16)$$

where we have set

$$\alpha = \frac{\pi la}{\lambda}; \qquad \beta = \frac{\pi mb}{\lambda} \quad (19.16a)$$

and I_0 is the intensity for $\alpha = \beta = 0$, *i.e.*, at the point O' in Fig. 259. Equation (19.16) gives the variation of intensity with position (given by the direction cosines l and m) in the pattern. Since the variation in the x-z plane (transverse to the length of the slit) is identical with that in the y-z plane (along the length of the slit), it will suffice to examine the intensity variation in the x-z plane. For all points P

in this plane, $m = 0$, since the angle between R (Fig. 259) and the y-axis is 90°. Thus $\beta = 0$, and $(\sin^2 \beta)/\beta^2 = 1$. For this case Eq. (19.16) becomes

$$\frac{I}{I_0} = \frac{\sin^2 \alpha}{\alpha^2} \tag{19.17}$$

and this is shown plotted in Fig. 260.

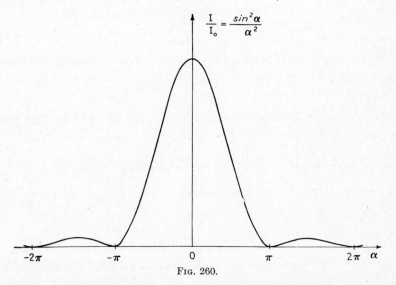

FIG. 260.

The maximum intensity occurs at the center, falls off to zero at $\alpha = \pm\pi, \pm 2\pi, \pm 3\pi$, etc., with secondary maxima approximately halfway between. If we take the positions of the maxima at the points

$$\alpha = \frac{\pi l a}{\lambda} = \pm \frac{3\pi}{2}, \pm \frac{5\pi}{2}, \cdots$$

the relative intensities at these points are

$$\left(\frac{2}{3\pi}\right)^2; \left(\frac{2}{5\pi}\right)^2; \left(\frac{2}{7\pi}\right)^2; \cdots; \quad \text{or} \quad 0.045; 0.016; \cdots$$

Thus we see that the intensities of the secondary maxima fall off very rapidly as one proceeds away from the central maximum, so that practically all the light is concentrated in the central diffraction band. The half angle θ subtended at the slit by this band is given by

$$\sin \theta = l = \frac{\lambda}{a}$$

or, for small angles,

$$\theta = \frac{\lambda}{a} \qquad (19.18)$$

This is shown in Fig. 261, in which we may imagine the slit dimension b to be so large compared to a that we have essentially a one-dimensional pattern. Note that the diffraction pattern becomes more extended, the narrower the slit dimensions, or the longer the wave-

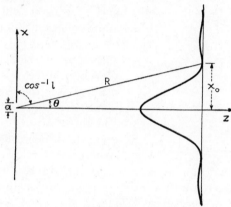

Fig. 261.

length. The general expression for the location of the minima is given by

$$\frac{\pi l a}{\lambda} = k\pi \qquad (k = 1, 2, 3, \dots)$$

or for the angles

$$\sin \theta = l = k\frac{\lambda}{a} \qquad (k = 1, 2, 3, \dots) \qquad (19.19)$$

The location of the minima can be obtained by an elementary argument. Consider the rays at an angle θ with the normal to the plane of the slit, as in Fig. 262. If the distance BB' is just one-half wavelength, there will be destructive interference between the rays originating at the slit edge A and the slit center B. Similarly, destructive interference will occur between the rays leaving any point in the region AB and the corresponding point in the region BC. Consequently this angle θ yields the first minimum of the diffraction pattern. From Fig. 262 it is clear that $BB' = \lambda/2 = (a/2) \sin \theta$, so that $\sin \theta = \lambda/a$ (first minimum). This agrees with Eq. (19.19) for $k = 1$. The argument is readily extended to obtain the locations of the other minima.

It is instructive to consider the vector-diagram method for the diffraction problem of a long narrow slit (one-dimensional pattern). We are confronted with the problem of constructing a vector diagram for an infinite number of infinitesimal vectors of equal amplitudes and continuously varying phase, corresponding to the integral of Eq. (19.7). First consider the slit area divided into a large but finite number of equal elementary areas. At a given observation point P, the waves coming from these elementary areas will be of equal amplitude and differ in phase one from the next by equal angles. The sum of the lengths of these vectors will be a constant, independent of the location of the point of observation. If we now add these vectors on a vector diagram in which the polygon construction is used, we have the vectors forming a portion of an equiangular polygon. The resultant vector is the vector from the starting point to the tip of the last elementary vector of the figure. This is illustrated schematically in Fig. 263a. If we now let the number of vectors approach infinity and the length of each approach zero, the polygon of Fig. 263a goes over

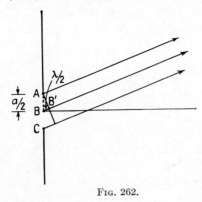

Fig. 262.

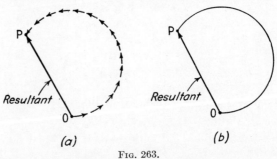

(a)   (b)

Fig. 263.

to the circle (continuous curve) of Fig. 263b. The arc length of the circle is constant for a given slit and wavelength, but the radius (and the curvature) varies with the position of the observation point. Thus when the observation point is directly ahead of the slit ($l = 0$), the infinitesimal vectors are all in phase, the radius of the circle is infinite, and we have the maximum resultant vector OP_1 (Fig. 264) as a straight line. As the observation point is moved, the radius of the circle becomes finite, and at a point P_2 the resultant vector is the chord OP_2

of Fig. 264, the arc OP_2 being equal to OP_1. Progressing further, the radius of the circle decreases, and finally at P_3 the arc length $OP_3 = OP_1$ is just equal to $2\pi R$, the circumference of the circle. At this point the chord OP_3 is zero, and we are at the first minimum of the diffraction pattern. Continuing further, the radius decreases still further, and the resultant vector increases again, reaching a value equal to the chord OP_4 at a point P_4. Here the arc length is greater than the circumference of the circle. The relative intensity at any point of diffraction pattern is the ratio of the square of the chord to the square of the length of arc. It is left to a problem to show that this

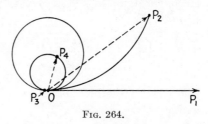

Fig. 264.

leads to Eq. (19.17). Thus we see how the diffraction pattern can be obtained from a vector diagram and in particular how the minima occur when the given arc length is an integer times the circumference of the circle.

4. Fraunhofer Diffraction by a Double Slit. In considering Young's experiment on the interference of light by two narrow slits close together, the assumption was tacitly made that the slits were narrow enough and close enough to each other to cause considerable overlapping of the central maxima of the diffraction patterns of each slit. We shall now examine the problem of the Fraunhofer diffraction pattern due to *two slits*, each of width a and separation d between centers. We shall, for simplicity, take the slit lengths very large compared to their widths, so that we have a one-dimensional pattern; *i.e.*, the intensity varies only in the x-direction on the observation screen. Even for slits not long compared to their width, the pattern is altered from the single-slit pattern only in this dimension, so that no generality is lost by taking $m = 0$ ($y_0 = 0$) for the points P at which we compute the intensity.

The method of calculation is identical with that employed for a single slit, except that the integration is to be carried out over two slits instead of one. Thus we may take over Eq. (19.11) as it stands, set $m = 0$, and have

$$u = Ab \left[\int_{-a/2}^{a/2} \cos\left(\omega t - kR + klx\right) dx \right.$$
$$\left. + \int_{d-(a/2)}^{d+(a/2)} \cos\left(\omega t - kR + klx\right) dx \right] \quad (19.20)$$

since, with an origin at the center of the first slit, the second extends from $x = [d - (a/2)]$ to $x = [d + (a/2)]$. If in the second integral we set $x' = x - d$, it becomes

$$\int_{-a/2}^{+a/2} \cos{(\omega t - kR + kd + klx')} \, dx'$$

Proceeding as before, each term of Eq. (19.20) yields an expression of the form of Eq. (19.14) with $m = 0$, and we obtain in place of Eq. (19.14)

$$u = Ab \left(\int_{-a/2}^{+a/2} \cos klx \, dx \right)$$
$$[\cos{(\omega t - kR)} + \cos{(\omega t - kR + kd)}] \quad (19.21)$$

The term in the brackets may be written in the form $B \cos{(\omega t - \delta)}$, with

$$B^2 = 2(1 + \cos kld) = 4 \cos^2{\left(\frac{kld}{2} \right)} = 4 \cos^2{\left(\frac{\pi ld}{\lambda} \right)} \quad (19.22)$$

using $k = 2\pi/\lambda$.

The phase δ is of no interest since it does not affect the relative intensities. Note that Eq. (19.22) corresponds exactly to Eq. (18.6) for the interference pattern in Young's experiment, since $l = \sin \theta$. The remaining terms of Eq. (19.21) yield just the relative intensity in the diffraction pattern of a single slit as expressed in Eq. (19.17). Thus we may write for the relative intensity in the double-slit pattern

$$\frac{I}{I_0} = 4 \frac{\sin^2 \alpha}{\alpha^2} \cos^2 \gamma \quad (19.23)$$

with $\alpha = \pi la/\lambda$ as before, and $\gamma = \pi ld/\lambda$.

Thus the intensity pattern is given by the product of two factors, one the diffraction pattern of a single slit and the other the interference pattern of two slits. In other words, the diffraction pattern is modulated by the interference pattern of the two slits. The *minima* occur either when
$$\gamma = (k + \tfrac{1}{2})\pi \qquad (k = 0, 1, 2, \ldots)$$
or when
$$\alpha = (j + 1)\pi \qquad (j = 0, 1, 2, \ldots) \qquad \left. \right\} \quad (19.24)$$

Now $\alpha = \pi la/\lambda = (\pi a/\lambda) \sin \theta$ and $\gamma = \pi ld/\lambda = (\pi d/\lambda) \sin \theta$, where θ is the angle which the diffracted rays make with the direction of the incident light. The conditions for the minima as given by Eq. (19.24) may be written in the form

$$\left. \begin{array}{l} d \sin \theta = (k + \tfrac{1}{2})\lambda \\ a \sin \theta = (j + 1)\lambda \end{array} \right\} \qquad (j, k = 0, 1, 2, \ldots) \qquad (19.25)$$

The locations of the *maxima* are not given by any simple relation, but near the center of the pattern, we may take $(\sin^2 \alpha)/\alpha^2$ practically constant.   Then the maxima occur approximately at the positions

$$d \sin \theta = k\lambda \qquad (k = 0, 1, 2, \ldots) \qquad (19.26)$$

Figure 265 shows a plot of the relative intensity for a double slit with $d = 3a$.

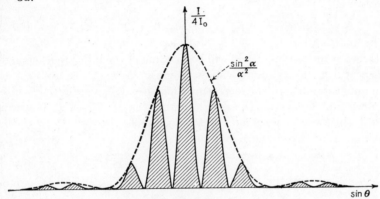

FIG. 265.

5. The Diffraction Grating; Many Slits.   In the preceding section we have seen that the interference effect between two slits produces comparatively sharp maxima in the otherwise slowly varying diffraction pattern of a single slit.   This effect can be enhanced tremendously by utilizing a large number N of slits, and in this form one has a plane diffraction grating, which is remarkably effective in making possible a spectral analysis of light consisting of a mixture of wavelengths.

Suppose we have N similar parallel slits of width a along the x-axis, with a spacing between centers equal to d.   This is the generalization of the double-slit problem.   The analysis may be accomplished in a manner similar to that employed for the double slit, but we shall omit the details of the calculation, since it becomes unnecessarily involved unless complex numbers are used.   The result turns out to be of a form just like that for a double slit; *i.e.*, the relative intensity distribution is that of the diffraction pattern of a single slit multiplied by the interference intensity distribution due to a system of N slits.   This can be expressed in the formula

$$\frac{I}{I_0} = \left(\frac{\sin^2 \alpha}{\alpha^2} \right) \frac{\sin^2 (\pi N l d/\lambda)}{\sin^2 (\pi l d/\lambda)} \qquad (19.27)$$

Note that this reduces to Eq. (19.23) for $N = 2$.   The factor $(\sin^2 \alpha)/\alpha^2$

has already been discussed. The second factor in Eq. (19.27) gives the intensity variations produced by N interfering beams [see Eq. (18.12)], and this has already been discussed in Sec. 3, Chap. 18. Let us review the principal aspects of this interference pattern. The oscillations of the numerator, $\sin^2(\pi Nld/\lambda)$, give rise to a pattern of interference fringes which are very closely spaced if N is large, since this function vanishes whenever l has one of the values

$$l = \sin\theta = j\frac{\lambda}{Nd} \qquad (j = 0, 1, 2, 3, \ldots) \qquad (19.28)$$

In between the minima there will be maxima of the interference fringes, which will have different values because of the variations of the denominator, $\sin^2(\pi ld/\lambda)$, corresponding to partial constructive interference, and because of the diffraction factor $(\sin^2\alpha)/\alpha^2$. If we disregard this slowly varying diffraction effect, then the *least intense* maxima occur when the denominator is unity (or very close to it), and these weakest maxima have intensities given by

$$I = I_0\frac{\sin^2\alpha}{\alpha^2} \cong I_0 \qquad \text{(least intense maxima)} \qquad (19.29)$$

This equation holds in the region of the center of the diffraction pattern where we may set $(\sin^2\alpha)/\alpha^2$ equal to unity. This region of validity of Eq. (19.29) becomes larger, the smaller the individual slit width a.

The most intense, or *principal*, maxima of the interference pattern occur when numerator and denominator of the second factor in Eq. (19.27) vanish simultaneously, corresponding to complete constructive interference of all the beams from the N slits. These occur for

$$\sin^2\frac{l\pi d}{\lambda} = 0$$

or for angles θ given by

$$l = \sin\theta = \frac{k\lambda}{d} \qquad (k = 0, 1, 2, \ldots) \qquad (19.30)$$

In Fig. 266, we show the elementary construction for locating the principal maxima. For those angles θ for which the path difference between successive slits and a wave front is a whole number of wavelengths, all the rays from the N slits will be in phase, and complete constructive interference will occur. Thus in Fig. 266 we show the angle θ for the first principal maximum (measured from the center of the pattern). The path difference between the rays from the first slit and the second is one wavelength.   For the kth principal maximum this path difference would be $k\lambda$, and since this is equal to $d \sin \theta$, we have

$$d \sin \theta = k\lambda$$

as the condition for locating the principal maxima, as in Eq. (19.30). Evidently the intensity of a principal maximum is N^2 times that of a

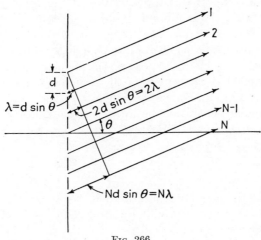

FIG. 266.

single slit, and if we take into account the slowly varying diffraction factor of Eq. (19.27), we have

$$I = N^2 I_0 \frac{\sin^2 \alpha}{\alpha^2} \qquad \text{(principal maxima)} \qquad (19.31)$$

Thus the ratio of most intense to least intense maxima is N^2, and this can be made extremely large by making N large.

In a diffraction grating, N is very large, of the order of 10^4 or 10^5, so that the secondary maxima are extremely weak compared to the principal maxima.   The latter, for monochromatic light, appear then as a series of very sharp lines with intensities given approximately by Eq. (19.31).   These lines occur at angles θ with the normal to the grating, θ being given by Eq. (19.30), and this is the ordinary diffraction-grating formula, with k determining the so-called *order of the spectrum*.   We have already seen in Sec. 3, Chap. 18 (and this section should be referred to in this whole discussion), that the most intense *secondary* maxima have intensities of about 4.5 per cent of those of the principal maxima and, although small, are not entirely negligible.

Finally, we must consider the resolving power of such a grating, *i.e.*, its ability to produce separated spectral lines for two wavelengths almost equal to each other. This depends on the width of the principal maxima and on their angular separation for the two wavelengths under consideration. (Note that the location of the zero-order principal maximum is independent of wavelength, so that this order is of no use.) The customary criterion of resolving power is to consider two spectral lines as just distinguishable if the center of the principal maximum for one lies just at the minimum adjacent to the principal maximum for the other. This is called the Rayleigh criterion and is quite arbitrary, since in practice the relative intensities of the lines in the incident light play a role, as well as the positions of the principal maxima.

We have seen that the centers of the principal maxima occur when the integer j in Eq. (19.28) has the values 0, N, $2N$, . . . , kN, ... Since the angular separation between two neighboring zeros of the term $\sin^2 (\pi N dl/\lambda)$ in the numerator of Eq. (19.27) is given by [see Eq. (19.28)]

$$\Delta l = \frac{\lambda}{Nd} \qquad (19.32)$$

it follows that the angular separation between a principal maximum, let us say the kth, and a neighboring minimum is also given by Eq. (19.32). Now the condition that the two kth-order principal maxima corresponding to two different wavelengths λ and $\lambda + \Delta\lambda$ have an angular separation Δl is given by Eq. (19.30) as

$$\Delta l = \frac{k\,\Delta\lambda}{d} \qquad (19.33)$$

Substituting this value of Δl in Eq. (19.32) we find

$$\frac{\lambda}{\Delta\lambda} = Nk \qquad (19.34)$$

This ratio of wavelength to wavelength difference of two spectral lines which are just resolvable is called the *resolving power* (more precisely, the *chromatic resolving power*) of the grating. It increases both with the order k of the spectrum and with the number of grating lines N.

6. Resolving Power of Optical Instruments. In our study of optical instruments we have entirely neglected diffraction effects, and we must now examine the limitations of these instruments due to these effects, *i.e.*, to the wave nature of light. A lens, for example, will not produce a point image of a point object, even if all aberrations are corrected, since the lens, being of finite cross section, transmits only a limited portion of a wave front incident on it and thus produces a diffraction pattern. An optical system is said to be able to resolve two point objects if the corresponding diffraction patterns are small enough or separated enough to be distinguished as two separate patterns in the image.

Let us consider the case of a telescope objective focused on infinity, and for the moment let us suppose that the lens is square, rather than circular, and of side a. The central diffraction pattern of a point object on the axis of the telescope, such as a very distant star, will subtend a half angle α at the objective given by [compare Eq. (19.18)]

$$\alpha = \frac{\lambda}{a} \qquad (19.35)$$

Since most of the light falls in this central pattern, we may disregard the presence of the outer diffraction pattern. For a circular lens the computation proceeds along lines similar to that given for the rectangle, but the integration is more difficult. The result turns out to be that the diffraction pattern consists of a central circular disk, on which falls about 85 per cent of the light, surrounded by a series of light and dark rings of rapidly diminishing intensity. The half angle subtended by this central disk is given by

$$\alpha = 1.22 \frac{\lambda}{D} = \frac{0.61\lambda}{r} \qquad (19.36)$$

where D is the diameter of the lens and r its radius. Suppose we agree that two point objects can just be resolved if the center of the diffraction disk of one lies just at the periphery of the diffraction disk of the second. One then sees immediately that two stars, for example, will be resolved by a telescope objective if their angular separation β at the objective is equal to or greater than α as given by Eq. (19.36). Thus we must have

$$\beta \geq \frac{1.22\lambda}{D} \qquad (19.37)$$

in order to have resolution of the two images. We see that the larger the diameter of the objective, the greater will be the resolving power. The eye itself may be considered as a telescope. If we take the diameter of the pupil to be 2 mm, then, for light of wavelength 5,500 A, Eq. (19.37) shows that the minimum angular separation of two point objects just resolvable by the eye is about 1 minute of arc.

Let us compute the radius ρ of the central diffraction disk formed at a distance l from a lens as the image of a point object (Fig. 267).

From the figure we see that $\alpha = \rho/l$ and that $\tan \theta_2 = D/2l$, so that, using Eq. (19.36), we have

$$\rho = \frac{0.61\lambda}{\tan \theta_2} = 1.22\lambda \frac{l}{D}$$

(In photography the distance l is approximately equal to the focal length f of the camera lens. The ratio f/D is known as the $f/$number of the lens, and the smaller the $f/$number, the better the resolving power of the lens.)   If the medium in which the image is formed has a refractive index n_2, then the wavelength λ is related to the wavelength λ_0 in air by $\lambda = \lambda_0/n_2$. Thus we may write

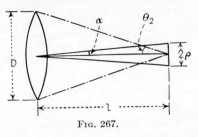

$$\rho = \frac{0.61\lambda_0}{n_2 \tan \theta_2} \qquad (19.38)$$

The resolving power of a microscope is conveniently expressed in terms of the linear separation, rather than the angular separation,

Fig. 267.

of two point objects which can just be resolved.   The distance given by Eq. (19.38) gives the separation of the centers of the diffraction disks which are the images of two point objects separated by a distance ρ_0. The object separation ρ_0 is related to the image separation ρ by the magnification of the lens, which, according to Abbe's sine condition [Eq. (16.12)], is

$$m = \frac{\rho}{\rho_0} = \frac{n_1 \sin \theta_1}{n_2 \sin \theta_2} \qquad (19.39)$$

where n_1 is the refractive index of the medium in which the object is located and θ_1 is the half angle subtended by the lens at the object. Since θ_2 is a small angle (for a microscope objective it is the order of 10^{-2} radian), we may replace $\tan \theta_2$ in Eq. (19.38) by $\sin \theta_2$ and obtain from Eq. (19.39)

$$\rho_0 = \frac{0.61\lambda_0}{n_1 \sin \theta_1} \qquad (19.40)$$

The quantity $n_1 \sin \theta_1$ is called the *numerical aperture* of the lens. The larger the numerical aperture, the better the resolving power of the lens.   For air the upper limit is about 0.95 in practice, but by immersing the object in oil, as is done in high-powered microscopes, the numerical aperture may be increased to 1.60.   Physically, the effect of the oil is to enable one to use waves of shorter wavelength than in air.

The numerical aperture of the unaided eye, using a pupillary radius of 1 mm and an object distance in air of 25 cm, is

$$\text{N.A.} = n_1 \sin \theta_1 = 1 \times \tfrac{1}{250} = 0.004$$

so that the smallest separation of two points just distinguishable as separate objects at a distance of 25 cm is, according to Eq. (19.40),

$$\rho_0 = \frac{0.61 \times 5 \times 10^{-5}}{4 \times 10^{-3}} = 0.075 \text{ mm}$$

for light of wavelength 5,000 A.

On the other hand, for a microscope objective with a numerical aperture of 1.60, this distance is smaller in the ratio

$$\frac{1.6}{0.004} = 400$$

so that it is about 2×10^{-5} cm, about half a wavelength of light. Since the microscope gives 400 times the resolving power of the naked eye, the magnifying power should be at least 400 times to take advantage of this. *The ratio of the numerical aperture of a microscope objective to that of the eye is called the normal magnifying power of a microscope.* A lower magnifying power will not take full advantage of the resolving power available, and a larger magnifying power gains nothing in detail and loses in brightness of the image. However, if enough light is available, one frequently employs higher magnifying powers for ease of observation. One defines the normal magnifying power of a telescope in a similar manner.

Problems

1. A plane monochromatic wave of wavelength 5,000 A is normally incident on an opaque screen containing a circular aperture of radius R. The diffraction pattern is observed on a second screen parallel to and 1 m distant from the first screen. What must be the radius R if the first three Fresnel zones giving rise to the intensity at the *center* of the pattern are uncovered? If the observing screen is moved slightly toward the aperture, will the intensity at the center of the pattern increase or decrease?

2. A parallel light beam of wavelength 5,500 A is normally incident on a circular opening in an opaque screen. Calculate the radius of the opening that will permit a point 20 cm from the screen and on the axis of the circular opening to be illuminated with twice the intensity on it when the screen is absent.

3. A so-called "zone plate" is made by constructing 20 Fresnel zones of the type discussed in Fig. 254 and by blocking off the light from every *other* zone. This zone plate, when held in the light from a distant point source, produces a bright spot on its axis 100 cm from the plate. Assuming a wavelength of 5,000 A, compute

    a. The areas of the zones on the plate.

    b. The radius of the zone plate.

    c. The intensity of the bright spot relative to its value in the absence of the zone plate.

    d. How would the above answers be changed, if the first uncovered zone has an inner radius of 2.0 mm?

    4. Monochromatic light of 5,000 A wavelength is normally incident on a circular aperture in an opaque screen. The light intensity at points on the axis of the aperture (on the far side of the screen) varies periodically. The position of the farthest minimum is at a distance of 1 m from the screen.

    a. Find the diameter of the circular aperture.

    b. Find the position of the minimum lying nearest to the one at 1 m.

    5. Plot a graph of the intensity of light at the point P of Fig. 257 as a function of distance D from a fixed circular aperture. A qualitative plot is all that is wanted.

    How would this graph be altered if the circular aperture were replaced by a circular obstacle of the same radius?

    6. Consider light from a *line* source S perpendicular to the plane of the page in Fig. 268, passing a straight-edged obstacle AB to a screen, as shown, the wave fronts being cylindrical. Show that the Fresnel zones are strips on the wave front cc. Find expressions for the angles subtended by these zones at the source S.

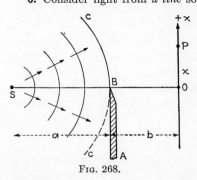

FIG. 268.

    7. In the experiment of Prob. 6, discuss qualitatively the variation of intensity on the screen as a function of x, the coordinate of P, when the obstacle AB is in the position shown. Prove that the diffraction pattern consists of a series of parallel light and dark fringes, the maxima being located at values of x (positive) given very nearly by

$$x = \sqrt{\frac{b}{a}(a + b)\lambda(2k + 1)}$$

and the minima at

$$x = \sqrt{\frac{b}{a}(a + b)2k\lambda}$$

    8. Derive expressions for the areas of the Fresnel zones on a spherical wave front of radius r_1 with its center at a source S for an observation point P lying at a distance R from S $(R > r_1)$.

    9. A single-slit Fraunhofer diffraction pattern is formed with white light. For what wavelength of light does the third maximum in its diffraction pattern coincide with the second maximum in the pattern for red light of wavelength 6,500 A?

10. A lens of focal length 40 cm forms a Fraunhofer diffraction pattern of a slit of 0.30 mm width. Calculate the distance from the center of the pattern to the first dark band and to the next bright band, using sodium light, $\lambda = 5,890$ A.

11. The Fraunhofer diffraction pattern of a single long slit of width 0.10 mm is observed on a screen in the focal plane of a lens of focal length 1 m placed directly in back of the slit. The incident light is a mixture of two wavelengths λ_1 and λ_2.

Find the ratio of these two wavelengths such that the position of the first-order maximum for one coincides with the position of the first minimum of the other. What is the distance from the center of the central image of the observation point on the screen where this condition is attained, if one of the wavelengths, say λ_1, is 4,000 A?

12. In the vector diagram of Fig. 264, if we denote the constant arc length OP_1 by A, show that the radius of the circle R is related to A by

$$\frac{R}{A} = \frac{\lambda}{2\pi a l}$$

for a slit of width a, where $l = \sin \theta$. From this show that the minima of the diffraction pattern lie at the angular positions given by Eq. (19.19).

Prove further that the relative intensity, given, for example, at P_2 of Fig. 264 by the ratio of the square of the chord OP_2 to A^2, is $(\sin^2 \alpha)/\alpha^2$ with $\alpha = \pi l a/\lambda$.

13. A plane light wave of wavelength 5,000 A is normally incident on a slit 1.0 mm wide and 4.0 mm long. A lens of focal length 100 cm is mounted just behind the slit and the light focused on a screen. Find the dimensions of the central part of the diffraction pattern in millimeters.

14. If the slit of Prob. 13 is square and 1.0 mm on a side, find the dimensions of one of the patterns lying next to the central diffraction region.

15. In Prob. 13 calculate the dimensions and area of a rectangle drawn on the observation screen which would contain all the light included in the five major diffraction maxima.

16. In the double-slit pattern show that if the slit separation is twice the width of either slit, all the even-order interference maxima will be missing. What order will be missing if the ratio is $3:1$?

17. Compute the relative intensities of the first five principal maxima of a double-slit diffraction pattern for which $d = 5a$. Sketch the intensity distribution for a sufficiently large angular range to include these five maxima.

18. Plot the intensity distribution, including the first five maxima, of the diffraction pattern formed by three slits, equally spaced, with $d = 2a$.

19. Plot the intensity distribution in the diffraction pattern formed by four equally spaced slits with $d = 3a$.

20. A plane grating is designed to spread the first-order visible spectrum,

4,000 to 7,000 A, over an angular range of 37°. How many lines per inch must this grating have and what are the diffraction angles for the red and violet limits of the spectrum?

21. Monochromatic light is incident on a plane transmission grating at an angle ϕ with the plane of the grating. Show that the positions of the principal maxima are determined by

$$d(\sin \theta + \cos \phi) = k\lambda \qquad (k = 0, 1, 2, \ldots)$$

22. The limits of the visible spectrum are nearly 4,000 to 7,000 A. Find the angular breadth of the first-order visible spectrum formed by a plane grating with 12,000 lines per inch. Does the violet of the third-order spectrum overlap the red of the second-order spectrum? If so, by how much (approximately)?

23. Light containing two wavelengths of 5,000 and 5,200 A is normally incident on a plane grating of grating spacing 10^{-3} cm. A 2-m lens is used to focus the spectrum on a screen. Find the distance between these two lines (in centimeters) on the screen for the first- and for the third-order spectrum.

24. The grating of Prob. 23 has 10,000 lines and is illuminated at normal incidence by light containing two wavelengths, 4,000 and 6,000 A.

a. Find the linear separation of the two lines in the second-order spectrum.

b. Find the separation between the second-order image of the 6,000-A line and the third-order image of the 4,000-A line.

c. If the 6,000-A line appears in the third order as a doublet which is just barely resolved, find the approximate separation of the doublet in angstrom units.

25. The sodium yellow line 5,893 A is a doublet with a separation of 6 A between the two lines.

a. What is the minimum number of lines of a grating which will just resolve these lines in the third-order spectrum?

b. If a lens of 30-ft focal length is used to focus the spectrum of this doublet using a grating of 30,000 lines per inch, what is the distance between these lines in the third-order spectrum?

26. The height-finding antenna on the Ground Control Approach radar consists of a vertical linear array of 100 parallel dipoles 1.6 cm apart radiating at a wavelength of 3.2 cm. The phase of the electric current fed to successive dipoles can be varied from 0 to $\pi/8$, and this is done continuously at a frequency of 30 cycles/sec.

a. Describe what happens to the radiated beam.

b. What constant phase shift "bias" is required so that the beam does not look down to the ground?

c. With the above arrangement where are the grating spectral orders which might be expected? Are there side lobes?

d. Find the angular width of the main lobe.

27. Compute the approximate radius of the central diffraction disk formed on the retina of the eye by a distant point object, assuming a pupillary diameter of 2.0 mm. The distance from the cornea to the retina is about 1 in., and the refractive index of the vitreous humor, the medium in which the image is formed, is 1.33.

28. On using a pinhole camera, it is observed that a photograph of two adjacent objects 10 m from the camera will just resolve these objects if they are 6.1 cm apart. Using an effective wavelength of 5,000 A, compute the diameter of the pinhole. (A pinhole camera is a lighttight box with a small circular hole in the center of one face.)

29. *a.* Find the angular separation in seconds of arc of the closest double star which can be resolved by the 100-in.-diameter Mount Wilson Observatory telescope. Use a wavelength of 6,000 A.

b. Suppose such a just-resolvable binary star is found at a distance of 100 light-years from the earth. What is the distance between the two stars in this binary star?

30. Two pinholes 1.0 mm apart are made in a screen and placed in front of a bright light source. They are viewed through a telescope with its objective stopped down to a diameter of 1.0 cm. How far from the telescope may the screen be and still have the pinholes appear as separate sources for a wavelength of 5,000 A?

31. A battleship displays two small red signal lights ($\lambda = 6,500$ A) at a vertical separation of 5 ft. These lights are observed from another vessel 20 miles away through binoculars with objective lenses 50 mm in diameter.

a. What is the separation between the centers of the diffraction disks, in terms of the radius of each disk?

b. Sketch the appearance of these two lights as viewed through the binoculars.

c. Would an observer be able to just resolve these two lights with his unaided eye?

32. The objective lens of a telescope is of 5.0 cm diameter and of 1 m focal length. The pupillary diameter of the normal eye is 2.0 mm.

a. What is the ratio of the angular resolving power of the telescope objective to that of the unaided eye?

b. What is the proper focal length for the ocular to be employed in conjunction with this objective lens to take full advantage of its resolving power?

33. An oil-immersion microscope will just resolve a set of test lines drawn 112,000 to the inch, using blue light of 4,200 A wavelength. Find the numerical aperture of the objective.

34. Ultraviolet light of wavelength 2,750 A is used in photomicrography in conjunction with a quartz-lens microscope of numerical aperture 0.85. Find the least separation of two points which can be just resolved.

35. If the focal length of a microscope is 5.00 mm and its numerical aperture is 0.85, an ocular of what focal length should be used? What is the minimum separation of two objects just resolvable with this instrument?

36. A microscope objective is 8.0 mm in diameter and has a focal length of 30 mm. It may be considered as a thin lens.

a. What is the numerical aperture of the microscope?

b. What minimum separation can be resolved when the microscope is used with light of 5,500 A wavelength?

c. What is the normal magnifying power of the microscope, if the pupil of the eye is 2.0 mm in diameter?

d. What focal length should the ocular have if maximum resolving power is to be obtained?

37. In observing cosmic-ray particle tracks in photographic emulsions it has been found that with light of 5,000 A wavelength and a high-magnification, oil-immersion microscope of numerical aperture 1.30, it is just possible to resolve adjacent silver bromide grains in the densest portions of such tracks. What is the distance between adjacent grains?

38. Prove that the maxima of the function $(\sin^2 \alpha)/\alpha^2$ occur for values of α given by $\alpha = \tan \alpha$.

Find the first three roots of this equation (excluding $\alpha = 0$), and compute the corresponding values of the function. Compare these values with the approximate values $(2/3\pi)^2$, $(2/5\pi)^2$, and $(2/7\pi)^2$ obtained by taking the maxima at positions midway between the minima.

CHAPTER 20

HEAT RADIATION

We have repeatedly stressed the fact that the radiation emitted by material bodies as heat, light, X rays, etc., is due to the combined effects of many molecules and atoms and is incoherent. The nature of this radiation depends, in general, on the mode of excitation of the emitting atoms and molecules and on their specific properties. By the nature of the radiation we mean its spectral distribution, polarization, intensity, etc. In this chapter we shall concern ourselves principally with that form of radiation known as *heat* or *thermal radiation,* because of the mode of excitation. It is a familiar fact that material bodies begin to emit invisible heat radiation (infrared waves) as they are heated; then, as the temperature is increased, they emit visible radiation with increasing intensity in the short-wavelength region. Furthermore, the total rate of emission of energy increases very rapidly with increasing temperature.

The transfer of energy by thermal radiation is a process which differs fundamentally from the corresponding transfer of energy by thermal conduction. In the latter case one can describe uniquely the process by a single vector (the heat current density) at each point of the medium, and this vector depends on the local temperature gradient. On the other hand, thermal radiation at a given point of space or of a material body cannot be represented by a single vector and does not in general depend on the temperature or temperature gradient at the point in question. In fact, it is necessary to employ the concept of an infinite number of rays passing through a point in all conceivable directions to describe the radiation state, and these rays are all mutually independent with regard to their intensities, frequencies, and polarizations. Even two rays of equal frequency and polarization and opposite directions of propagation do not combine to form a single ray but maintain their individual identities.

1. Emission and Absorption; Kirchhoff's Law. In building appropriate definitions to describe the state of radiation, we must keep in mind the fact that radiation of finite energy content can never be emitted from point sources but must come from bodies of finite size, and inasmuch as the radiation emerges through the surface of a radiating body, one may say that radiation always comes from, impinges on, or passes through an element of surface but not a point.   We shall, in our study, employ the approximation of geometrical optics, so that

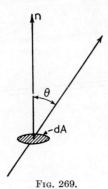

we may follow the propagation of energy in terms of bundles of rays.   This implies that we may choose elementary areas large compared to the wavelengths under consideration $(dA \gg \lambda^2)$ but very small compared to ordinary dimensions. Furthermore, it should be pointed out that one can never realize a beam of strictly parallel rays, but the bundle of rays must form a converging or diverging cone of given direction and small solid angle.

Fig. 269.

Let us consider a material medium or a region of empty space which is being traversed by radiation and focus our attention on an elemen-

tary area dA at a given point.   This area will be traversed by rays propagating in all directions, and the energy crossing this area per unit time in a direction making an angle θ with the normal to this surface (Fig. 269) will evidently be proportional to $dA \cos \theta$, *i.e.*, to the projection of dA on a plane which is perpendicular to the chosen direction.   The bundle of rays traversing dA in this direction forms a small cone or narrow pencil with vertex at dA, and the energy flow from or to dA per unit time will be proportional to the solid angle $d\omega$ at the vertex of this cone (Fig. 270).   Thus we may write for the energy per unit time (the energy flux dF) crossing dA in a bundle of

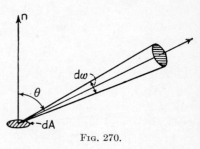

Fig. 270.

rays subtending a solid angle $d\omega$ at dA, when the bundle has a direction θ with the normal,

$$dF = K \cos \theta \, dA \, d\omega \qquad (20.1)$$

The proportionality constant K is called the *specific intensity* or *brightness* of this pencil of rays.   This brightness K may be further resolved into the specific intensities of those rays in the bundle corresponding to different frequencies or wavelengths in the radiation and hence has a definite spectral composition.   If we consider those rays whose frequencies lie between ν and $\nu + d\nu$, we may write as the contribution to K from this spectral range $d\nu$,

$$dK = K_\nu\, d\nu$$

so that

$$K = \int_0^\infty K_\nu\, d\nu \qquad (20.2)$$

Now let us consider the nature of the radiation which is in thermal equilibrium with a material body. For this purpose consider an evacuated enclosure or cavity of arbitrary shape, and let us suppose that we have attained thermal equilibrium. The walls of the enclosure will all be at the same temperature T, and they will be constantly emitting and absorbing ratiation. If the walls are constructed of material which absorbs *all* the radiation incident on them and reflects none, we say that they are *black*. The radiation in the cavity will then be isotropic and homogeneous, the specific intensity K will be independent of position and direction at any point in the radiation field, and there will be no preferred state of polarization. The *energy density* of the radiation, which has the same value at every point, will depend only on the temperature of the walls, and there will be a definite spectral distribution of this energy density at each temperature. Under these conditions we say that the radiation is *black*, or that it is *black-body radiation*.

There is a simple relation between the brightness K and the energy density u of radiation at a given point for the case of isotropic radiation. To obtain this relation, we must consider the energy arriving at the point under consideration as coming from all directions. Consider the energy arriving at an elementary area dA in a direction θ with the normal to dA. In time dt the energy transported across dA by these rays fills an infinitesimal cylinder of slant height $c\, dt$ (Fig. 271), where c is the velocity of propagation, and of base dA, so that it fills a volume equal to $c \cos\theta\, dt\, dA$. According to Eq. (20.1), this energy is equal to

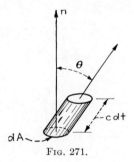

Fig. 271.

$$dF\, dt = K \cos\theta\, dA\, d\omega\, dt$$

Hence this bundle yields a contribution du to the energy density equal to

$$du = \frac{K \cos\theta\, dA\, d\omega\, dt}{c \cos\theta\, dt\, dA} = \frac{1}{c} K\, d\omega \qquad (20.3)$$

The total energy density u is the sum of the contributions from all the pencils crossing dA in *all* directions, and this is evidently obtained by integrating Eq. (20.3) over all these directions.   Hence we may write

$$u = \frac{1}{c} \int K \, d\omega$$

and since for isotropic radiation K is independent of direction, this becomes

$$u = \frac{K}{c} \int d\omega = \frac{4\pi}{c} K \tag{20.4}$$

using the fact that the solid angle encompassing all directions at a point is 4π.

Now consider the case for which the walls of our enclosure are perfectly reflecting surfaces (diffuse reflectors) for all wavelengths, so that no energy is absorbed.   In this case the radiation in the cavity may have any composition whatsoever, since the various rays do not interact with each other and there is no mechanism by which the existing spectral distribution or the state of polarization may be altered.   If we introduce a tiny black body which is at the same temperature as the walls, it will absorb and reemit radiation so that, after thermal equilibrium for the whole system is established, we again have black-body radiation at temperature T.   Since the black body so introduced may be made as small as we please, its contribution to the energy of the system may be disregarded, and it acts simply as a catalyst which ensures the black-body distribution and composition of the radiation in the cavity.   The black-body radiation in a perfectly reflecting enclosure (with a speck of black body at temperature T) may be said to have a temperature T equal to that of the black body with which it is in equilibrium, since its space distribution and spectral composition are determined uniquely by this temperature.   If we place an arbitrary body (not black) of the *same temperature* in the cavity, the state of the radiation must remain unchanged (thermal equilibrium).   Now the total rate of energy flow across a closed surface surrounding this body must be zero; hence

$$F = \int_{\substack{\text{closed} \\ \text{surface}}} S_n \, dA = 0$$

where S_n is the normal component of the Poynting vector at dA. F is composed of the incident radiation F_0 which enters the surface from outside; the reflected radiation F_r; the radiation F_e emitted by the body; and finally the radiation F_t which is transmitted through the body and emerges through the other side of the surface. Hence we must have

$$F_0 = F_r + F_e + F_t \tag{20.5}$$

In traversing the body, a fraction a of the incident radiation is absorbed. a is called the *absorption power* of the body. Evidently for the radiation absorbed, we must have

$$aF_0 = F_0 - F_r - F_t \tag{20.6}$$

From Eqs. (20.5) and (20.6) here follows immediately

$$aF_0 = F_e$$

or, dividing by A, the area of the body,

$$E = \frac{F_e}{A} = a\frac{F_0}{A} \tag{20.7}$$

E is the *emissive power* of the body at temperature T, and we see that it is greatest when $a = 1$, *i.e.*, for a black body which absorbs all incident radiation. For this reason, a black body is often referred to as an ideal radiator, and it yields the maximum thermal radiation which can be obtained at a given temperature. For such a black body, Eq. (20.7) becomes

$$\bar{E} = \frac{F_0}{A} \tag{20.8}$$

where $\bar{E}$ is the emissive power of the black body. Using this relation, Eq. (20.7) may be written as

$$E = a\bar{E} \tag{20.9}$$

The above relations hold not only for the total radiation of all frequencies, but also for that portion of the radiation in the spectral range, $d\nu$, *i.e.*, for frequencies lying between ν and $\nu + d\nu$. We have thus obtained a fundamental result known as *Kirchhoff's law: The emissive power of a body is equal to its absorption power multiplied by the emissive power of a black body at the same temperature.* It simplifies the discussion of radiation considerably, since the emission of radiation by any material can be referred to that emitted by an ideal black body, and the properties of the body which one requires are simply its absorption power. If a body is transparent for any range of frequencies or wavelengths, it cannot radiate energy of these wavelengths. The ratio of the emissive power E of a body to that of a black body $\bar{E}$ is termed the *emissivity* ϵ. It is equal to the absorbing power a of the body.

Finally, let us consider the dependence of the emissive power of a surface element on the angle θ which the emitted bundle of rays makes with the normal to the surface. The energy incident on the area element dA per unit time in this bundle of angular opening $d\omega$ is given by Eq. (20.1), so that we have

$$dF_0 = K \cos\theta \, dA \, d\omega$$

If dA is an element of area of a black body, all this incident energy will be absorbed, and if the radiation state is not disturbed (thermal equilibrium), the body must emit a similar bundle; hence

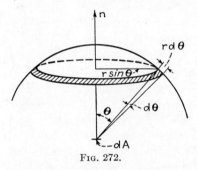

FIG. 272.

$$dF_e = K \cos\theta \, dA \, d\omega \quad (20.10)$$

The specific intensity or brightness K is that corresponding to black-body radiation and is related to the energy density thereof by Eq. (20.4). To calculate the total emission rate from this surface element, consider the radiation emitted in the hollow conical bundle between θ and $\theta + d\theta$ (Fig. 272). The solid angle of this hollow cone is $d\omega = 2\pi \sin\theta \, d\theta$, since, on a sphere of radius r, the area of the ring is

$$2\pi r^2 \sin\theta \, d\theta$$

and by definition $d\omega$ is this area divided by r^2. Thus from Eq. (20.10) we have

$$F_e = 2\pi K \, dA \int_0^{\pi/2} \cos\theta \sin\theta \, d\theta \quad (20.11)$$

as the emission rate from one side of the surface element dA (the outside). The value of the integral is $\frac{1}{2}$, so that we obtain

$$F_e = \pi K \, dA \quad (20.12)$$

The energy radiated per unit time per unit area is the emissive power $\bar{E}$ of the surface, so that

$$\bar{E} = \pi K \quad (20.13)$$

When applied to sources emitting visible radiation, this equation is known as *Lambert's law*, and although we have shown it to be true for black bodies, it turns out experimentally to be very nearly true for some sources which are not black. When applied to such cases, the brightness K of the source will in general be different from that of a black body.

2. Radiation Pressure. When an electromagnetic wave impinges on the surface of a material body, it exerts a mechanical force on the body in the direction of propagation of the wave. In general, one must deal with both normal stresses (pressures) and shearing stresses on the surfaces of bodies on which radiation is incident (or from which radiation is emitted). For the case of normal incidence, or for the case of isotropic radiation, which is fundamental in our study of heat radiation, one has to do with the pressure of radiation, and before proceeding further with the question of the laws of emission of thermal radiation, we must derive the relation between radiation pressure and the energy density of the radiation exerting the pressure.

Let us start with the simple case of a plane electromagnetic wave normally incident on the surface of an ideal metal of infinite conductivity. Inside the metal there can be no electric field and hence no magnetic field nor electromagnetic wave; therefore the metal is a perfect reflector. There will be a surface current of surface density J induced on the conductor surface, as shown in Fig. 273, and this alternating current emits the reflected wave. The magnitude of J will be such that its magnetic field inside the metal just cancels that of the incoming wave and doubles the magnetic field just outside the conductor surface. The electric vectors of the incident and reflected waves must be equal and opposite at each instant of time just outside the metal surface, since the tangential component of $\mathcal{E}$ is continuous at any boundary. The mechanical force on the induced surface current

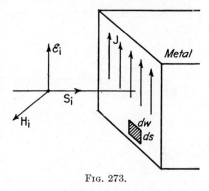

exerted by the magnetic field of the incident wave is directed into the metal, as is evident from Fig. 273, and this is the origin of the pressure of radiation for this case.

Consider an element of area of width dw and length ds as shown in Fig. 273. The current on this area forms a current element

$$i \, ds = J \, dw \, ds = J \, dA$$

and since the magnitude of the force on this current element is given by

$$dF = i \, ds \, B_i = J B_i \, dA$$

we have for the pressure p

$$p = JB_i = J\mu_0 H_i \tag{20.14}$$

B_i is the magnetic induction vector of the incident plane wave just at the metal surface. Now the general boundary condition on H, the resultant magnetic field intensity of both incident and reflected waves [Eq. (14.24)], requires that the difference between the tangential components of H as one crosses any surface be equal to the surface current density on this surface. In our case, the resultant H is zero just inside the metal surface, and the resultant H is tangential to the metal just outside. We thus have

$$H = J \tag{20.15}$$

Now inside the metal we have H_r, the magnetic intensity of the reflected wave generated by the surface current, just equal and opposite to H_i, so that there is no wave inside the metal, whereas just outside the surface the resultant magnetic intensity is

$$H = H_i + H_r = 2H_i = 2H_r \tag{20.16}$$

Using Eqs. (20.15) and (20.16) in Eq. (20.14), there follows

$$p = \frac{\mu_0 H^2}{2} \tag{20.17}$$

and since the electric energy density is zero just at the conductor surface ($\mathcal{E} = 0$), we may write

$$p = u \tag{20.18}$$

where u is the electromagnetic energy density at the surface of the reflector. It is instructive to interpret this result in terms of the energy densities of the incident and reflected waves. The energy density of the incident wave is

$$u_i = \frac{1}{2}(\epsilon_0 \mathcal{E}_i^2 + \mu_0 H_i^2) = \mu_0 H_i^2 = \frac{S_i}{c} \tag{20.19}$$

where S_i is the magnitude of the Poynting vector, and we have used the relation $\epsilon_0 \mathcal{E}_i^2 = \mu_0 H_i^2$, which is valid for a traveling plane wave. Similarly, for the reflected wave,

$$u_r = \frac{1}{2}(\epsilon_0 \mathcal{E}_r^2 + \mu_0 H_r^2) = \mu_0 H_r^2 = \frac{S_r}{c} \tag{20.20}$$

and since $H_i = H_r$ just outside the conductor surface, we may write in place of Eq. (20.17)

$$p = 2\mu_0 H_i^2 = 2\mu_0 H_r^2$$

or

$$p = \mu_0 H_i^2 + \mu_0 H_r^2 = u_i + u_r \tag{20.21}$$

so that the radiation pressure on the metal equals the sum of the energy densities of the incident and reflected waves at its surface. Needless to say, the results just obtained hold for instantaneous as well as for average values of the pressure and energy densities.

Thus we are led to the conclusion that electromagnetic waves transport not only energy (the flow given by the Poynting vector) but also momentum. The momentum carried by these waves may be thought of as distributed throughout space in a manner similar to the energy; hence we introduce the idea of a space density of electromagnetic momentum g. Consider an element of area ΔA of the conductor surface. In time dt, the momentum incident on this surface is given by

$$g_i \, \Delta A \, c \, dt$$

and the momentum carried away from this surface element by the reflected wave in time dt is similarly given by

$$g_r \, \Delta A \, c \, dt$$

where $g_i = g_r$ for the case under consideration. The change of momentum in time dt is the sum of these two expressions, and consequently the force on the area ΔA is, by Newton's second law,

$$\Delta F = c(g_i + g_r) \, \Delta A$$

and the pressure

$$p = cg_i + cg_r \tag{20.22}$$

Comparing this with Eq. (20.21), we see that the momentum density in an electromagnetic wave is related to the energy density, and hence to the Poynting vector, by

$$g = \frac{u}{c} = \frac{S}{c^2} \tag{20.23}$$

More generally, the vector relation between $\mathbf{g}$ and $\mathbf{S}$ is

$$\mathbf{g} = \frac{1}{c^2} \mathbf{S} \tag{20.23a}$$

The concept of electromagnetic momentum now enables us to compute the pressure of isotropic radiation. Before doing so, however, we must emphasize the fact that the relation given by Eq. (20.18) for normal incidence is true, not only for perfect reflectors, but for arbitrary surfaces, if by u we mean the *total* electromagnetic energy density at the surface.   For example, let us suppose that we have a perfectly absorbing surface, so that there is no reflection, and that this surface is at such a low temperature that it emits negligible radiation. Then Eqs. (20.22) and (20.23) show that the pressure of normally incident radiation is still equal to the energy density at the surface

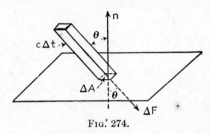

FIG. 274.

($p = u_i$ and $u_r = 0$), but since the energy density is now that of the incident wave alone, which is half as large as for the case of perfect reflection, the pressure is reduced by half also.   Now let us consider radiation impinging on an element ΔA of the surface of a body at an angle θ with the normal.   The momentum transferred to the surface element in time Δt is that contained in a slant prism of base ΔA and slant height $c\ \Delta t$ (Fig. 274). This gives rise to a force ΔF in the direction shown given by

$$\Delta F = gc \cos \theta\ \Delta A$$

or, since by Eq. (20.23) $g = u/c$, this can be written as

$$\Delta F = u \cos \theta\ \Delta A \tag{20.24}$$

This gives rise to a component normal to the surface

$$\Delta F_n = u \cos^2 \theta\ \Delta A \tag{20.25}$$

and a tangential component

$$\Delta F_t = u \cos \theta \sin \theta\ \Delta A \tag{20.26}$$

For isotropic radiation (u independent of direction) the tangential components of ΔF as given by Eq. (20.26) sum up to zero, and the pressure is obtained from Eq. (20.25).   Since the average value of $\cos^2 \theta$ over a hemisphere is $\frac{1}{3}$, this yields for the *pressure of isotropic radiation*

$$p = \frac{u}{3} \tag{20.27}$$

This is a fundamental equation in radiation theory.   One more remark may be appropriate at this point.   Let us suppose that we have a hollow enclosure containing black-body radiation at a temperature T, and let the temperature of the walls (which may be of arbitrary composition) be T, so that the system is in thermal equilibrium. From the second law of thermodynamics we must also have mechanical equilibrium for this system, since otherwise mechanical work could be obtained at the expense of the internal energy of an isolated system, all parts of which are at the same temperature. It thus follows that the pressure must be the same at all points of the walls, independent of their absorbing or reflecting powers, and it is related to the energy density by Eq. (20.27).

3. The Stefan-Boltzmann Law. We have already pointed out that the energy density of black-body radiation depends only on its temperature. The law expressing this dependence was found experimentally by *Stefan* and later deduced theoretically by *Boltzmann*. It states that the emissive power of a black body is proportional to the fourth power of its absolute temperature. If, as before, $\bar{E}$ denotes the emissive power of a black body, we can write

$$\bar{E} = \sigma T^4 \qquad (20.28)$$

where σ, the Stefan-Boltzmann constant, has the value

$$\sigma = 5.67 \times 10^{-8} \text{ joule/m}^2\text{-sec-}°\text{C}^4$$
$$= 1.36 \times 10^{-12} \text{ cal/cm}^2\text{-sec-}°\text{C}^4 \qquad (20.28a)$$

We have written Eq. (20.28) for the emissive power $\bar{E}$, but we can readily see that a similar expression holds for the radiation density u. Using Eq. (20.13) to express $\bar{E}$ in terms of K, and Eq. (20.4) to express K in terms of u, we find readily that

$$u = \frac{4\pi}{c} K = \frac{4}{c} \bar{E} = \frac{4\sigma}{c} T^4 = \alpha T^4 \qquad (20.29)$$

The thermal radiation from many real surfaces which are not black is found experimentally to be very nearly proportional to the fourth power of the absolute temperature, but with a proportionality constant which is smaller than σ as given by Eq. (20.28a). This is the case for metals such as platinum and tungsten and also for carbon. For such surfaces, one can write

$$E = \epsilon\sigma T^4 \qquad (20.30)$$

where ϵ, the emissivity, has already been referred to and is equal to the absorbing power of the body [Eq. (20.9)]. The emissivity of a hot tungsten-lamp filament is about $\frac{1}{3}$.

The Stefan-Boltzmann law can be derived theoretically from the second law of thermodynamics in the following manner: Consider a cylinder with a tightly fitting frictionless piston and perfectly diffuse reflecting walls which contains black-body radiation at temperature T. Let the volume in which the radiation is present be V and the walls be at the temperature T (Fig. 275). As we have shown, the radiation exerts a pressure $p = \frac{1}{3}u$ on the piston, and the energy density u is uniformly distributed throughout the volume. The internal energy of the system is uV, where u depends only on the temperature T. Now let an amount of heat dQ flow reversibly into the system. The first law of thermodynamics requires that

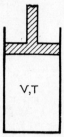

V,T

FIG. 275.

$$d(uV) = dQ - p\,dV$$

where dV is the volume change corresponding to a small motion of the piston. Since

$$d(uV) = u\,dV + V\,du$$

the above equation may be written in the form

$$dQ = V\,du + (p + u)\,dV$$

and since $p = u/3$, this takes the form

$$dQ = V\left(\frac{du}{dT}\right)dT + \frac{4}{3}u\,dV \tag{20.31}$$

where we have used the fact that u is a function of T only and not of V.

Now the second law of thermodynamics requires that the heat dQ added in a reversible process divided by the absolute temperature T (the change of entropy) depend only on the initial and final states of the system and not on the intermediate stages of the process. This is equivalent to saying that if we divide each term of Eq. (20.31) by T, the left-hand side becomes a total differential. Thus in the equation

$$dS = \frac{dQ}{T} = \frac{V}{T}\left(\frac{du}{dT}\right)dT + \frac{4}{3}\frac{u}{T}\,dV \tag{20.32}$$

$(V/T)(du/dT)$, the coefficient of dT, is $(\partial S/\partial T)_V$; and $\frac{4}{3}u/T$, the coefficient of dV, is $(\partial S/\partial V)_T$. Since, in general, the rules of partial differentiation demand that

$$\frac{\partial^2 S}{\partial T\,\partial V} = \frac{\partial^2 S}{\partial V\,\partial T}$$

there follows

$$\frac{\partial}{\partial V}\left(\frac{V}{T}\frac{du}{dT}\right) = \frac{\partial}{\partial T}\left(\frac{4}{3}\frac{u}{T}\right)$$

Remembering that u depends only on T, this becomes

$$\frac{1}{T}\frac{du}{dT} = \frac{4}{3T}\frac{du}{dT} - \frac{4}{3}\frac{u}{T^2}$$

or

$$\frac{du}{dT} = 4\frac{u}{T}$$

Separating variables,

$$\frac{du}{u} = 4\frac{dT}{T}$$

and integrating

$$\ln u = \ln T^4 + \text{constant}$$

or

$$u = \alpha T^4 \tag{20.33}$$

which is identical with Eq. (20.29).

4. The Planck Radiation Law; Wien's Displacement Law. There still remains the fundamental question of the spectral composition of black-body radiation. The Stefan-Boltzmann law gives the temperature dependence of the total energy density u but places no limitations whatsoever on the possible spectral distribution of this energy density among the various wavelengths or frequencies of the electromagnetic spectrum. Indeed, thermodynamics alone cannot provide a unique answer to this question. The situation is somewhat analogous to the theory of gases. Here thermodynamics can provide us with a number of relations involving the nternal energy of the gas, but the velocity distribution of the molecules is a matter for atomic theory. The researches of Planck, about 1900, in connection with this problem led to the foundations of the now famous quantum theory. Classical physics led to an impossible law, as we shall point out shortly. It would be beyond the scope of this book to attempt a discussion of the quantum theory, and we must content ourselves with a statement and discussion of the results.

If we denote the energy density per unit frequency range of the spectrum by u_ν, then in the frequency range $d\nu$ there will be a contribution to the total energy density equal to $u_\nu\,d\nu$, and consequently

$$u = \int_0^\infty u_\nu\,d\nu \tag{20.34}$$

As we have seen in connection with the Stefan-Boltzmann law, the brightness K and the emissive power of a black body $\bar{E}$ are proportional to u. Similarly a proportionality exists between these quantities per unit frequency or per unit wavelength range. Although it is more convenient from a theoretical standpoint to deal with frequency distribution, it is more convenient experimentally to deal with the distribution with respect to wavelength, and we must say a word or two concerning these two modes of description. For the sake of concreteness, consider the emissive power of a black body. This can be written as

$$\bar{E} = \int_0^\infty E_\lambda \, d\lambda = \int_0^\infty E_\nu \, d\nu$$

where E_λ and E_ν are the emissive powers per unit wavelength and frequency range, respectively. The spectral distribution of black-body radiation can be specified either by giving E_λ as a function of λ or by giving E_ν as a function of ν. The resulting formulas will *not* be identical in form, as we can see from the following: Consider a range of frequencies between ν and $\nu + d\nu$ and a corresponding range of wavelengths $d\lambda$. The energy of these wavelengths radiated per unit time per unit area by a black body is given by

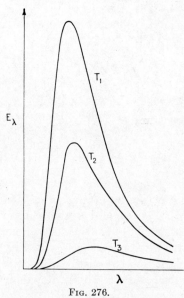

FIG. 276.

$$d\bar{E} = E_\nu \, d\nu = E_\lambda \, d\lambda$$

and since the relation between frequency and wavelength is

$$\nu = \frac{c}{\lambda}$$

we have immediately

$$|d\nu| = \frac{c}{\lambda^2} |d\lambda|$$

so that E_ν and E_λ are related by the equation

$$E_\lambda = \frac{c}{\lambda^2} E_\nu \qquad (20.35)$$

Similarly for energy densities, we have $u_\lambda = (c/\lambda^2)u_\nu$. Equation (20.35) must be kept in mind when translating experimental results from a wavelength to a frequency scale. Figure 276 shows the shape of the curves for E_λ for black-body radiation as a function of wavelength, as obtained from experiment. In these curves $T_1 > T_2 > T_3$. Note that the maxima of these curves moves toward shorter wavelengths as the temperature is increased, as one would expect from the color changes which occur when the temperature of a body is raised. The curves of Fig. 276 may be looked upon as plots of u_λ as function of λ, since there would only be a difference of a scale factor.

The equation describing the normal spectrum (black-body spectrum) obtained by Planck is as follows:

$$u_\nu = \frac{8\pi h \nu^3}{c^3} \frac{1}{e^{h\nu/kT} - 1} \tag{20.36}$$

Here h is a fundamental atomic constant known as Planck's constant and has the value

$$h = 6.62 \times 10^{-34} \text{ joule-sec}$$

k is Boltzmann's constant (1.38×10^{-23} joule/°C) and T the absolute temperature. For the wavelength distribution, we have, using the fact expressed by Eq. (20.35),

$$u_\lambda = \frac{8\pi hc}{\lambda^5} \frac{1}{e^{hc/\lambda kT} - 1} = \frac{c_1/\lambda^5}{e^{c_2/\lambda T} - 1} \tag{20.37}$$

which is the form usually employed by experimentalists. There are two limiting cases for which we may rewrite Eq. (20.36) which have interesting historical significance. For long wavelengths, *i.e.*, for a frequency range such that $h\nu \ll kT$, we may expand the exponential in Eq. (20.36) and neglect powers of $h\nu/kT$ higher than the first. We have

$$e^{h\nu/kT} = 1 + \frac{h\nu}{kT} + \frac{(h\nu)^2}{2!(kT)^2} + \cdots$$

so that very nearly

$$e^{h\nu/kT} - 1 = \frac{h\nu}{kT}$$

Using this value in Eq. (20.36), there follows

$$u_\nu = \frac{8\pi \nu^2}{c^3} kT \tag{20.38}$$

which is valid for the long-wavelength portion of the spectrum. It is of interest to note that this is the law predicted by classical theory for the whole spectral range and is known as the *Rayleigh-Jeans law*. It is obviously an impossible law, since it predicts an infinite total energy density at any finite temperature.

On the other hand, for the high-frequency, short-wavelength region of the spectrum, in which $h\nu \gg kT$, we may set

$$e^{h\nu/kT} - 1 \cong e^{h\nu/kT}$$

and obtain

$$u_\nu = \frac{8\pi h\nu^3}{c^3} e^{-h\nu/kT} \tag{20.39}$$

This is the form of the radiation law obtained by *Wien* by semiempirical methods and is known by his name. It is more convenient than the Planck law for calculation purposes in the short-wavelength region of the spectrum.

The Stefan-Boltzmann law may be derived from Planck's law by performing the integration indicated by Eq. (20.34). We have

$$u = \frac{8\pi h}{c^3} \int_0^\infty \frac{\nu^3\, d\nu}{e^{h\nu/kT} - 1}$$

and if we set $h\nu/kT = x$, we find

$$d\nu = \frac{kT}{h}\, dx$$

$$\nu^3 = \left(\frac{kT}{h}\right)^3 x^3$$

and substituting

$$u = \frac{8\pi k^4 T^4}{c^3 h^3} \int_0^\infty \frac{x^3\, dx}{e^x - 1} = \alpha T^4 \tag{20.40}$$

where

$$\alpha = \frac{8\pi k^4}{c^3 h^3} \int_0^\infty \frac{x^3\, dx}{e^x - 1}$$

The integral has the value $\pi^4/15$, so that

$$\alpha = \frac{8\pi^5 k^4}{15 c^3 h^3}$$

Finally, the position of the maximum of any one of the curves of Fig. 276 may be obtained by differentiating Eq. (20.37). The result may be expressed in the form

$$\lambda_m T = \text{constant} = b \tag{20.41}$$

where λ_m is the wavelength for which E_λ is a maximum and the constant b has the numerical value

$$b = 0.00288 \text{ m-}^\circ\text{C} = 0.288 \text{ cm-}^\circ\text{C}$$

This important law is known as *Wien's displacement law* and was derived by Wien with the help of thermodynamic considerations.

5. Photometric Units; Visibility of Radiant Energy. Photometry is the study of the measurement of radiant energy in the visible region of the spectrum, and, although bearing an intimate relation to the general theory of radiation discussed in the preceding sections, it possesses its own peculiar units which differ somewhat from those which we have been employing. There are two reasons for the unique procedure adopted when dealing with visible radiation: (1) Photometric units were introduced independently of those employed in other branches of physics, very much as the calorie is introduced in heat as an energy unit; and (2) the human eye is not equally sensitive to radiations of different wavelengths (even in the visible range), so that the so-called *relative visibility* of radiation must be included in the definition of photometric units.

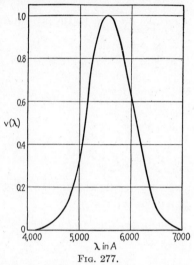

Fig. 277.

Suppose we consider an experiment in which an observer looks at a number of essentially monochromatic sources. The energy radiated from the sources is varied so that they all seem equally bright to a normal observer. It is found that the least radiant power (E_λ) is needed for the source of wavelength 5,550 A. The ratio of E_λ for this source to its value for any other source at wavelength λ to produce the sensation of equal brightness for a normal eye is called the *relative visibility* of this wavelength. Figure 277 is a plot of this relative visibility $v(\lambda)$ as a function of λ for a normal eye. Because of this selective action of the eye, a statement of the emissive power E in absolute units of a light source is insufficient to determine its visual effect. For this reason it is conventional to introduce a photometric unit of the total rate of emission of energy (energy flux) called the *lumen*. For a normal observer it is equivalent to $\frac{1}{621}$ watt at the wavelength 5,550 A. The numerical factor of 621 arises from the arbitrary definition of a unit of light intensity (see below), the *candle*. Thus 1 watt radiated at 5,550 A equals 621 lumens of light flux, and at any other wavelength the luminous flux F_l in lumens is given by

$$F_l = v(\lambda) \cdot 621F \qquad (20.42)$$

where F is the radiated power in watts from a monochromatic source of wavelength λ and $v(\lambda)$ is the relative visibility of this wavelength. The ratio F_l/F is called the *luminous efficiency* of the source. If the source is not monochromatic, then one must integrate over the spectrum to obtain the luminous efficiency. The number of lumens radiated per unit area of the surface of the source is called the *luminosity* of the source, L. It is clear that the contribution to L from the wavelength range $d\lambda$ is given by

$$dL = 621 v(\lambda) E_\lambda \, d\lambda$$

where $E_\lambda \, d\lambda$ is in watts per square centimeter, so that the luminosity becomes

$$L = 621 \int_0^\infty v(\lambda) E_\lambda \, d\lambda \tag{20.43}$$

in lumens per square centimeter, and the luminous efficiency is given by

$$\text{Eff.} = 621 \frac{\int_0^\infty v(\lambda) E_\lambda \, d\lambda}{\int_0^\infty E_\lambda \, d\lambda} \tag{20.44}$$

since $\int_0^\infty E_\lambda \, d\lambda$ is equal to E, the emissive power of the surface in watts per square centimeter.

The *intensity* I of a light source of dimensions sufficiently small that it may be considered a point source is defined as follows: Consider a pencil of rays coming from the source of solid angular opening $d\omega$ (Fig. 278). Then the intensity of the source in the direction n is defined as the luminous flux crossing the area dA' divided by the solid angle $d\omega$. Thus we have

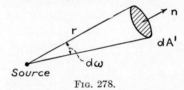

Fig. 278.

$$I = \frac{dF_l}{d\omega} \tag{20.45}$$

and if the source radiates uniformly in all directions,

$$I = \frac{F_l}{4\pi} \tag{20.46}$$

where F_l is the total flux coming from the source. The photometric unit of intensity is an arbitrary unit, the *candle*, defined as a source which (emitting uniformly in all directions) emits 4π lumens, so that 1 candle equals 1 lumen per unit solid angle. Actually the standard candle was chosen arbitrarily, the unit flux obtained from Eq. (20.46). Experiment then yielded the numerical factor 621 used above.

Consider the area dA' of Fig. 278. The illumination E' on this surface is defined as the ratio of the luminous flux incident on it to its area. Thus

$$E' = \frac{dF_l}{dA'} = \frac{dF_l}{d\omega} \frac{d\omega}{dA'} = \frac{I}{r^2} \qquad (20.47)$$

using Eq. (20.45) and the fact that $dA' = r^2 \, d\omega$ for the case in which dA' is normal to r. If the normal to the surface element makes an angle θ with the direction of the pencil, then Eq. (20.47) evidently becomes

$$E' = \frac{I}{r^2} \cos \theta \qquad (20.48)$$

Finally, the brightness K of a pencil of rays has already been defined by Eq. (20.1). The same definition is utilized in photometry except for a change in units. If, in Eq. (20.1), one expresses dF in lumens, then we have

$$K = \frac{\Delta I}{\cos \theta \, \Delta A} \qquad (20.49)$$

where $\Delta I = dF/d\omega$ in candles and K is measured in candles per square centimeter. Equation (20.49) gives the brightness of the radiation at the surface ΔA. If the surface element ΔA is self-luminous, then K is called the *brightness of the surface*. If such a surface obeys Lambert's law [Eq. (20.12) or (20.13)], it is convenient to define a new unit of brightness B, the *lambert*, defined by the relation

$$B = \pi K \qquad (20.50)$$

where K is in candles per square centimeter. Thus the lambert is $1/\pi$ times as large as the candle per square centimeter.

In terms of this new unit, Eq. (20.13) becomes

$$\bar{E} = E' = B \qquad (20.51)$$

since, for a black surface, the illumination (energy incident per unit time per unit area) equals the emissive power $\bar{E}$. For surfaces which diffusely reflect or transmit light and obey a law similar to Eq. (20.10) for the reflected or transmitted light (this is essentially Lambert's law), one writes for the surface brightness

$$B = kE' \qquad (20.52)$$

where k is the fraction of the incident light reflected or transmitted and E' is the illumination of the surface.

Problems

1. Consider a black body whose surface A is everywhere convex, so that none of the radiation leaving any point of this surface is directly incident on any other point of the surface. This body is completely surrounded by an enclosure, and both the body and the walls of the enclosure are at an absolute temperature T_1. Show that the rate at which radiant energy falls on the body is given by

$$\sigma A T_1^4$$

independent of the area and nature of the walls.

Using the above result, show that if the black-body temperature is maintained at T_2 and that of the surrounding walls at T_1, the net rate of gain or loss of energy by radiation of the black body is given by

$$A\sigma(T_2^4 - T_1^4)$$

What condition must be satisfied for this law to be valid?

2. A closed graphite crucible at 27°C is placed inside a furnace with walls maintained at 1730°C. Treating the crucible as a black body of 40 cm² area, compute the initial rate at which the crucible gains heat from the furnace walls, using the results of Prob. 1. If the crucible is of mass 100 g and mean specific heat 0.30, how long will it take for the crucible to reach a temperature of 100°C? (Note that the ratio of crucible to wall temperature is small compared to unity for the temperature range in question.)

3. Taking 15°C as an average temperature of the entire earth's surface and assuming the earth as a whole (including the atmosphere) absorbs the sun's radiation and radiates like a black body, compute the absolute temperature of space (*i.e.*, of the radiation in empty space around the earth). Take the solar energy incident on the earth's surface as 2.2 cal/cm²-min, when the sun is directly overhead.

4. A small hole of area ΔA is made in the walls of a furnace containing black radiation at temperature T. A black sphere of radius r is placed in front of the hole at a distance R from it. Neglecting the radiation from the outer furnace walls, show that the energy falling on the black sphere per unit time is given by

$$\sigma \, \Delta A \; T^4 \, \frac{r^2}{R^2}$$

5. A black sphere 8.0 cm in diameter is placed in front of a small (10 cm²) opening in the walls of a furnace with its center 40 cm from the opening. The furnace walls are shielded so that only the radiation from the opening is incident on the sphere. The steady temperature reached by the sphere is the same as can be maintained by supplying 2.80 watts of electrical power to a heating unit inside the sphere, when the hole in the furnace walls is covered. Compute the temperature of the furnace radiation, assuming it to be black.

6. A small hole of area 5.0 cm² is cut in the wall of a furnace containing black-body radiation at 2000°abs. A blackened metal disk of 20 cm radius is mounted parallel to the furnace walls with its center at a distance of 40 cm from the walls on the normal to the furnace wall at the opening. The mass of the disk is 0.20 kg, and its mean specific heat is 0.20.

If the furnace walls are shielded so that only the radiation from the hole is incident on the disk, compute the initial rate of increase of the disk temperature. The disk is initially at room temperature.

7. A hole of area 4.0 cm² is made in one of the walls of a furnace containing black-body radiation at a temperature of 727°C. A hollow cylinder with open ends and with perfectly absorbing inner walls is mounted on the furnace wall with the center of its base coincident with the hole. The inner radius of the cylinder is 17.3 cm.

   a. What must be the altitude of the cylinder if it is to absorb 75 per cent of the radiation from the hole?

   b. How much energy is absorbed by the cylinder walls in 1 min?

8. Prove that the net rate of heat transfer per unit area by radiation between two plane-parallel surfaces, of separation small compared with the linear dimensions of the surfaces, is given by

$$\frac{\sigma(T_1^4 - T_2^4)}{(1/\epsilon_1) + (1/\epsilon_2) - 1}$$

where ϵ_1, T_1 and ϵ_2, T_2 are the emissivities and absolute temperatures of the two surfaces. σ is the Stefan-Boltzmann constant.

9. The temperature of the water in a thermos bottle is observed to fall from 100 to 99°C in 30 min when the outer shell of the bottle is at 25°C.

Find the time required for the temperature of the same amount of ice water at 0°C to rise to 1°C if the outer shell is at 20°C. Neglect the heat loss through the cork stopper.

10. The inner bottle of a thermos bottle (unsilvered) contains 1 liter of ice water, and the outer shell is at 25°C. The emissivity of a glass surface is 0.85, and the area of the outer surface of the inner bottle (and also the inner surface of the outer shell) is 175 cm².

Neglecting heat losses through the cork, find how long it takes for the water's temperature to rise from 0°C

   a. To 1°C.

   b. To 10°C. (Use reasonable approximations for part *b*.)

11. The temperature of the outer surface of a closed tungsten crucible is measured by a radiation pyrometer as 2400°abs, assuming the crucible to be black. If the emissivity of the crucible is 0.45, find the actual temperature of the crucible.

12. An object of surface area A_1 is maintained at a temperature T_4 by a constant supply of electrical power P, while radiating to remote surroundings which are at a temperature T_3. A "radiation shield" consisting of a thin metal spherical shell of surface area A_2 is placed so as to surround but not touch the object. It is found that with the same power P supplied to the inner object, the radiation shield comes to a steady temperature T_2 and the temperature of the inner object rises to a new value T_1. Consider the object and the radiation screen as black bodies.

   a. Find expressions for the power loss from the object before and after insertion of the radiation shield, and for the power loss from the radiation shield.

   b. Using the equations of part *a*, deduce an equation for T_1 in terms of T_4, T_3, and the known surface areas.

   13. Prove that Wien's displacement law follows from the Planck formula (20.36) or (20.37) or from Eq. (20.39).

   14. The wavelength of maximum intensity in the solar spectrum is 5,000 A. Assuming the sun to radiate like a black body, find its surface temperature.

   15. To what temperature would the blackened bulb of a thermometer rise in full sunlight if the bulb were surrounded by a perfectly transparent, evacuated glass bulb? The surroundings are at 25°C. Assume the thermometer bulb to behave like a black body.

   16. Compute the ratio of the increase of brightness of black-body radiation at a wavelength of 6,410 A for an increase of temperature from 1200 to 1500°abs.

   17. Starting from Planck's law or from Wien's law [Eq. (20.39)], prove that the maximum value of the emissive power *per unit wavelength range* (E_λ) for black-body radiation varies with the fifth power of the absolute temperature. What is the corresponding law for E_ν?

   18. What is the radiation pressure of black-body radiation at a temperature of 6000°abs?

   19. Starting from Planck's law, compute the value of b in Wien's displacement law [Eq. (20.41)]. Repeat this calculation starting from Eq. (20.39), and compare your result with the experimental value.

   20. Calculate the force exerted by a beam of parallel light from the sun on a particle 1.0 cm in radius in the tail of a comet. Take the sun as a black-body radiator at 5750°abs.

   21. Find the brightness of a sheet of paper which is placed on a desk at a distance of 1 m below a 250-cp point source. The paper diffusely reflects 80 per cent of the light incident on it.

   22. *a.* The brightness of a spherical diffusing shade 10.0 cm in radius placed about a point source is $1/2\pi$ candle/cm². What is the brightness expressed in lamberts and the intensity of the point source?

   b. What is the brightness of a book page 10 by 10 cm held 0.8 m below a 75-cp point source if the page reflects 65 per cent of the incident light?

APPENDIX I

ELECTROMAGNETIC UNITS

As has been indicated in the text, a number of different systems of electromagnetic units have been employed in the study of electricity and magnetism. Of these, the so-called *Gaussian* system of units has enjoyed the widest popularity, and it is the purpose of this appendix to present the basis for this system in sufficient detail so that the reader may translate the principal equations in rationalized mks units to the Gaussian system, and vice versa. The Gaussian system itself is a mixture of two older systems of units, the so-called absolute electrostatic system (esu) and the absolute electromagnetic system (emu), both of which are unrationalized systems.

1. The Electrostatic System of Units. The electrostatic system of units is based on the choice of a unit charge, the so-called *statcoulomb*, or electrostatic unit of charge, derived from Coulomb's law. The mechanical units employed are centimeters, grams, and seconds, and the proportionality constant in Eq. (3.1) is placed equal to the pure number unity (a *dimensionless* number). Thus Coulomb's law [Eq. (3.3)] takes the form

$$F = \frac{q_1 q_2}{r^2} \tag{1}$$

so that the dimensions of charge can be expressed in terms of those of mass, length, and time. *Then the unit charge in the electrostatic system, the statcoulomb, is defined so that two such similar charges separated by a distance of one centimeter in vacuum repel each other with a force of one dyne.* The dimensions of the square of a charge become

$$[q^2] = ml^3 t^{-2} \tag{2}$$

The field and potential of a point charge in empty space are then

$$\mathcal{E} = \frac{q}{r^2} \tag{3}$$

and

$$V = \frac{q}{r} \tag{4}$$

and the electric displacement vector D becomes identical with $\mathcal{E}$ in vacuum, both in magnitude and dimensions. Gauss's theorem now takes the form

$$\int_{\substack{\text{closed} \\ \text{surface}}} D_n \, dS = 4\pi q \tag{5}$$

and the presence of the factor 4π is characteristic of the unrationalized nature of this system of units.

In order to convert any of the equations of the text in Chaps. 2 to 4, covering electrostatics in empty space, to electrostatic units, one replaces $4\pi\epsilon_0$ by unity and D by $D/4\pi$. Thus, for example, the capacity of a parallel-plate condenser [Eq. (4.15)] becomes

$$C = \frac{A}{4\pi d} \tag{6}$$

and that for the energy density of the electrostatic field [Eq. (4.33)] becomes

$$u = \frac{1}{8\pi} \, \mathcal{E}^2 = \frac{1}{8\pi} \, \mathcal{E}D \tag{7}$$

in electrostatic units. *The electrostatic unit of current, the statampere, is defined as one statcoulomb per second.*

In the case of dielectrics (Chap. 13), the polarization vector P has the same dimensions as $\mathcal{E}$ or D (statcoulombs per square centimeter). The relation between D and $\mathcal{E}$ is still written in the form

$$D = \epsilon\mathcal{E} \tag{8}$$

where now ϵ is a pure number and equal to the dielectric constant κ of the dielectric. Essentially the same rule as above (replacement of $4\pi\epsilon_0$ by unity, $4\pi\epsilon$ by ϵ or κ, and D by $D/4\pi$) will convert the equations of this chapter to electrostatic units. Thus the definition of D [Eq. (13.8)] becomes

$$\frac{D}{4\pi} = \frac{\mathcal{E}}{4\pi} + P$$

or

$$D = \mathcal{E} + 4\pi P \tag{9}$$

The definition of *electric susceptibility* χ provides the one exception to the foregoing procedure. In the electrostatic system of units the susceptibility χ is defined as

$$\chi = \frac{P}{\mathcal{E}} \tag{10}$$

so that Eq. (13.19) becomes

$$\kappa = 1 + 4\pi\chi \tag{11}$$

Finally, we present a few of the more important numerical conversion factors relating electrostatic to mks units. Any others can then be derived with the help of these.

$$1 \text{ coulomb} = 3.00 \times 10^9 \text{ statcoulombs}$$
$$300 \text{ volts} = 1 \text{ statvolt}$$
$$1 \text{ farad} = 9.00 \times 10^{11} \text{ statfarad (cm)}$$

The charge on an electron is

$$1.60 \times 10^{-19} \text{ coulomb} = 4.80 \times 10^{-10} \text{ statcoulomb}$$

2. The Electromagnetic System of Units. The electromagnetic system of units is based on the choice of a unit charge (or unit electric current), the so-called *abcoulomb* (or *abampere*), derived from the law of force between two current-carrying conductors. The mechanical units employed are centimeters, grams, and seconds (just as in the electrostatic system), and the proportionality constant in Eq. (7.1) is placed equal to the pure number unity (a dimensionless number). Thus, the equation for the attractive force between the two parallel current elements [Eq. (7.7)] takes the form

$$dF = \frac{i^2 \, ds \, ds'}{r^2} \tag{12}$$

so that the dimensions of current, and hence of charge, can be expressed in terms of those of mass, length, and time. *The unit current in the electromagnetic system of units, the abampere, is defined as that current existing in similar parallel current elements separated by a distance of one centimeter in vacuum which results in an attractive force of one dyne per centimeter of each element.* This is entirely similar to the definition of the ampere.

From Eq. (12) we see that current in emu has dimensions given by

$$[i^2]_{\text{emu}} = mlt^{-2}$$

and hence a charge q in emu has dimensions given by

$$[q^2]_{\text{emu}} = ml \tag{13}$$

In sharp contrast to this, we have for the dimensions of q^2 in esu, according to Eq. (2),

$$[q^2]_{\text{esu}} = ml^3t^{-2}$$

from which there follows the surprising fact that the dimensions of electric charge in esu and in emu are different from each other. This has been a source of much confusion to the student of electromagnetism.   In fact the ratio of the dimensions of q in esu to those of q in emu is readily seen to be

$$\frac{[q]_{esu}}{[q]_{emu}} = \frac{l}{t} \quad \text{(a velocity!)} \tag{14}$$

and this velocity is expressed in centimeters per second.

In the electromagnetic system of units, the unit of magnetic induction B is called *one gauss, and this equals one dyne per abampere-centimeter*, according to the defining Eq. (6.7).   The unit of magnetic flux is called *one maxwell, and this is equal to one gauss-cm²*.   In empty space $B = H$ so that H (termed *oersteds* in emu) is identical with B in magnitude and dimensions.   The Ampère rule [Eq. (7.5)] in emu takes the form

$$\mathbf{dH} = i\left(\frac{\mathbf{ds} \times \mathbf{r}}{r^3}\right) \tag{15}$$

and the Ampère circuital law for steady currents [Eq. (7.18)] becomes

$$\oint H_s \, ds = 4\pi i \tag{16}$$

and once again the factor 4π shows the unrationalized character of this electromagnetic system of units.

In order to convert any of the formulas in Chaps. 6 to 8 to emu, one replaces μ_0 by 4π and H by $H/4\pi$.   For example, the formula (8.14) for the inductance of a long solenoid in air becomes

$$L = \frac{4\pi^2 N^2 r^2}{l} \tag{17}$$

and the energy density in a magnetic field [Eq. (8.30)] becomes

$$u_m = \frac{B^2}{8\pi} = \frac{H^2}{8\pi} \tag{18}$$

In the case of magnetic materials (Chap. 14), the magnetization vector M has the same dimensions as B or H (abamperes per centimeter).   The relation between B and H is still written in the form

$$B = \mu H \tag{19}$$

where now μ is a pure number and equal to the relative permeability of the magnetic material.   Essentially the same rule as above (replacement of μ_0 by 4π, μ by $4\pi\mu$, and H by $H/4\pi$) will convert the equations of this chapter to electromagnetic units.   Thus the defining equation for H [Eq. (14.16)] becomes

$$\frac{H}{4\pi} = \frac{B}{4\pi} - M$$

or

$$B = H + 4\pi M \tag{20}$$

The definition of *magnetic susceptibility* χ_m again is the exception to the foregoing rule. In emu the magnetic susceptibility χ_m is defined as

$$\chi_m = \frac{M}{H} \tag{21}$$

so that Eq. (14.21) becomes

$$\mu = 1 + 4\pi\chi_m \tag{22}$$

Finally, we list a number of the numerical conversion factors relating electromagnetic to mks units:

$$10 \text{ amp} = 1 \text{ abamp}$$
$$10 \text{ coulombs} = 1 \text{ abcoulomb}$$
$$1 \text{ volt} = 10^8 \text{ abvolts}$$
$$1 \text{ weber/m}^2 = 10^4 \text{ gauss}$$
$$1 \text{ henry} = 10^9 \text{ abhenrys (cm)}$$

3. The Gaussian System of Units. The Gaussian system is a mixed system, partly electrostatic and partly electromagnetic, in which the magnetic field vectors B, H, and M are expressed in emu and other quantities such as electric field intensity $\mathcal{E}$, current, and charge are expressed in esu. None of the equations of the text involving both magnetic and electric quantities are valid as they stand in Gaussian units, and we must obtain the correct forms. This involves the inclusion of a conversion factor (and it is a dimensional factor), owing to the different dimensions and magnitudes of the same physical quantity in esu and in emu.

Let us consider the general expression for the force on a charge moving in a combined electric and magnetic field. This is [Eq. (6.14)]

$$\mathbf{F} = q\mathcal{E} + q(\mathbf{v} \times \mathbf{B}) \tag{23}$$

This equation is valid as it stands if *all* the quantities entering into it are expressed in the same system of units. To find the correct form in the Gaussian system, we write

$$F_{\text{dynes}} = q_{\text{esu}}\mathcal{E}_{\text{esu}} + q_{\text{emu}}(v_{\text{cm/sec}} \times B_{\text{gauss}})$$

and if we denote the ratio $q_{\text{esu}}/q_{\text{emu}}$ by c, the above equation becomes

$$F_{\text{dynes}} = q_{\text{esu}} \left[\mathcal{E}_{\text{esu}} + \frac{1}{c} \left(v_{\text{cm/sec}} \times B_{\text{gauss}} \right) \right]$$

According to Eq. (14), the conversion factor c between charge in esu and in emu has the dimensions of a velocity, and its numerical value as determined experimentally is

$$c = 3.00 \times 10^{10} \text{ cm/sec} \tag{24}$$

so that c is the velocity of light in vacuum. Thus Eq. (23) in Gaussian units is

$$\mathbf{F} = q \left[\mathbf{\mathcal{E}} + \left(\frac{\mathbf{v}}{c} \times \mathbf{B} \right) \right] \tag{25}$$

(Note that $\mathcal{E}$ and B or $\mathcal{E}$ and H have the same dimensions in this Gaussian system.)

Some of the more important equations will now be given in Gaussian units. The above example illustrates the method of proceeding from one system to the other.

The Faraday induction law [Eq. (8.1)] is, in Gaussian units,

$$E = -\frac{1}{c} \frac{d\Phi}{dt} \tag{26}$$

and the motional emf of Eq. (8.5) becomes

$$E = \oint \mathcal{E}'_s \, ds = \frac{1}{c} \oint (\mathbf{v} \times \mathbf{B})_s \, ds \tag{27}$$

Equation (10.9) takes the form

$$\oint H_s \, ds = \frac{4\pi}{c} \left(i + \frac{1}{4\pi} \int \frac{\partial D_n}{\partial t} \, dS \right) \tag{28}$$

The Maxwell equations (10.10) are

$$\left. \begin{aligned} \oint \mathcal{E}_s \, ds = -\frac{1}{c} \int \frac{\partial B_n}{\partial t} \, dS; \qquad \oint H_s \, ds &= \frac{4\pi}{c} \int J_n \, dS \\ &+ \frac{1}{c} \int \frac{\partial D_n}{\partial t} \, dS \\ \int B_n \, dS = 0; \qquad \int D_n \, dS &= 4\pi \int \rho \, dv \end{aligned} \right\} \tag{29}$$

with corresponding changes in (10.11) and (10.12).

For a traveling plane wave in vacuum, Eq. (10.22) relating $\mathcal{E}$ and H now becomes

$$\mathcal{E} = H \tag{30}$$

so that the electric and magnetic intensities are equal.

The Poynting vector S is, instead of Eq. (10.28),

$$\mathbf{S} = \frac{c}{4\pi}\,(\boldsymbol{\mathcal{E}} \times \mathbf{H}) \tag{31}$$

The magnitudes of $\mathcal{E}$ and H in the wave field of an oscillating dipole are given, in Gaussian units, by

$$|\mathcal{E}| = |H| = \frac{\omega^2 P}{c^2 r}\,\sin\,\theta\,\sin\,\omega\left(t - \frac{r}{c}\right) \tag{32}$$

instead of Eqs. (11.14) and (11.15), and the average rate of radiation from this dipole is

$$\frac{\overline{dE}}{dt} = \frac{\omega^4 P^2}{3c^3} \tag{33}$$

in place of (11.18).

In dielectrics, the relation between $\mathcal{E}$ and H as given by Eq. (15.12) takes the form

$$n\mathcal{E} = H \tag{34}$$

In Chap. 17, the scattered power $\bar{P}_s$ of Eq. (17.28) in Gaussian units is

$$\bar{P}_s = \frac{e^4 \mathcal{E}_0^2}{3m^2 c^3}\left(\frac{\omega^2}{\omega_0^2 - \omega^2}\right)^2 \tag{35}$$

4. The Unrationalized MKS System.   In view of the fact that the first edition of this book employed the unrationalized rather than the rationalized mks system of units, it seems appropriate to say a word concerning the relations between these two systems.   The two systems are identical dimensionally and differ only in the sizes of the units of a few quantities.   If, in the rationalized equations of this text, one replaces

$4\pi\epsilon_0$ by ϵ_0 or $4\pi\epsilon$ by ϵ
$\mu_0/4\pi$ by μ_0 or $\mu/4\pi$ by μ
D by $D/4\pi$
H by $H/4\pi$

then all the equations become expressed in unrationalized mks units (with the trivial exceptions of those of electric and magnetic susceptibilities as explained in the preceding paragraphs).   Thus the transition from one system to the other is exceedingly simple.

APPENDIX II

PHYSICAL CONSTANTS

Velocity of light, c............................ 2.998×10^8 m/sec

Gravitational constant, γ...................... 6.670×10^{-11} m³/kg-sec²

Electronic charge, e........................... 1.602×10^{-19} coulomb

Mass of an electron........................... 9.106×10^{-31} kg

Ratio of charge to mass of an electron........... 1.759×10^{11} coulomb/kg

Mass of a proton.............................. 1.673×10^{-27} kg

Ratio of charge to mass of a proton............. 9.564×10^7 coulomb/kg

Ratio of mass of a proton to that of an electron.. $1,837$

Planck's constant, h........................... 6.623×10^{-34} joule-sec

Boltzmann's constant, k....................... 1.380×10^{-23} joule/°C abs

Avogadro's number........................... 6.024×10^{23} per mole

Permittivity of free space, ϵ_0................... 8.854×10^{-12} farad/m

Permeability of free space, μ_0.................. $4\pi \times 10^{-7}$ henry/m

Stefan-Boltzmann constant, σ................. 5.672×10^{-8} joule/m²-sec-°C⁴

INDEX